FUNDAMENTALS
OF TECHNOLOGY

Volume Two

Second Edition

DeWayne R. Brown, PhD
Derrek B. Dunn, PhD

D1530290

Change the course.

ISBN: 978-1-58390-230-1 (Vol. 1–3 bundled)
ISBN 978-1-58390-227-1 (Volume 1 only)
ISBN 978-1-58390-228-8 (Volume 2 only)
ISBN 978-1-58390-229-5 (Volume 3 only)

Change the course.

530 Great Road
Acton, Massachusetts 01720
800-562-2147

This book is dedicated to the most influential and inspirational women in Dewayne's life:

Mrs. Dora Mae Hanna Brown Redden (Mother)

Mrs. Josephine Coward Hanna (Grandmother) [deceased]

Dr. Lisa Hope Antoine

Ms. Arneitha Roberta Nesmith

Dr. Cynthia Thompson

CONTENTS

PREFACE

This book is intended to be used for students at vocational, associate or baccalaureate degree programs who are studying to become technicians or technologists. The book will start with a comprehensive review of the past and the present history of technology. The various careers in technology will be covered. The role of the technologist in the technical lab will be emphasized. The book will provide information about student success that will help them with retention and realizing their personal goal. Students will begin preparing for their careers in technology by developing cover letters, writing resumes, learning to critique interviews and will receive valuable advice for effective writing and listening. Topics that will be vital to students' careers, in the private sector and government such as leadership and diversity, will be included. The fundamental mathematics and measurements that are used in various fields in technology is studied. Plotting data and statistics will be covered where MATLAB will be used as the instrumental tool for computation and graphing.

Changes in the Second Edition

- The most extensive improvements in the *Fundamentals of Technology, Second Edition* are:

- Employ and salary information in Chapter 1 has been updated.

- History of Technology has been updated to reflect the second decade of the 21st century.

- The section on Ethics and Professionalism for Computer Professionals in Chapter 2 was updated to reflect new information on copyright laws, trademark, servicemark and patents.

- A new section was added to Chapter 2 to address six types of interviews.

- More information was added in Chapter 2 for preparing for the initial interview (screening interview) and the on-site interview (selection interview).

- A new section was added to Chapter 2 that provide information on the tone of voice during interview.

- A new section was created in Chapter 2 to help students address tough job interview questions.

- There is a new chapter on effective communication skills.

- There is new chapter on leadership and diversity.

- There is a new chapter featuring student success.

To the Student

Today, the key to survival in the fierce job market will involve the embracement of diversity and the employment of people with capable leadership potential. Corporations and their customers have been forced to react not only to the changing face of America, but the mindsets of the global marketplace. Innovation will continue to thrive even in the online world. The demand for professionals to produce, install, and maintain state-of-the-art equipment, train and supervise industry's skilled workers, and support research and development efforts will remain on the rise. This book will allow you to answer questions like:

- How can I start now and continue to persist to my goals of graduation and job employment?

- Am I communicating effectively and managing my time efficiently?

- What challenges am I facing to remain productive in my technical career as corporations reinvent themselves with diversity?

This textbook will provide a lot of information for succeeding in college, preparing for a career after graduation and maintaining your success through your professional years. Emphasis is placed on ethics, attitude, professionalism, communicating effectively, valuableness of find resources and using your time wisely. The authors encourage the students to sharpen their problem-solving abilities by working the math problems because it will help them build their critical thinking skills.

To the Instructor

The text material has been used in the classroom and has worked well for our four-year college students who pursued a bachelor's degree in technology. It usage is encouraged for two-year college students, too. This book is user-friendly for students without a strong background in technology. *Fundamentals of Technology, Second Edition* is recommended to be used as the primary text for Orientation to Technology or Engineering Technology courses or as a supplement for courses requiring the use of applied mathematics, computers, or scientific calculators. The text also may be used in technical or vocational schools.

All chapters of the textbook have a homework section in Appendix A. Chapters 1 – 6 consist of comprehension that will help reinforce the concepts from the chapters. Some of the comprehension will require consulting resources outside the book, such as the internet to stimulate critical thinking. Chapters 7 – 10 contain numerous practical applications, computer simulation/scientific calculator computations, and critical-thinking mathematical problems to help the students to think more abstractly and be able to analyze.

Organization

Chapter 1 will provide an introduction to technology. First the history of technology will be discussed, from the Stone Age through the second decade of the 21th Century. Various growing fields in technology such as Information Technology (IT), Computer Engineering (CET), Biomedical Technology, and Environmental Technology are investigated. The differences among the job responsibilities of scientists, engineers, technologists and technicians are examined.

Chapter 2 focuses on the career development of a technologist. The importance of professionalism and ethics are covered. Emphasis is placed on personal and professional development, work habits and job performance, personal conduct and human relations. Tips and pointers on cover letters, and resumes for hard copy and email are featured. There are samples of cover letters and resumes. Students are taught how to write letters to acknowledge an offer as well as how to reject an offer. The textbook will cover the entire process of preparing for interviews whether if it is an initial or on-site interview and whether it is in person, by telephone, by computer or will be video-conferenced. Addition information on the tone of voice during interviews is provided. There is a valuable section that addresses how to respond to sample tough interview questions.

In **Chapter 3** the job responsibilities of the technologist in the technical laboratory will be discussed. The importance of lab safety training is covered. Some rules for lab safety are offered. How to develop good lab skills is addressed. The types of errors that occur in measurements in the laboratory such as gross, systematic, and random are reviewed. Strategies for reducing these errors are included. Percentage error calculations are done. The importance of significant figures and their effects on computations are emphasized. In addition, how to write lab reports and tips on giving oral reports are discussed in this chapter, too. A brief review of common errors in lab reports is given. Some popular technological tools to enhance performance in the technical laboratory as well as the classroom, such as the scientific graphical calculator and the computer algebraic systems are covered.

Chapter 4 addresses how to communicate effectively. The chapter emphasizes the process of how communication works. Students will learn how to communicate exactly what they want to say and what mode of communication is best for that particular message. In addition, factors that influence your ability to speak clearly and listen critically are discussed. This chapter addresses the four types of communication styles and provides advice on how to communicate if you have that style or dealing with someone else who has that style.

In **Chapter 5** the importance of leadership and diversity are emphasized. Leadership is defined and its attributes and qualities are described. This chapter will help students to develop leadership skills to be successful leaders through education and modeling leadership rubrics. The importance of embracing diversity as a culture is addressed. Factors that affect diversity will be covered to help students appreciate and market the

new direction that corporations are now taking to implement diversity and inclusion in their infrastructures. Students will learn first-hand hoe companies and institutions are re-inventing themselves through diversity matrices and competency models for diversity management from domestic and global perspectives. Students will understand the newly role of Diversity & Inclusion (D&I) practitioners in the corporate and the visionary and strategic planning that they must bring to help corporations remain successful.
.

Chapter 6 explains how student success is beneficial to society. The most potent principles of student success are identified in this chapter. The factors that influence students' success in college are addressed. This chapter is helpful for freshmen students who are making that transition to college by providing advice and recommendations for common changes and common stressors that freshmen can expect in their first year on campus. Student time management is emphasized and some of the common barriers to student time management are discussed. Advice will be offered for improvement of techniques for studying.

Chapter 7 will cover some of the basic mathematics used in the various fields of technology. Topics such as arithmetic, simple algebraic equations, and basic matrix algebra are covered. MATLAB as a software simulation tool for computation will be introduced in this chapter as reinforcement of the learned concepts. Computer software tools such as MATLAB will be valuable for students entering the corporate work environment or graduate school. MATLAB is one of the most powerful and popular software tools for science-related fields on the market. MATLAB is a programming language and data visualization tool. MATLAB has many capabilities for solving problems in engineering, technology, scientific, computing and mathematical disciplines.

Chapter 8 covers measurement systems. First the U.S. customary system of measurement is discussed. Next the metric system is studied. Conversions between the U.S. customary and metric systems are performed. Temperature conversions are done. Mathematical applications that can be solved by the usage of a circle are addressed. The relationship among various units of time is covered. Lastly, students are taught how to effectively determine the time in different time zones.

Chapter 9 emphasizes the fundamentals of graphing data. After data is collected it must be presented to others in a meaningful way. Oscilloscopes, spectrum analyzers, logic analyzers etc. are examples of some of the instruments that display graphical information. Students will learn how to graph linear equations and non-linear equations. Selecting scales for graphs will be reviewed. The concepts of interpolation and extrapolation applications to graphing will be covered. In addition, students will use MATLAB to plot fundamental two-dimensional graphics. They will be able to graph trigonometric functions, such as the sine wave, cosine wave, and the tangent wave. They will be able to graph linear and non-linear equations. Students will be able to label the x- and y-axes. They will be able to give graphs a title name.

Chapter 10 covers the background of statistics. This chapter covers a range of techniques and procedures for analyzing data, interpreting data, and displaying data. In this chapter, students will use MATLAB to perform statistical analyses on data sets. They will compute the mean, standard deviation and variance of data sets by both hand calculation and computer simulation. Students will use MATHLAB to create histograms. They will apply MATLAB curve fitting techniques to data sets for straight-line approximation, quadratic approximation and other higher order approximations.

About the Authors

Dr. Dewayne Randolph Brown is a Full Professor of Computer Systems Technology Department within the School of Technology at North Carolina Agricultural & Technical State University in Greensboro, North Carolina, United States of America. Dr. Brown teaches undergraduate and graduates courses in electronic and wireless communications. In addition, Dr. Brown has taught orientation to technology courses for nine-teen years. Dr. Brown has written four previous textbooks relevant to the field of technology, *Fundamentals of Technology* (XanEdu, 2012), *Fundamental Mathematics for Electronics and Information Technology* (XanEdu, 2008), *Mathematics for Technologists in Electronics, Second Edition* (Prentice-Hall, 2002), and *Mathematics for Technologists in Electronics* (Pearson Custom Publishing, 2000). Dr. Brown received his Bachelors of Science in electrical engineering from the University of South Carolina in 1990. Dr. Brown received his Masters of Science in electrical engineering from North Carolina Agricultural & Technical State University in 1992. Dr. Brown received his Ph.D. in electrical engineering from Virginia Polytechnic Institute and State University in 1997. Dr. Brown has been a member of Association for Technology, Management, and Applied Engineers (ATMAE) formerly known as the National Association of Industrial Technology (NAIT) since 2000. Dr. Brown is a Certified Senior Technology Manager (CSTM) within ATMAE.

Dr. Derrek B. Dunn is currently a Full Professor and Chairperson of the Department of Technology in the School of Business and Technology at University of Maryland at Eastern Shore (UMES). Dr. Dunn has taught college level courses in such fields as Wireless Communication Systems, Computer Networks, Telecommunication Management, Global Positioning Systems, and Optical Systems.

Dr. Dunn received his Bachelor of Science in Electrical Engineering and a Bachelor of Science in Mathematics from North Carolina A&T State University. He also received a Master of Science in Electrical Engineering, Master of Science in Mathematics and a Doctor of Philosophy in Electrical Engineering from Virginia Polytechnic Institute and State University.

Dr. Dunn bring nearly 15 years of experience in teaching and research on learners and learning at a distance, and experience on the use of distance education in technology and engineering.

Dr. Dunn's past experience with The Association of Technology, Management, and Applied Engineering (ATMAE) formerly known as the National Association of Industrial Technology (NAIT) includes membership of NAIT/ATMAE for the past eleven years, certified industrial technologist, ATMAE accreditation training, Regional Director - Student Division and member and elected to a second term as Vice-President of the Electrical, Electronics and Computer Technology (EECT) Division and is currently the President of the Electrical, Electronics and Computer Technology (EECT) Division.

CHAPTER 2
Preparing for a Career in Technology

CHAPTER 2
PREPARING FOR A CAREER IN TECHNOLOGY

2.1 PROFESSIONALISM AND ETHICS

Ethical issues are not clear-cut; but are based on believing there is a difference between right and wrong, deciding to do what you think is right when under pressure and assuming that other people are trying to do their best. Ethics can be violated in any profession, ranging from political leaders, lawyers, law enforcement officers, medical doctors, etc. It is believed that cheating in school, at sports and in business makes it more likely that someone will progress to a level of violating ethics and will feel comfortable in repeating these violations. There are pressures in the workplace that can possibly cause an employee to violate ethics and become unprofessional, such as productivity, solving a bad problem during a crisis and just the fear of not being able to do your job.

There are many unfortunate circumstances that can lead to a violation of ethics in the workplace; some of them are:

- Decrease in Morale
- Breakdown in change of command
- Burn-out
- Grievances and lawsuits
- Loss of productivity
- Damage to image and repudiation

Typical behaviors and mentalities that can lead to a violation of ethics:

- Misuse of funds
- Abuses of authority
- Winning at all costs
- Using people as a means to an end
- Making oneself an exception
- Not recognizing an ethical trap

Negative characteristics and devastating consequences that can lead to a violation of ethics:

- Not efficient
- An organizational liability
- Not a team player
- Damage to Career
- Damage to Future
- Unfit role model

Training, modeling, reinforcements and a sense of reality are the resolution to maintaining ethics. Family, School, Church and the media can play a strong influential role in valuing ethics. When people acknowledge right from wrong, respect the human feeling of others, recognize the sanctity of human life and live by the Golden Rule then ethical violations will be very low to no existence.

The Six pillars of character that will positively influence professionalism and ethics:

- Trustworthiness

    a. Honesty
    b. Integrity
    c. Promise keeping
    d. Loyalty

- Respect

- Responsibility

    1. Accountability
    2. Pursuit of Excellence
    3. Self-restraint

- Justice and Fairness

- Caring

- Civil Virtue and Citizenship

The five P's of Ethical Power:

1. Purpose
2. Pride
3. Patience
4. Persistence
5. Perspective

The Principles of a Morally Good Person:

a. Just
b. Trustful

c. Trustworthy
d. Moral Courage
e. Moral Autonomy

Living by principles, acting consistently, striving to be fair, practicing, seeking advice, realizing that the job will not be easy and not taking yourself for granted are inner strength realistic goals that can help prevent an employee from violating ethics. Having organizational values, walking the walk—talking the talk, training, modeling, discussion and nipping it in the bud are outer strength realistic goals that can help prevent an employee from violating ethics.

2.1.1 WHAT IS ETHICAL BEHAVIOR?

Ethics involves the definition and achievement of what is good or bad, right or wrong, in relation to moral duty and obligation. It also includes the need to act in accordance with the principles of right and wrong governing the conduct of a particular group, such as doctors and lawyers. In the study of ethics, it is critical to understand that the motive is as important as the act. If a person refrains from stealing only because she or he fears prison, she or he cannot really be viewed as ethical.

Ethics is concerned with encouraging you to do what you know you should do:

- Consider all relevant sides of an ethical problem.

- Consider basic ethical values.

- Act in accordance with the code of your profession.

Moral progress depends on our willingness to improve the consistency of our ethical judgment and behavior and to apply the same principles more thoroughly to our conduct involving other people. Primitive man recognized few, if any, obligations to those outside his tribe. But modern man in his shrinking world must recognize his obligations to humanity in general. It is much easier to hold ideals than to live up to them. To convince someone of his or her duty by reasoning, does not necessarily induce him or her to do it. Our decision of what to do in a given situation depends on our understanding of basic ethical principles and our common sense knowledge of the way of the world and its people.

EXAMPLE 1: An example of how ethics start with you.

If you obey the law, you will set a good example for others and spare your fellow Explorers or Advisors the discomfort of having to intervene in your private life.

One way to develop an ethical basis for decisions is to read, attend meetings, and cultivate an awareness of the kinds of situations that tempt people to behave unethically. An excellent starting point is to periodically review applicable codes of ethics, and apply them to recent situations in your experience. Discuss these situations with associates and friends in informal settings.

As you develop awareness, you will also develop foresight. You will learn to recognize situations early for their dangers. When you sense such a circumstance arising, stall for time or find a gracious way to defer a decision until you can think the matter over and consult with others. Always think ahead. Where could this situation go? Will it place me in a position where my ethical standards will be challenged?

Learn to see marginal or ambiguous situations more clearly.

Frequently ask yourself:

- "Is this ethical?"

- "Could it lead me to act unethically in the future?"

Ask certain questions during the early stages:

- "How would it look to someone else?"

- "Who else is affected by this decision and how?"

- "Is there an angle I'm not seeing?"

Cultivate one or more friendly but tough mentors – not yes-people. Your mentor need not be your boss, though you are fortunate if your boss would be tough-minded but helpful. You may need to try a few people out for their advice before finding those with the necessary depth of experience and understanding, and an interest in your development. A mentor who always gives you the easy answer – "No, there's no problem here" – is only teaching excessive regard for expediency. Find another one. They who walk with the wise shall be wise.

2.1.2 WHAT IS PROFESSIONALISM?

Professional behavior and ethics are interrelated. Ethics is the route through which professionalism becomes understandable, relevant, and practical. The topics of professionalism and ethics should be introduced early and reinforced throughout any professional program. Figure 2.1 shows an example of un-professionalism.

FIGURE 2.1

But it should be our job. Hopefully we can all agree. Isn't it important to work in a place where professionalism is exercised and understood by all your fellow co-workers and employees? Wouldn't we be serving our consumers and fulfilling the agenda appropriately? What is **professionalism** anyway? A lot of people don't know. Companies can go through training after training and discuss its importance and still professionalism is somehow lost. Some people just can't redeem themselves as professionals because they tend to forget one simple thing. Keep your personal business, personal. By doing this we are better able to prepare for a day that has criteria to be followed and completed. Whether or not that criteria needs to be met daily or yearly, like annual goals, it is important to play the part so that the short or long-term goal could be met. If we are not aware of our attitudes and behaviors at work, we could be responsible for not creating a healthy and professional work environment.

Four Tips on Professionalism:

- Loosen up at the same rate as your prospect or customer.

- Avoid bringing up personal matters in a new business relationship.

- Bashing competitors is taboo.

- Be punctual for all appointments.

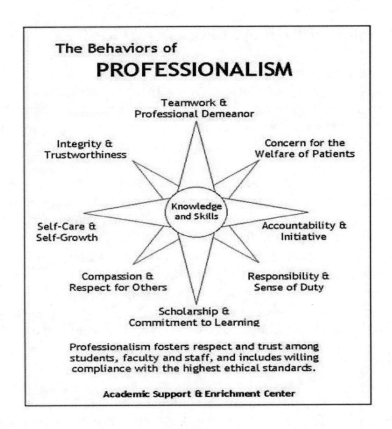

FIGURE 2.2

Teamwork & Professional Demeanor is at the top of Figure 2.2. Teamwork at the workplace is very important because working as a team will allow all members to feel free to lend their ideas to collaborate and reinforce stronger ones. Teamwork will build strong work relationships and good work ethics.

FIGURE 2.3

2.1.3 THE CHALLENGE OF ETHICAL DECISION-MAKING

The term "moral behavior" is applied in evaluating the personal conduct of a citizen and is judged in comparison to society's norms. The term "ethical behavior" is applied to that citizen's conduct in professional matters and is judged in comparison to the standards of the profession, which are formally expressed in statements called codes of ethics.

Distinguishing between moral and ethical behavior is necessary because people have a wider array of value obligations when functioning as professionals than when resolving value dilemmas in their personal lives. A professional has specialized knowledge that must be applied to serve four entities: the employer, the client of the employer, the profession, and, most importantly, society. A professional also has legitimate moral obligations. In addition to the application of technical knowledge and the proper consideration of economic factors, the professional must properly balance the value obligations to each of the four entities. For example, the employee should be loyal to the employer, honest with the client, respectful of the profession, and sensitive to the health and safety of the public. Values such as loyalty, honesty, respect, and sensitivity to public safety are emphasized in professional codes of ethics.

For example in one scenario, rational ethical judgment by professional water managers is important because of the significant implications of their decisions to society. They make decisions that affect the environment, allocate water resources, influence public health and safety, distribute public monies, and affect the lives of future generations. Ethical conduct, or professional decision-making, is a necessary requisite to being called a professional. A professional must be able to properly balance competing values in making decisions that affect both society and the client, especially where personal, societal, and cultural values conflict. The value issues must be properly balanced within the framework of economic, political, and sociological constraints. Professional ethics must not be overlooked but valued as a critical factor in the successful management of water resources. Situations with ethical concerns require mature and rational value decisions. Mature ethical decision-making is not easy, and the professional often is criticized by those who feel adversely affected by the decisions.

In another scenario, the preservation of wetland systems is often in value conflict with economic development of the land. Worthwhile values are legitimately associated with both sides of the issue. The difficulty in quantifying the worth of public amenities provided by wet-lands often complicates decision-making. The water professional who supports wetland development may appear unethical. It is difficult to quantify the value of a wetland to fish and waterfowl in terms that can be compared to the economic value of transforming the wetland into a shopping mall that will be used daily by thousands of people. Would a code of ethics lead a water professional to preserve the wetland for reasons of public welfare, or to develop the land and thus serve the client and the public with fidelity?

FIGURE 2.4

"Codes of ethics" are the value guidelines that a professional must follow in order to remain registered as a member of the profession. Codes are not a list of do's and don'ts. Therefore, to a young professional, they may appear to be vague statements. For example, a code might state that the professional should hold paramount the safety, health, and welfare of the public, or that they should act as faithful agents in professional matters for each employer or client. The emphasis on values is evident through the terms "public safety" and "faithful."

When one is confronted by decisions related to water resources issues, such as sustainable development and wetland systems, interpretation of these guidelines is not always clear-cut. Differences of opinion can lead a professional to blow the whistle. Misinterpreting the codes or ignoring them can result in a person's losing his or her job, or even being expelled from the profession. Thus, understanding value issues and being able to make mature value decisions are just as important to the water resources practitioner as is technical knowledge.

2.1.4 PROFESSIONALISM AND ETHICS WHEN DEALING WITH CLIENTS

There is no substitute for professionalism and ethics when dealing with clients - common sense tells us that.

It is this professionalism and ethical conduct that gives certain contractors a competitive edge over others that fail to act like professionals.

When you have a written code of conduct that you present to your clients, and the client sees that you are in fact acting in accordance with that code, then there is a foundation for trust established. Satisfied customers become loyal customers that recommend your company to neighbors and friends.

Professional conduct for contractors:

- Treat customers with respect, being courteous and at all times law abiding.

- Enter into contracts for work they know they are qualified to perform, and stand behind their work, offering warranties.

- Are honest and straightforward with their clients, submitting reasonable proposals and answering all questions pertaining to those proposals.

- Communicate with clients, following up with any concerns or questions and responding quickly to any problems.

- Ensure daily clean-up of the job site and daily safety inspection before departing from the job site each day.

- Promote safety and recognize that everyone's health and safety are of paramount concern.

- Encourage proper dress and professional behavior, including refraining from the use of profanity on job sites and assuring a drug and alcohol free job site.

- Always strive to better service customers and promote professionalism and ethical behavior in every facet of their daily operations.

2.1.5 ETHICS AND PROFESSIONALISM IN THE WORKPLACE

Conducting yourself in the utmost professional manner is a great way to succeed in the workplace. Treat this time as opportunity to hone your professional skills by gaining valuable experience in the following:

ATTITUDE – Remember that you are representing your company, agency, institution, etc. At all times, do your best to present yourself in the best possible light. Many times, a positive attitude can make up for deficiencies in other areas, so be sure to put your best foot forward whenever possible. This is your chance to make a positive impression on the organization and to gain valuable skills necessary for success in the workplace. Make the most of every learning opportunity and be cordial and friendly with everyone you meet!

COMMUNICATION – Depending on the layout of the site, you may or may not have your own workspace. Remember to respect others' privacy by not asking about a coworker's age, relationship status, sexual orientation, politics, religion or health unless they offer the information first. Likewise, respect others by keeping your voice down when talking, as well as controlling your phone and/or computer volume. Be sure to turn off your cell phone or PDA when in the workplace.

DRESS – Be sure to follow the dress code of the office, if stated. If there isn't a set standard, observe what others wear and dress accordingly. A good rule of thumb is to dress as if you already have the job you want to get, which means you should always dress in a presentable manner. Likewise, practicing good hygiene is essential, and limiting makeup and fragrances is important. Finally, be aware of your jewelry, your hairstyle and visible tattoos as these are all important aspects of your professional image.

ETHICS - If you are faced with what you believe to be an ethical dilemma, be sure to address this with your site coordinator before making a decision. Likewise, be sure to talk about the issues with coworkers to get their advice. Be honest with yourself in what you are prepared to do. Remember, at no time should you be expected to engage in any illegal activity. Your actions and those of the organization should promote learning and a positive experience at all times. Again, don't be afraid to ask questions with your site coordinator or others within the organization.

NETWORKING - Your practice experience is meant to be primer for finding a position upon graduation. Learning about the organization is important, but so is learning from the professionals you will be working with. Take time to get to know them by learning what they do and make your presence known by asking pertinent questions, getting involved in projects and over-delivering on assignments. Be sure to follow up with contacts internally and externally even if they can't immediately help you. Remember, networking is a two-way street- being helpful to others can pay dividends for you in the long run.

PREPAREDNESS – Just as you would not want to be unprepared for a class, you do not want to underperform on your job site. Be mindful of deadlines and absolutely deliver on all promises. If asked to conduct research, work on a project or give a presentation, take on these assignments happily. Be sure to communicate progress and any difficulties with your site coordinator or the appropriate person. Remember that you are at the site to learn, so arrive ready to work without distraction. And don't be afraid to ask plenty of questions. Expect to learn about the organization and the industry and be able to speak intelligently when asked.

SEXUAL HARASSMENT & RELATIONSHIPS – Workplace relationships are generally subject to strict guidelines. Be sure to adhere to company policies should you enter into a relationship with a coworker. Should that or any work relationship cross certain boundaries, it may be considered sexual harassment. There are two types – quid pro quo and hostile work environment. Quid pro quo means "something for something", which refers to an employee performing sexual favors in return for a promotion or preferential treatment. Hostile work environment entails a coworker feeling uncomfortable about another's actions, including touching, flirting or inappropriate comments or materials. Sexual harassment is against the law and is taken very seriously. If you have questions regarding what is and isn't acceptable behavior, don't be shy in asking your site coordinator for direction.

TIMELINESS – Since you will be travelling to your site, plan to arrive early each day. Plan accordingly if you will be using public transportation, and be sure to factor in time to and from your parking site if you will be parking on site. You will be asked to set a schedule with your site coordinator, so be sure to discuss any tests or any conflicts early on. Never leave your assignment before the end of your schedule unless previously approved by your site coordinator. Communicate with your site coordinator as soon as possible if absent and be sure to discuss alternatives to make up any time missed.

2.1.6 MAINTAINING AND NURTURING YOUR REPUDIATION

Adhering to ethical standards is a very important attribute in having a solid professional career; however there are four key categories of attributes which deserve attention:

Personal and Professional Development

A professional should never stop learning. Formal and informal means of education are continually available. Strengthen your skills and keep up with changes and innovations, particularly in the area of technology. Read into other fields of study (we need to know each other's areas of learning). The act of communicating comes from the communications curriculum, what we are supposed to communicate comes from the other fields of knowledge. Helping you gain knowledge, obtain a membership in at least one professional association and actively pursue the educational opportunities offered.

Read the newspaper and professional journals, read the important new book that everyone's reading. Read magazines that broaden your knowledge of the world around you and keep yourself up to date on current events. As a professional, you will be interacting with people in personal, social and professional situations so you need to be able to converse about a wide range of current events topics such as technology, politics, sports and entertainment.

Learn from your colleagues, organize yourself and take part in the networking opportunities. Serve in organizations and do good work. Be a mentor to other up-and-coming professionals, and seek mentors you can ask questions and advice. Send appropriate notes of encouragement, thanks and congratulations. Send lots of holiday cards; this helps in keeping your network alive. Overconfidence often masks incompetence, always ask questions and be teachable and remain humble, and yet still remain confident. Admit to yourself that you always have more to learn.

Work Habits and Job Performance

Know your own strengths and weaknesses and own up to your mistakes. Otherwise, you'll never overcome your challenges. Prioritize tasks, allocate time, and work within constraints. Don't think about how long you have worked; focus on the success and results. Be goal-oriented, not just task-oriented. Pay attention to detail and always deliver work on time. Work hard and be absolutely dependable.

If you want to be promoted, do your job well and then help do the job of the person you would like to replace. Help that person whenever possible. When people are promoted, they often have a hand in selecting a replacement. Make yourself the obvious choice.

Personal Conduct

Always act in a professional manner and dress professionally. Always be on time. Be aware of what goes on around you. Observe procedures and power structures (formal and informal) and work with them. Always be ethical and never allow yourself to be persuaded to compromise your personal standards. The respect of others is directly proportional to your respect for yourself and your respect for them. Work towards a balance in your life. Don't live to work or you'll burn out. You will be too stressed to maintain other vital relationships in life. If all you have in life is your job, you might be good at what you do, but you'll be very dull. Cultivate other interests and relationships and be a generous contributor to charitable causes and serve in your community.

Human Relations

Be personable and likeable. Learn to work well with people, treating them as equals. Work with and respect administrative assistants and other staffers. They can help you succeed or cause you to fail. Know people's names (and proper spelling) and use them. Don't hold grudges and stay out of office politics for at least the first year in any organization. It will take that long to understand the formal and informal power and communications structure. Never ever believe the job could not be done without you, cooperation is the key to success. Show your gratitude to other team members openly and often. Give others credit freely for their contributions.

2.1.7 ETHICS AND PROFESSIONALISM FOR COMPUTER PROFESSIONALS

A. Ethics

1. Ethics and Responsible Decision-Making

The foundation of all security systems is formed by moral principles and practices of those people involved and the standards of the profession. That is, while people are part of the solution, they are also most the problem. Security problems with which an organization may have to deal include: responsible decision making, confidentiality, privacy, piracy, fraud & misuse, liability, copyright, trade secrets, and sabotage. It is easy to sensationalize these topics with real horror stories; it is more difficult to deal with the underlying ethical issues involved.

The student should be made aware of his individual responsibility in making ethical decisions associated with information security.

2. Confidentiality & Privacy

Computers can be used symbolically to intimidate, deceive or defraud victims. Attorneys, government agencies and businesses increasingly use mounds of computer generated data quite legally to confound their audiences. Criminals also find useful phony invoices, bills and checks generated by the computer. The computer lends an ideal cloak for carrying out criminal acts by imparting a clean quality to the crime.

The computer has made the invasion of our privacy a great deal easier and potentially more dangerous than before the advent of the computer. A wide range of data are collected and stored in computerized files related to individuals. These files hold banking information, credit information, organizational fund raising, opinion polls, shop at home services, driver license data, arrest records and medical records. The potential threats to privacy include the improper commercial use of computerized data, breaches of confidentiality by releasing confidential data to third parties, and the release of records to governmental agencies for investigative purposes.

The basic law that protects our privacy is the Fourth Amendment to the United States Constitution, which mandates that people have a right to be secure in homes and against unreasonable search and seizure. In addition, many laws have been enacted to protect the individual from having damaging information stored in computerized databases.

3. Piracy

Microcomputer software presents a particular problem since many individuals are involved in the use of this software. Section 117 of the copyright laws, specifically the 1980 amendment, deals with a law that addresses the problem of backup copies of software. This section states that users have the right to create backup copies of their software. That is, users may legally create a backup copy of software if it is to be held in archive. Many software companies provide a free backup copy to users that preclude the need for to users purchase software intended to defeat copy protection systems and subsequently create copies of their software. If the software purchased is actually leased, you may in fact not even be able to make backup copies of the software. The distinction between leasing and buying is contained within the software documentation. The copyright statement is also contained in the software documentation. The copyright laws regarding leased material state that the leaser may say what the leaseholder can and cannot do with the software. So it is entirely up to the owner of the software as to whether or not users may make backup copies of the software. At a time when federal laws relating to copyright protection are evolving, several states are considering legislation that would bar unauthorized duplication of software.

The software industry is prepared to do battle against software piracy. The courts are dealing with an increasing number of lawsuits concerning the protection of software. Large software publishers have established the Software Protection Fund to raise between $500,000 and $1 million to promote anti-piracy sentiment and to develop additional protection devices.

4. Fraud & Misuse

The computer can create a unique environment in which unauthorized activities can occur. Crimes in this category have many traditional names including theft, fraud, embezzlement, extortion, etc. Computer related fraud includes the introduction of fraudulent records into a computer system, theft of money by electronic means, theft of financial instruments, theft of services, and theft of valuable data.

5. Liability

Under the UCC, an express warranty is an affirmation or promise of product quality to the buyer and becomes a part of the basis of the bargain. Promises and affirmations made by the software developer to the user about the nature and quality of the program can also be classified as an express warranty. Programmers or retailers possess the right to define express warranties. Thus, they have to be realistic when they state any claims and predictions about the capabilities, quality and nature of their software or hardware. They should consider the legal aspects of their affirmative promises, their product demonstrations, and their product description. Every word they say may be as legally effective as though stated in writing. Thus, to protect against liability, all agreements should be in writing. A disclaimer of express warranties can free a supplier from being held responsible for any informal, hypothetical statements or predictions made during the negotiation stages.

Implied warranties are also defined by the UCC. These are warranties that are provided automatically in every sale. These warranties need not be in writing nor do they need to be verbally stated. They insure that good title will pass to the buyer, that the product is fit for the purpose sold, and that it is fit for the ordinary purposes for which similar goods are used (merchantability).

6. Types of Intellectual Property

Some people confuse patents, copyrights, and trademarks. Although there may be some similarities among these kinds of intellectual property protection, they are different and serve different purposes.

What Is a Copyright?

Copyright is a form of protection provided to the authors of "original works of authorship" including literary, dramatic, musical, artistic, and certain other intellectual works, both published and unpublished. The 1976 Copyright Act generally gives the owner of copyright the exclusive right to reproduce the copyrighted work, to prepare derivative works, to distribute copies or phono-records of the copyrighted work, to perform the copyrighted work publicly, or to display the copyrighted work publicly.

The copyright protects the form of expression rather than the subject matter of the writing. For example, a description of a machine could be copyrighted, but this would only prevent others from copying the description; it would not prevent others from writing a description of their own or from making and using the machine. Copyrights are registered by the Copyright Office of the Library of Congress.

What Is a Trademark or Servicemark?

A trademark is a word, name, symbol or device which is used in trade with goods to indicate the source of the goods and to distinguish them from the goods of others. A servicemark is the same as a trademark except that it identifies and distinguishes the source of a service rather than a product. The terms "trademark" and "mark" are commonly used to refer to both trademarks and servicemarks.

Trademark rights may be used to prevent others from using a confusingly similar mark, but not to prevent others from making the same goods or from selling the same goods or services under a clearly different mark. Trademarks which are used in interstate or foreign commerce may be registered with the Patent and Trademark Office. The registration procedure for trademarks and general information concerning trademarks is described in a separate pamphlet entitled "Basic Facts about Trademarks."

What Is a Patent?

A patent for an invention is the grant of a property right to the inventor, issued by the Patent and Trademark Office. The term of a new patent is 20 years from the date on which the application for the patent was filed in the United States or, in special cases, from the date an earlier related application was filed, subject to the payment of maintenance fees. US patent grants are effective only within the US, US territories, and US possessions.

The right conferred by the patent grant is, in the language of the statute and of the grant itself, "the right to exclude others from making, using, offering for sale, or selling" the invention in the United States or "importing" the invention into the United States. What is granted is not the right to make, use, offer for sale, sell or import, but the right to exclude others from making, using, offering for sale, selling or importing the invention.

7. Patents and Copyright Laws for Software

A patent can protect the unique and secret aspect of an idea. It is very difficult to obtain a patent compared to a copyright (please see discussion below). With computer software, complete disclosure is required; the patent holder must disclose the complete details of a program to allow a skilled programmer to build the program. Moreover, a United States software patent will be unenforceable in most other countries.

Copyright law provides a very significant legal tool for use in protecting computer software, both before a security breach and certainly after a security breach. This type of breach could deal with misappropriation of data, computer programs, documentation, or similar material. For this reason the information security specialist will want to be familiar with basic concepts of the copyright law.

The United States, United Kingdom, Australia, and many other countries have now amended or revised their copyright legislation to provide explicit copyright laws to protect computer program. Copyright law in the United States is governed by the Copyright Act of 1976 that preempted the field from the states. Formerly, the United States had a dual state and Federal system. In other countries, such as Canada, the courts have held that the un-revised Copyright Act is broad enough to protect computer programs. In many of these countries the reform of copyright law is actively underway.

8. Trade Secrets

A trade secret protects something of value and usefulness. This law protects the unique and secret aspects of ideas, known only to the discoverer or his confidants. Once disclosed the trade secret is lost as such and can only be protected under one of the following laws. The application of trade secret law is very important in the computer field, where even a slight head start in the development of software or hardware can provide a significant competitive advantage.

9. Sabotage

The computer can be the object of attack in computer crimes such as the unauthorized use of computer facilities, alternation or destruction of information, data file sabotage and vandalism against a computer system. Computers have been shot, stabbed, short-circuited and bombed.

B. Laws and Legislation

The types and numbers of security laws and legislation at all governmental levels are expanding rapidly. Often, we forget that such legislation may affect each of us, as well as the organization.

Some additional differences between a copyright and a trademark are as follows:

1. The purpose of a copyright is to protect works of authorship as fixed in a tangible form of expression. Thus, copyright covers: a) works of art (2 or 3 dimensional), b) photos, pictures, graphic designs, drawings and other forms of images; c) songs, music and sound recordings of all kinds; d) books, manuscripts, publications and other written works; and e) plays, movies, shows, and other performance arts.

2. The purpose of a trademark is to protect words, phrases and logos used in federally regulated commerce to identify the source of goods and/or services.

3. There may be occasions when both copyright and trademark protections are desired with respect to the same business endeavor. For example, a marketing campaign for a new product may introduce a new slogan for use with the product, which also appears in advertisements for the product. However, copyright and trademark protection will cover different things. The advertisement's text and graphics, as published in a particular vehicle, will be covered by copyright - but this will not protect the slogan as such. The slogan may be protected by trademark law, but this will not cover the rest of the advertisement. If you want

both forms of protection, you will have to perform both types of registration.

4. If you are interested in protecting a title, slogan, or other short word phrase, generally you want a trademark. Copyright law does not protect a bare phrase, slogan, or trade name.

5. Whether an image should be protected by trademark or copyright law depends on whether its use is intended to identify the source of goods or services. If an image is used temporarily in an ad campaign, it generally is not the type of thing intended to be protected as a logo.

6. The registration processes of copyright and trademark are entirely different. For copyright, the filing fee is small, the time to obtain registration is relatively short, and examination by the Copyright Office is limited to ensuring that the registration application is properly completed and suitable copies are attached. For trademark, the filing fee is more substantial, the time to obtain registration is much longer, and examination by the Trademark Office includes a substantive review of potentially conflicting marks which are found to be confusingly similar. While copyright registration is primarily an administrative process, trademark registration is very much an adversarial process.

7. Copyright law provides for compulsory licensing and royalty payments - there is no analogous concept in trademark law. Plus, the tests and definition of infringement are considerably different under copyright law and trademark law.

CLOTHING ITEMS

Here are a few guidelines about clothing items when it comes to copyright vs. trademark:

1. Anything you silk screen or otherwise display prominently on the front or back of a shirt, top, cap or hat is generally considered artwork, and therefore covered by copyright. In fact, if you send a photo of a clothing item to the U.S. Trademark Office showing your design, logo or slogan prominently displayed on the front or back, they will refuse to register it as a trademark.

2. To qualify as a trademark, your logo or slogan must be used as the brand of the clothing item itself. In other words, your logo or slogan must be used the way clothing brands are typically used and displayed on clothing, namely, sewn into a waistband, collar, hem or pocket, or applied to a label, sticker or tag, and NOT in a way that dominates the appearance of the clothing item.

3. The caveat, of course, is that when your design, logo or slogan is regarded as artwork - even though it can be protected by copyright - the protection only extends to the artistic configuration used. To put it more bluntly, if you have a slogan or name, copyright law can protect the artistic way you display it, but the text itself is NOT protected. Copyright law does not cover names, words or short phrases.

4. The only way to protect a name, word, short phrase or other text, is to register it as a trademark. But this means that you have to change the way you use the mark from an artistic

display to a brand name usage.

5. Yes, it is possible to register a design, logo, name or phrase under both copyright law and trademark law, so long as you use it in two different ways and you do it consistently. Keeping the two usages of the same design or text at the same time is not an easy task, and you can end up compromising your rights under copyright or trademark, or both, very easily if you aren't careful.

C. Professionalism

Students should be encouraged to become involved professionally while they are in school and to continue their professional involvement throughout their career. Several societies and professional organizations are concerned with security, including:

- The Computer Security Institute
- Computer Professionals for Social Responsibility
- Data Processing Management Association
- Security Management Magazine
- Licensing and Certification

2.1.8 ETHICS AND PROFESSIONALISM IN TEACHING

Teachers are not only masters of the content they teach, but they are also relay to their students' common societal values such as responsibility, respectfulness and conscientiousness. Teachers are always teaching, even when not delivering formal instruction, by virtue being a primary adult influence in a student's life. For this reason, professionalism and ethics are important topics in teacher preparation courses just as they are important considerations to parents of students and employers of teachers.

2.1.8.1 TEACHERS AS PROFESSIONALS-- STUDENTS

Professionalism in teaching refers to teacher interaction with students as well as teacher interaction with other teachers and supervisors. The former involves impartial teaching and appropriate teaching of all students, regardless of ethnicity, academic performance or personality. The professional teacher works hard to establish an equitable and safe classroom in which all students feel cared for and fairly treated.

2.1.8.2 TEACHERS AS PROFESSIONALS--COLLEAGUES AND SUPERVISORS

Professional teacher behavior with regard to colleagues refers to the way in which teachers interact with each other. A professional teacher is collaborative and individualistic; he or she will share materials when appropriate but does not become a burden to his or her colleagues. A professional teacher does not create personal alliances or feuds with his or her colleagues. With regard to supervisors and employers, the professional teacher is respectful and approachable; however, he or she maintains his or her sense of individual integrity. Clear communication with colleagues and supervisors is a mark of professionalism in a teacher.

2.1.8.3 ETHICS

Historically, ethics is the study of philosophical ideas of morality. The study of ethics is built around the question: What defines good and bad? Philosophers have considered this question to be of chief importance as a conceptual pursuit because it has application beyond the theoretical; good and bad and what defines something as such has a direct influence on society. Since educational practices do not take place outside of society and are directly related the culture in which they are based, ethics are an important part of any school or teacher.

2.1.8.4 ETHICS OF TEACHING

Because society still largely depends on the idea that there is good or bad, or acceptable and unacceptable, teachers must consider the ethical ramifications of their teaching styles and personal actions. This includes equitable treatment of all students as well as maintaining the proper student and teacher relationship. Ethics in education dictate that a high degree of responsibility comes with the privilege of teaching and mentoring a society's children, and teachers are to act accordingly.

2.1.8.5 PROFESSIONALISM AND ETHICS

The relationship between professionalism and ethics is significant. Professionalism in any discipline is defined by the responsibility to society of that discipline as determined by the society in which it is practiced. The responsibility of teachers is profound, and the professionalism expected great. Similarly, the ethics of teaching are derived from societal values and the importance placed on education. Teachers, as professionals who serve society, should abide with integrity by the expectations of professionalism and ethics set by that society.

2.1.8.6 PROFESSIONAL TIPS FOR SUCCESS

A professional learns every aspect of the job. An amateur skips the learning process whenever possible.

A professional carefully discovers what is needed and wanted. An amateur assumes what others need and want.

A professional looks, speaks and dresses like a professional. An amateur is sloppy in appearance and speech.

A professional keeps his or her work area clean and orderly. An amateur has a messy, confused or dirty work area.

A professional is focused and clear-headed. An amateur is confused and distracted.

A professional does not let mistakes slide by. An amateur ignores or hides mistakes.

A professional jumps into difficult assignments. An amateur tries to get out of difficult work.

A professional completes projects as soon as possible. An amateur is surrounded by unfinished work piled on unfinished work.

A professional remains level-headed and optimistic. An amateur gets upset and assumes the worst.

A professional handles money and accounts very carefully. An amateur is sloppy with money or accounts.

A professional faces up to other peoples. An amateur avoids others.

A professional uses higher emotional tones: Enthusiasm, cheerfulness, interest, and contentment. An amateur uses lower emotional tones: anger, hostility, resentment, fear, and victim.

A professional persists until the objective is achieved. An amateur gives up at the first opportunity.

A professional produces more than expected. An amateur produces just enough to get by.

A professional produces a high-quality product or service. An amateur produces medium-to-low quality product or service.

A professional earns higher pay than amateurs, and with that high pay come an higher expectation of professionalism and ethics.

A professional has a promising future. An amateur has an uncertain future.

The first step to making yourself a professional is to decide you are a professional.

2.2 TYPES OF FORMAL LETTERS WRITTEN TO EMPLOYERS

2.2.1 COVER LETTER

A cover letter is a letter of introduction to an employer, which is used to formally submit a resume for employer review. The purpose of the cover letter is to identify your intent to "apply for" or "seek out" a specific position within a company. It also formally presents you as available for a job position or range of positions within a company.

Most importantly, the cover letter is an opportunity to quickly introduce you and grab the employer's attention. Like the resume, it is another chance to market yourself to the hiring manager, promoting them to read your resume and ultimately grant a job interview.

A cover letter is a critical part of the job search process. It allows you the first opportunity to gain some interest from the employer. For most careers a cover letter must be submitted with every resume.

Cover letters generally fall into two categories:

1. Letter of application: applying for a specific, advertised opening.

2. Letter of inquiry: expressing interest in an organization, but you are not certain if there are current opening.

2.2.1.1 SELECT A COVER LETTER TYPE

When you need to write a cover letter, it's sometimes the small things that make a big difference. There are several types of cover letters that can be sent to employers and contacts. Be sure to choose a type of cover letter that reflects how you are applying for the job or the type of job search assistance you are requesting. Your cover letter should be designed specifically for the purpose you are writing and customized for each position you seek.

First of all, your cover letter needs to include your contact information (name, address, phone, email) so prospective employers can get in touch with you.

Your cover letter should include at least three paragraphs:

1. What you are applying for and where you found the job posting - First Paragraph
2. What you have to offer - Middle Paragraph(s)
3. How you will follow-up - Final Paragraph

In the first paragraph, if you are writing in response to a job posting, indicate where you learned of the position and the title of the position. More importantly, express your enthusiasm and the likely match between your credentials and the position's qualifications.

The second paragraph of your cover letter should refer specifically to the qualifications listed in the job posting and illustrate how your particular abilities and experiences relate to the position for which you are applying.

The final paragraph of your letter should reiterate your interest in the job and let the employer know how they can reach you and include your phone number and email address.

2.2.1.2 FORMAT YOUR COVER LETTER

How you format your cover letter, both from content (the information you include) and a presentation (what your cover letter looks like) perspective is important. Even when applying online or via email, your cover letter needs to be properly formatted, readable, and without any mistakes.

Cover Letter Format:

Your Contact Information
Name
Address
City, State, Zip Code
Phone Number
Email Address

Date

Employer Contact Information (if you have it)
Name
Title
Company
Address
City, State, Zip Code

Salutation
Dear Mr./Ms. Last Name, (leave out if you don't have a contact)

Body of Cover Letter
The body of your cover letter lets the employer know what position you are applying for, why the employer should select you for an interview, and how you will follow-up.

First Paragraph
The first paragraph of your letter should include information on why you are writing. Mention the position you are applying for and where you found the job listing. Include the name of a mutual contact, if you have one.

Middle Paragraph(s)
The next section of your cover letter should describe what you have to offer the employer. Mention specifically how your qualifications match the job you are applying for. Remember, you are interpreting your resume, not repeating it.

Final Paragraph
Conclude your cover letter by thanking the employer for considering you for the position. Include information on how you will follow-up.

Complimentary Close

Respectfully yours,

Signature

Handwritten Signature (for a mailed letter)

Typed Signature

2.2.1.3 REVIEW COVER LETTER EXAMPLES

Take the time to review cover letter examples; then make sure that your letter explains how your skills relate to the criteria listed in the job posting. When applying for a job a cover letter should be sent or posted with your resume. Your cover letter should be specific to the position you are applying for, relating your skills and experience to those noted in the job posting. Your cover letter is your first (and best) chance to make a good impression!

2.2.1.4 START FROM A COVER LETTER TEMPLATE

A cover letter template can be a good way to get started writing cover letters to send with resumes when you apply for jobs. Use a cover letter template as a starting point for creating your own personalized cover letter. Once you have a template ready to use on your computer, add your information to the cover letter template, then tweak and edit it to personalize your cover letter, so it highlights your qualifications for the job.

FIGURE 2.5

2.2.1.5 WRITE A CUSTOM COVER LETTER

It is important to customize your cover letter, so it presents your candidacy for employment effectively. It may be time consuming to write a custom cover letter for each job you apply for, but it's important to take the time and effort to show the company why you are a good match. Don't be afraid to try switching the format i.e. bulleted accomplishments versus. a paragraph, because the template is just a starting point for creating your own cover letter. Write a new customized cover letter for each job you apply for.

Save the original version of your cover letter, before you start making changes, so you can go back and start over, if you need to. Also, that way you'll be able to edit your original cover letter when applying for new jobs.

2.2.1.6 WRITE A PERSONALIZED COVER LETTER

When it comes to cover letters, taking the time to get personal is really important. Find out as much as you can about the company and the hiring manager. Personalize your cover letter and, if you can, address it to the individual responsible for hiring. If need be, research online or make a phone call to find out whom the hiring manager is.

If you know someone at the company, mention their name in your cover letter. Name dropping works - your cover letter will get a closer look if it mentions someone who works at the company. That's important both from your perspective and from the employee's, especially if the company has an Employee Referral Program and is eligible for a bonus. As an aside, be sure to ask your contact if they can recommend you for the job and help get your cover letter and resume a closer look from the hiring manager.

Mention how you learned about the job in the first paragraph of your cover letter. The company wants to know how the job was sourced, especially when you found the listing on a job board or other site where they paid to post. That sentence can simply say, for example, "I learned of this position from the posting I read on Monster."

Take it one step further and mention something about the company, from the mission statement on the company web site, for example, in your cover letter.

2.2.1.7 SEND AN EMAIL COVER LETTER

The most important part of sending an email cover letter is to follow the employer's instructions. If the job posting says to include your cover letter and resume as an attachment, attach Microsoft Word or Adobe PDF files to your email message. Save the files with your name, so they don't get mixed up with other applicant's materials i.e. alisondoyleresume.doc, alisondoylecover.doc.

When the employers requests a cover letter and resume in the body of an email message, paste your cover letter and resume into your email message. Use a basic font and remove the formatting. Don't use HTML. You don't know what email client the employer is using, so, simple is best because the employer may not see a formatted message the same way you do.

Be sure to include a Subject Line in your email with the position for which you are applying and your name. For example: Alison Doyle, Social Media Manager Position.

Include a signature with all your contact information - name, address, phone, and email address, so it's easy for the hiring manager to get in touch with you.

Send the email message to yourself first to test that the formatting works. If everything looks good, resend to the employer.

Figure 2.6

2.2.1.8 ADDRESS YOUR COVER LETTER

How to address a cover letter can be tricky if you are responding to a blind ad and don't have a contact person's name to include or you don't know the hiring manager's gender. Review Figure 2.7 to see how to address this type of cover letter.

Dear Mr. Jones

Dear Jane Doe

Dear Hiring Manager

To whom it may concern

Dear Human Resources Manager

Dear Sir or Madam

Dear Hiring Manager

FIGURE 2.7

There a variety of cover letter salutations you can use to address your letter. Employers who responded to a recent employer survey conducted by Saddleback College preferred:

- Dear Hiring Manager (38%)
- To whom it may concern (26%)
- Dear Sir/Madam (18%)
- Dear Human Resources Director (9.5%)
- Leave it blank (8%)

Once you have chosen a salutation, follow it with a colon or comma, a space, and then start the first paragraph of your letter. For example:

Dear Hiring Manager:

2.2.1.9 SEND YOUR COVER LETTER AS AN ATTACHMENT

When you apply for jobs via email, you may need to send your resume and cover letter as an attachment. It's important to send your cover letter and resume attachments correctly, to include all the information you need so your email message is read, and to let the receiver know how they can contact you to schedule an interview. Figure 2.8 shows how to send a cover letter as an attachment.

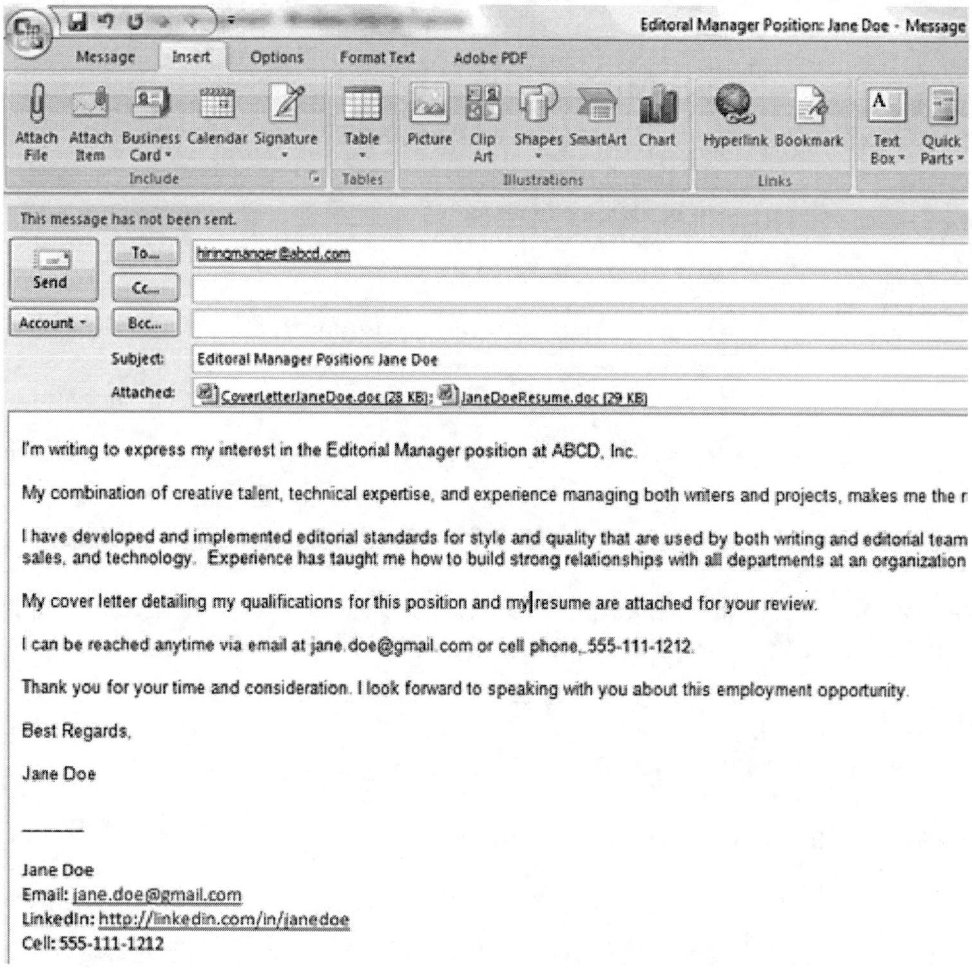

FIGURE 2.8

2.2.1.10 EXPLAIN AN EMPLOYMENT GAP

When you have recent gaps in your resume, whether from being laid-off and out of work, taking time out from the workplace to spend with your family, traveling, going back to school, or for any reason, your cover letter gives you an opportunity to explain an employment gap.

When you address the gap in your cover letter, the hiring manager will be aware that there's an explanation for you being out of the workforce. If you did volunteer work or consulting you can mention it. However, you don't need to provide a lengthy explanation - be brief and to the point.

Do keep in mind, that given the job market, there are many resumes with gaps, so deciding whether to reference the employment gap is optional.

If the gap was in the past, you don't need to mention it. In fact, you don't need to include all your experience on your resume, especially if you have been in the workforce for years. It's acceptable to limit the "years of experience" you include on your resume to fifteen years when seeking a managerial or professional position and ten years when looking for other positions.

Figure 2.9

2.2.1.11 COVER LETTER CORRESPONDENCE

Cover letter presentation matters as much as what you include. When writing cover letters it's important to use a basic font that is easy to read. Depending on the hiring process your cover letter may be viewed in an applicant tracking system or other online hiring system. Those systems work best reading simple text rather than fancy formatting.

It's also important for the hiring manager to be able to easily read your resume. Using a basic 12 point font will ensure that your cover letter is easy to read. Basic fonts like Arial, Verdana, and Times New Roman work well. Don't forget to leave space between paragraphs and to proof your letter before you send or upload it. Do remember that your cover letter fonts should match your resume.

Main **differences** between e-mail and hard copy correspondence:

Format: your **signature block** (address, etc.) goes below your name in e-mail, while it goes at the top of the page on hard copy.

E-mail requires a **subject line** logical to the recipient. E-mail subject lines can make or break whether your e-mail is opened and read. Hard copy can have a subject line too, but it's on the letter (after recipient's address block and before "Dear...," and it's seen after the letter is opened.

Signature: Of course you won't have a handwritten signature on e-mail, but don't forget this on hard copy.

All cover letters should:

Explain why you are sending a resume.
Don't send a resume without a cover letter.

Don't make the reader guess what you are asking for; be specific: Do you want a summer internship opportunity, or a permanent position at graduation; are you inquiring about future employment possibilities?

Tell specifically how you learned about the position or the organization — a flyer posted in your department, a web site, a family friend who works at the organization. It is appropriate to mention the name of someone who suggested that you write.

Convince the reader to look at your resume.
The cover letter will be seen first.
Therefore, it must be very well written and targeted to that employer.

Call attention to elements of your background — education, leadership, experience — that are relevant to a position you are seeking. Be as specific as possible, using examples.

Reflect your attitude, personality, motivation, enthusiasm, and communication skills.

Provide or refer to any information specifically requested in a job advertisement that might not be covered in your resume, such as availability date, or reference to an attached writing sample.

Indicate what you will do to follow-up.

In a letter of application — applying for an advertised opening — applicants often say something like "I look forward to hearing from you." However, if you have further contact info (e.g. phone number) and if the employer hasn't said "no phone calls," it's better to take the initiative to follow-up, saying something like, "I will contact you in the next two weeks to see if you require any additional information regarding my qualifications."

In a letter of inquiry — asking about the possibility of an opening — don't assume the employer will contact you. You should say something like, "I will contact you in two weeks to learn more about upcoming employment opportunities with (name of organization)." Then mark your calendar to make the call.

Page margins, font style and size

For hard copy, left and right page margins of one to 1.5 inches generally look good. You can adjust your margins to balance how your document looks on the page.

Use a font style that is simple, clear and commonplace, such as Times New Roman, Arial or Calibri. Font SIZES from 10-12 points are generally in the ballpark of looking appropriate. Keep in mind that **different font styles in the same point size are not the same size.** A 12-point Arial is larger than a 12-point Times New Roman.

If you are having trouble fitting a document on one page, sometimes a slight margin and/or font adjustment can be the solution.

Serif or sans serif? Sans (without) serif fonts are those like Arial and Calibri that don't have the small finishing strokes on the ends of each letter. There is a great deal of research and debate on the pros and cons of each. Short story: use what you like, within reason; note what employers use; generally sans serif fonts are used for on-monitor reading and serif fonts are used for lengthy print items (like books); serif fonts may be considered more formal. Test: ask someone to look at a document for five seconds; take away the document; ask the person what font was on the document; see if s/he even noticed the style. A too-small or too-large font gets noticed, as does a weird style.

Should your resume and cover letter font style and size match? It can be a nice touch to look polished. But it's also possible to have polished documents that are not in matching fonts. A significant difference in style and size might be noticed. Remember that you can have your documents reviewed through advising, and that might be a fine-tuning question you ask.

A Cover Letter Template (Style 1):

Your Contact Information
Name
Address
City, State, Zip Code
Phone Number
Email Address

Date

Employer Contact Information (if you have it)
Name
Title
Company
Address
City, State, Zip Code

Salutation
Dear Mr./Ms. Last Name, (leave out if you don't have a contact)

Body of Cover Letter
The body of your cover letter lets the employer know what position you are applying for, why the employer should select you for an interview, and how you will follow-up.

First Paragraph
The first paragraph of your letter should include information on why you are writing. Mention the position you are applying for and where you found the job listing. Include the name of a mutual contact, if you have one.

Middle Paragraph(s)
The next section of your cover letter should describe what you have to offer the employer. Mention specifically how your qualifications match the job you are applying for. Remember, you are interpreting your resume, not repeating it.

Final Paragraph
Conclude your cover letter by thanking the employer for considering you for the position. Include information on how you will follow-up.

Complimentary Close

Respectfully yours,

Signature

A Cover Letter Template (Style 2):

*(Hard copy: sender address and contact info at top. **Your address and the date can be left-justified, or centered.**)*

Your Street Address
City, State Zip Code
Telephone Number
E-mail Address

Month, Day, Year

Mr./Ms./Dr. FirstName LastName
Title
Name of Organization
Street or P. O. Box Address
City, State Zip Code

Dear Mr./Ms./Dr. LastName:

Opening paragraph: State why you are writing; how you learned of the organization or position, and basic information about yourself.

2nd paragraph: Tell why you are interested in the employer or type of work the employer does (Simply stating that you are interested does not tell why, and can sound like a form letter). Demonstrate that you know enough about the employer or position to relate your background to the employer or position. Mention specific qualifications which make you a good fit for the employer's needs. (Focus on what you can do for the employer, not what the employer can do for you.) This is an opportunity to explain in more detail relevant items in your resume. Refer to the fact that your resume is enclosed. Mention other enclosures if such are required to apply for a position.

3rd paragraph: Indicate that you would like the opportunity to interview for a position or to talk with the employer to learn more about their opportunities or hiring plans. State what you will do to follow up, such as telephone the employer within two weeks. If you will be in the employer's location and could offer to schedule a visit, indicate when. State that you would be glad to provide the employer with any additional information needed. Thank the employer for her/his consideration.

Sincerely,

(Your handwritten signature [on hard copy])

Your name typed
(In case of e-mail, your full contact info appears below your printed name [instead of at the top, as for hard copy], and of course there is no handwritten signature)

Enclosure(s) (refers to resume, etc.)

(Note: the contents of your letter might best be arranged into four paragraphs. Consider what you need to say and use good writing style.)

Sample Cover Letter A—Letter of Application, e-mail version

Subject line: *(logical to recipient!)* Application for sales representative for mid-Atlantic area

April 14, 2010

Mr. William Jackson
Employment Manager
Acme Pharmaceutical Corporation
13764 Jefferson Parkway
Roanoke, VA 24019
jackson@acmepharmaceutical.com

Dear Mr. Jackson:

From the Acme web site I learned about your need for a sales representative for the Virginia, Maryland, and North Carolina areas. I am very interested in this position with Acme Pharmaceuticals, and believe that my education and employment background are appropriate for the position.

You indicate that a requirement for the position is a track record of success in meeting sales goals. I have done this. After completion of my B.S. in biology, and prior to beginning my master's degree in marketing, I worked for two years as a sales representative with a regional whole foods company. My efforts yielded success in new business development, and my sales volume consistently met or exceeded company goals. I would like to repeat that success in the pharmaceutical industry, using my academic background in science and business. I will complete my M.S. in marketing in mid-May and will be available to begin employment in early June.

Attached is a copy of my resume, which more fully details my qualifications for the position.

I look forward to talking with you regarding sales opportunities with Acme Pharmaceuticals. Within the next week I will contact you to confirm that you received my e-mail and resume and to answer any questions you may have.

Thank you very kindly for your consideration.

Sincerely,
Layne A. Johnson
5542 Hunt Club Lane, #1
Blacksburg, VA 24060
(540) 555-8082
lajohnson@vt.edu

Resume attached as MS Word document *(assuming company web site instructed applicants to do this)*

Sample Cover Letter B—Letter of Application, e-mail version

Subject line: *(logical to recipient!)* Application for marketing research position #031210-528

March 14, 2010

Ms. Charlene Prince
Director of Personnel
Large National Bank Corporation
Roanoke, VA 24040
cprince@largebank.com

Dear Ms. Prince:

As I indicated in our telephone conversation yesterday, I would like to apply for the marketing research position (#031210-528) advertised in the March 12th *Roanoke Times and World News*. With my undergraduate research background, my training in psychology and sociology, and my work experience, I believe I could make a valuable contribution to Large National Bank Corporation in this position.

In May I will complete my B.S. in Psychology with a minor in Sociology at Virginia Tech. As part of the requirements for this degree, I am involved in a senior marketing research project that has given me experience interviewing and surveying research subjects and assisting with the analysis of the data collected. I also have completed a course in statistics and research methods.

My experience also includes working part-time as a bookkeeper in a small independent bookstore with an annual budget of approximately $150,000. Because of the small size of this business, I have been exposed to and participated in most aspects of managing a business, including advertising and marketing. As the bookkeeper, I produced monthly sales reports that allow the owner/buyer to project seasonal inventory needs. I also assisted with the development of ideas for special promotional events and calculated book sales proceeds after each event in order to evaluate its success.

I believe my combination of business experience and social science research training is an excellent match for the marketing research position you described. Enclosed is a copy of my resume with additional information about my qualifications. Thank you very much for your consideration. I look forward to receiving your reply.

Sincerely,
Alex Lawrence
250 Prices Fork Road
Blacksburg, VA 24060
(540) 555-1234
alex.lawrence@vt.edu

Resume attached as MS Word document

Sample Cover Letter C—Letter of Application, hard copy version

-2 Apartment Heights Dr.
Blacksburg, VA 24060
(540) 555-0101
abcd@vt.edu

February 22, 2011

Dr. Michelle Rhodes
Principal, Wolftrap Elementary School
1205 Beulah Road
Vienna, VA 22182

Dear Dr. Rhodes:

I enjoyed our conversation on February 18th at the Family and Child Development seminar on teaching elementary children and appreciated your personal input about balancing the needs of children and the community during difficult economic times. This letter is to follow-up about the Fourth Grade Teacher position as discussed at the seminar. I will complete my M.Ed. in Curriculum and Instruction at Virginia Tech in May 2011, and will be available for employment as soon as needed for the 2011-12 school year.

My teacher preparation program at Virginia Tech has included a full academic year of student teaching. Last semester I taught second grade and this semester am teaching fourth grade. These valuable experiences have afforded me the opportunity to:

- Develop lesson plans on a wide range of topics and varying levels of academic ability,
- Work with emotionally and physically challenged students in a total inclusion program,
- Observe and participate in effective classroom management approaches,
- Assist with parent-teacher conferences, and
- Complete in-service sessions on diversity, math and reading skills, and community relations.

My experience includes work in a private day care facility, Rainbow Riders Childcare Center, and in Virginia Tech's Child Development Laboratory. Both these facilities are NAEYC-accredited and adhere to the highest standards. At both locations, I led small and large group activities, helped with lunches and snacks, and implemented appropriate activities. Both experiences also provided me with extensive exposure to the implementation of developmentally appropriate activities and materials.

I enthusiastically look forward to putting my knowledge and experience into practice in the public school system. Next week I will be in Vienna, and I plan to call you then to answer any questions that you may have. I can be reached before then at (540) 555-7670. Thank you very much for your consideration.

Sincerely,
(handwritten signature)
Donna Harrington

Enclosure

Sample Cover Letter D—Letter of Application, hard copy version

1000 Terrace View Apts.
Blacksburg, VA 24060
(540) 555-4523
stevemason@vt.edu

March 25, 2010

Ms. Janice Wilson
Personnel Director
Anderson Construction Company
3507 Rockville Pike
Rockville, MD 20895

Dear Ms. Wilson:

I read in the March 24th *Washington Post* classified section of your need for a Civil Engineer or Building Construction graduate for one of your Washington, DC, area sites. I will be returning to the Washington area after graduation in May and believe that I have the necessary credentials for the project.

Every summer for the last five years I have worked at various levels in the construction industry. As indicated on my enclosed resume, I have worked as a general laborer, and moved up to skilled carpentry work, and last summer served as assistant construction manager on a two million dollar residential construction project.

In addition to this practical experience, I will complete requirements for my B.S. in Building Construction in May. As you may know, Virginia Tech is one of the few universities in the country that offers such a specialized degree for the construction industry. I am confident that my degree, along with my years of construction industry experience, make me an excellent candidate for your job.

The Anderson Construction Company projects are familiar to me, and my aspiration is to work for a company that has your excellent reputation. I would welcome the opportunity to interview with you. I will be in the Washington area during the week of April 12th and would be available to speak with you at that time. In the next week to ten days I will contact you to answer any questions you may have.

Thank you for your consideration.

Sincerely,
(handwritten signature)
Jesse Mason

Enclosure

Subject: *(logical to recipient!)* Inquiry about software engineering position after completion of M.S. in computer engineering

December 12, 2009

Mr. Robert Burns
President, Template Division
MEGATEK Corporation
9845 Technical Way
Arlington, VA 22207
burns@megatek.com

Dear Mr. Burns:

Via online research in Hokies4Hire through Career Services at Virginia Tech, I learned of MEGATEK. Next May I will complete my master of science in computer engineering. From my research on your web site, I believe there would be a good fit between my skills and interests and your needs. I am interested in a software engineering position upon completion of my degree.

As a graduate student, I am one of six members on a software development team in which we are writing a computer-aided aircraft design program for NASA. My responsibilities include designing, coding, and testing of a graphical portion of the program which requires the use of ZX-WWG for graphics input and output. I have a strong background in CAD, software development, and engineering, and believe that these skills would benefit the designing and manufacturing aspects of template software. Enclosed is my resume with further background information.

My qualifications equip me to make a contribution to the project areas in which your division of MEGATEK is expanding efforts. I would appreciate the opportunity to discuss a position with you, and will contact you in a week or ten days to answer any questions you may have and to see if you need any other information from me. Thank you for your consideration.

Sincerely,
Morgan Stevens
123 Ascot Lane
Blacksburg, VA 24060
(540) 555-2556
mstevens@vt.edu

Resume attached as MS Word document

Sample Cover Letter F—Letter of Inquiry about Internship Opportunities, hard copy version

2343 Blankinship Road
Blacksburg, VA 24060
(540) 555-2233
StacyLeeGimble@vt.edu

January 12, 2010

Ms. Sylvia Range
Special Programs Assistant
Marion County Family Court Wilderness Challenge
303 Center Street
Marion, VA 24560

Subj: Wilderness Challenge internship position

Dear Ms. Range:

This semester I am a junior at Virginia Tech, working toward my bachelor's degree in family and child development. I am seeking an internship for this summer 2010, and while researching opportunities in the field of criminal justice and law, I found that your program works with juvenile delinquents. I am writing to inquire about possible internship opportunities with the Marion County Family Court Wilderness Challenge.

My work background and coursework have supplied me with many skills and an understanding of dealing with the adolescent community; for example:

- 10 hours per week as a volunteer hotline assistant for a local intervention center. After a 50-hour training program, I counseled teenagers about personal concerns and referred them, when necessary, to appropriate professional services for additional help.

- Residence hall assistant in my residence hall, which requires me to establish rapport with fifty residents and advise them on personal matters, as well as university policies. In addition, I develop social and educational programs and activities each semester for up to 200 participants.

My enclosed resume provides additional details about my background.

I will be in the Marion area during my spring break, March 6-10. I will call you next week to see if it would be possible to meet with you in early March to discuss your program.

Thank you for your consideration.

Sincerely,
(handwritten signature)
Stacy Lee Gimble

Encl.

23 Roanoke Street
Blacksburg, VA 24060
(540) 555-1123
K.Walker@vt.edu

October 23, 2010

Mr. James G. Webb
Delon Hampton & Associates
800 K Street, N.W., Suite 720
Washington, DC 20001-8000

Dear Mr. Webb:

Next May I will complete my bachelor's degree in Architecture at Virginia Tech, and am researching employment opportunities in the Washington area. I obtained your name from Professor (last name) who teaches my professional seminar class this semester. S/he indicated that you had volunteered to provide highly motivated graduating students with career advice, and I hope that your schedule will permit you to allow me to ask for some of your time and advice. I am particularly interested in historic preservation and have done research on the DHA website to learn that your firm does work in this area. I am also interested in learning how the architects in your firm began their careers. My resume is enclosed simply to give you some information about my background and project work.

Within two weeks I will call you to arrange a time to speak to you by telephone or perhaps visit your office if that would be convenient. I will be in the Washington area during the week of November 22. I very much appreciate your time and consideration of my request, and I look forward to talking with you.

Sincerely,
(handwritten signature)
Kristen Walker

Encl.

2.2.1.12 AFTER INTERVIEW | THANK-YOU LETTERS | FOLLOW-UP

Following an interview, promptly (within 2 business days) write the interviewer a letter expressing appreciation and thanks for the interview.

The purpose of this letter is to:

- Show appreciation for the employer's interest in you.

- Reiterate your interest in the position' and in the organization.

- Review or remind the employer about your qualifications for the position. If you thought of something you forgot to mention in the interview, mention it in your follow-up / thank-you letter.

- Demonstrate that you have good manners and know to write a thank-you letter.

- Follow up with any information the employer may have asked you to provide after the interview.

Thank-you letters can be hard copy typed, handwritten or e-mailed.

Hard copy not-handwritten are most formal and are appropriate after an interview.

Handwritten are more personal, and can be appropriate for brief notes to a variety of individuals you may have met during an on-site interview.

E-mail is appropriate, particularly as a supplement (i.e. do both e-mail and hard copy) when that has been your means of contact with the person you want to thank, or if your contact has expressed a preference for e-mail, or you know your contact is travelling and will not have access to hard copy mail in a timely fashion.

Before your interview ended, your interviewer should have informed you of the organization's follow-up procedures — from whom (same person who interviewed you, someone else), by what means (phone, e-mail, etc.), and when you would hear again from the organization. If the interviewer did not tell you, and you did not ask, use your follow-up / thank-you letter to ask.

If more than a week has passed beyond the date when you were told you would hear something from the employer (and barring some major event in the news like a merger or acquisition or other event that would be taking employees' attention), call or e-mail to politely inquire about the status of the organization's decision-making process. Someone (or something) or an unexpected circumstance may be holding up the process. A polite inquiry shows that you are still interested in the organization and may prompt the employer to get on schedule with a response. In your inquiry, mention the following: name of the person who interviewed you, time and place of the interview, position for which you are applying (if known), and ask the status of your application.

400C Hunter Ridge
Blacksburg, VA 24060
(540) 555-1111
boles@vt.edu

October 26, 2010

Ms. Glenna Wright
Human Resources Manager
Fashion Department Store
2000 Line Drive
Fairfax, VA 22030

Dear Ms. Wright:

Thank you so much for your time and the privilege of having an interview with you yesterday, October 25, during your recruiting visit to Virginia Tech. The management trainee program you outlined sounds both challenging and rewarding and I look forward to your decision concerning an on-site visit.

As mentioned during the interview, I will be graduating in December with a B.S. in Fashion Merchandising. Through my education and experience I've gained many skills, as well as an understanding of retailing concepts and dealing with the general public. I have worked seven years in the retail industry in various positions from sales associate to assistant department manager. I think my education and work experience would complement Fashion's management trainee program.

I have enclosed a copy of my college transcript and a list of references that you requested.

Thank you again for the opportunity to be considered by Fashion Department Store. The interview served to reinforce my strong interest in becoming a part of your management team. I can be reached at (540) 555-1111 or by e-mail at boles@vt.edu should you need additional information.

Sincerely,

Marianne Boles

Enclosures

170 Roanoke Street
Blacksburg, VA 24060
(540) 555-6241
JRichardson@vt.edu

March 3, 2011

Ms. Patricia Smith
Personnel Manager
Sheldon E-Solutions
1212 Lark Lane
Richmond, VA 23230

Dear Ms. Smith:

Thank you for the opportunity to visit with you and see your facilities last Wednesday. Both the interview and the tour made for an exciting and complete day.

I was so very impressed with your warehousing procedures. Mr. Allen was so thorough in explaining your process to me, and I will be corresponding directly with him to express my appreciation. Incidentally, the process you use is quite similar to one I have been researching through an independent study this term. Perhaps I can share my final report with you and Mr. Allen.

The expense report you requested is enclosed.

Again, thank you for your hospitality during my time in Richmond and for all your efforts to arrange my visit. Having seen your operation, I am all the more enthused about the career opportunity that Sheldon E-Solutions offers. I look forward to your decision.
Sincerely,

Jan Richardson
Enclosure

2.2.1.13 ACKNOWLEDGING OFFER | DECLINE OFFER | REQUEST EXTENSION

Courtesy dictates that you acknowledge a written job offer, even if you are not ready to accept or decline it. Take note of the details of the offer, as specified in your offer letter, and respond appropriately.

You may respond verbally and in writing; whether via e-mail or hard-copy depending on the pattern and mode of communication you have had with the employer, and instructions from the employer.

Items to remember:

- Thank the employer for the opportunity presented.
- If you understand the terms of the offer, indicate that. If you don't, ask for clarification.
- A smart employer will know that you may be considering various employment options and need to make a deliberative decision; you may need to compare the offer to another pending offer.
- However, you might need to make a decision before you know if you will receive another offer.

Sample Letter J—Acknowledging a Job Offer, neither Accepting nor Declining

444 University Road
Blacksburg, VA 24060
(540) 555-9876
gguthrie@vt.edu

February 1, 20xx

Mr. Chris Afton
Grand Hotel Inc.
8899 Jefferson Street
Roanoke, VA 24022

Dear Mr. Afton:

This is to acknowledge your letter offering me the catering and sales representative position with Grand Hotel, Incorporated. Thank you very much for offering me this exciting opportunity. I understand the terms of the offer, and will be able to give you my response by your requested deadline of February 16. I appreciate your allowing me ample time to consider your offer so as to be sure my decision will be in the best interests of both my career goals and the needs of your organization.

In the meantime, I will be in contact with you if I have any additional questions, and I will respond promptly should you need to reach me. Again, thank you so much for this wonderful opportunity.

Yours truly,

(your signature)

George Guthrie

If you choose to decline a job offer, do so courteously, in writing, after making a phone call.

Never say anything negative in writing about the employer, even if you had a negative experience. If you had a very negative experience, it is best to share this information with Career Services.

A decision to decline an offer is usually based on the fact that another offer is a better fit for your interests and goals. It is fine to state this, without giving details about why the declined offer is not a fit.

It is not necessary to state whose offer you accepted, but you may do so if you wish. Remember that this employer may be a contact for you in the future. Maintain the relationship with professional, courteous interactions.

Sample Letter J—Declining a Job Offer

900 Town Road
Blacksburg, VA 24060
(540) 555-9009
email: myname@vt.edu

April 20, 2010

Dr. Joan Swietzer
Citizens Network for Foreign Affairs
343 Third Street, NW
Washington, DC 20201-0343

Dear Dr. Swietzer:

Thank you very much for your telephone call and letter offering me the position of Assistant Project Coordinator with the Citizens Network for Foreign Affairs. While I believe firmly in the mission of your organization and appreciate the challenging opportunity you offer, I have had another offer which I believe more closely aligns with my current career goals and interests. Therefore, although it was a difficult decision, as I explained when we spoke by phone this morning, I must decline your offer. I do appreciate all the courtesy and hospitality extended to me by your office, and I wish you the best in your endeavors.

In the position I have accepted with Public Policy Watch, I will occasionally be on Capitol Hill to attend hearings and monitor legislation, so I hope we can get together again and talk about common interests.

Best regards,

(your signature)
Chris Hancock

In some cases you may need more time than the employer has allowed for your decision.

What to do:

You may ask for an extension; the employer does not have to grant it.

Make sure you have a concrete and appropriate reason for asking for an extension. Expecting to hear soon from another employer with whom you've interviewed is a legitimate reason. If you just hoping to get more interviews, that's not a concrete reason.

Don't wait until the last minute to ask for an extension; this looks like you don't think ahead and may indicate that you might behave the same way on the job.

Be tactful and diplomatic in your wording. You will need to explain your reasons to the employer. For example, if you have an upcoming, previously scheduled interview with another employer, you may explain that it is important to you to keep your commitment to the other employer, and that in order to make the best decision; you need to attend the other interview.

For the sake of speed, phone the employer to discuss the situation. For the record, you should follow up in writing. Since this is a request that needs to be handled quickly, e-mail is probably the best method to confirm your request.

Sample Email —Requesting an Extension of Deadline to Accept or Decline Job Offer

(sample of e-mail)

(March 1, 201x)

Dr. Thomas G. Jones
Oregon Department of Fish and Wildlife
2300 Main Street
Portland, OR 90001
tgjonesemailaddress@agency.gov

Dear Dr. Jones:

Thank you for your telephone call and letter that I received yesterday offering me the position of wildlife biologist with the Oregon Department of Fish and Wildlife. I am excited about the opportunity this position offers both in terms of job duties and location, and I very much appreciate your confidence in offering me the job.

You asked that I make a decision by next week on March 7. This is an important decision, and unfortunately I do not have all the information I need in order to make this decision by that date. To confirm our phone conversation of this afternoon, I am asking you to consider whether it would be possible for me to supply you with my decision by March 28. I would very much appreciate such an extension, and assure you that I will be able to make a firm decision by that date.

Thank you very much for your consideration of my request.

Sincerely,
Hannah Lenke
Fish and Wildlife Sciences & Biology double-major | Virginia Tech
343 Jefferson Street
Blacksburg, VA 24060
(540) 555-8754
HannahLenke@vt.edu

If this were sent as hard-copy, your address and contact info would appear at the top. Since this type of request needs to be handled quickly, most likely you would communicate verbally and use e-mail for confirmation in writing.

2.2.1.14 ACCEPTANCE OF A JOB OFFER

Accepting a job offer (in addition to cause for celebration!) ethically obligates you to:

- Keep your word.
- Cease job search efforts.

If you have accepted a co-op or internship position, e-mail your co-op / internship advisor.

- Promptly notify other employers who have communicated to you that you are under consideration that you must withdraw your name from their consideration.

- First means of notice: a courteous phone call. Make every effort to speak to your contact in person rather than leaving a voice mail message for this purpose.

- Follow up your phone call in writing; please review Sample Letter K. Use e-mail or hard copy depending on the pattern and mode of communication you have had with the employer. Hard copy is more formal; if you have already had an interview with the employer, that more formal means of communication may be advisable.

Failing to notify employers that you are withdrawing from the job search is discourteous, and potentially dishonest. It's essentially leaves the employer with a misperception that you are still interested in the job.

Sample Letter K—Accepting a Job Offer

1234 College Road
Blacksburg, VA 24060
(540) 555-0000
firslastname@vt.edu

March 1, 20xx

Mr. Johnathon P. Summers
Summers Fruit Company
1678 Plantation Road
Atlanta, GA 46201

Dear Mr. Summers:

Thank you for your offer of employment as a horticultural associate at your Fruitville, Florida, site. As we discussed on the phone this morning, I am delighted to accept your offer and look forward to beginning work with Summers Fruit Company.

You indicated that I will be receiving a salary of $_____ per year, and will have initial duties reporting to Andrea Caruso. As your offer stated, I will begin work on August 1st. In mid-July, after relocating to the area, I will call you to see what information or materials I may need before August 1st. In the meantime, please let me know if I can provide you with any information.

Again, thank you for offering me this exciting opportunity. I am very enthused about beginning my career with you after graduation.

Sincerely,

(your signature)

Jason Banyon

Ethical Issues related to accepting a Job Offer:

- Your acceptance of a job offer is binding.
- Don't accept a job offer, even verbally, until you are certain you are committed.
- Don't back out after accepting; that's called reneging, and is unethical.
- An employer should never pressure you to renege on another employer.
- Once you have accepted a job offer, notify any other employers with whom you are in discussion about employment that you are no longer a candidate. Cancel any upcoming interviews by courteously explaining that you have accepted another job offer.

2.2.1.15 YOU HAVE ONE OFFER, BUT YOU ARE HOPING FOR ANOTHER

The situation: Not uncommon for job seekers:

You have an offer from employer B.

You've gone through the interview process with employer A, and you're hoping for, and perhaps expecting an offer. You really want the job with employer A.

B has given you a deadline, perhaps two weeks from the offer date.

You haven't heard from A, and you might not hear until near or after B's deadline.

You'd rather work for A, but B has given you a great offer, and you don't want to turn that down if A doesn't want you.

<u>What to do?</u>

The solution:

First, never accept an offer and then back out later.
That's called reneging, and it's considered highly unethical and inappropriate and is very disturbing to employers (and they do talk to each other). You may hear opinions that it's okay. It's not. Ask yourself what your ethical standards are.)

Without delay, call employer A and let your contact know the situation. Keep your information simple and factual regarding the offer from B. You don't have to mention organization B's name, but you might be asked. Reiterate to employer A that you really want to work for A. Ask where you stand in the evaluation process and if there is any possibility to have definitive information from A before B's deadline, and if not, when that might be.

Your goals: Diplomatically learn more about your status with A, let A know your interest in them, and perhaps stimulate A to speed up their process if they really want you.

Next, without delay, call employer B. Express appreciation for the offer. Indicate that you don't yet have all the information you need to make your decision. (Good organizations will want you to make a well-informed decision and they are aware job seekers are looking at multiple options.)

If A will give you a final decision by or shortly after B's deadline, you have the option to ask B for a deadline extension — just don't wait until the last minute to ask. B can say yes or no to your request; you won't know until you ask.

Your goals: Maintain your good relationship with B, and perhaps gain some time to make your decision.

Bottom line: Be as honest as you can while being diplomatic. Treat everyone with respect; maintaining good relationships with organizations and individuals (who may change organizations) will serve your long-term career success.

Need more help sorting out your individual situation?

Consult a Career Services advisor — via walk-in advising or an appointment. They are there to help you sort through these kinds of situations.

2.3 RESUME

A **resume** is a summary of your experiences and skills relevant to the field of work you are entering. It highlights your accomplishments to show a potential employer that you are qualified for the work you want. It is not a biography of everything you have done. Its purpose is to get you an interview. A resume can (and often should) reflect more than just your paid work experience. Current students, in particular, should consider including the details of your more important extracurricular, volunteer and leadership experiences. Tailor separate resumes to fit each career field in which you are job searching. Some people create slightly different resumes tailored to each job opening. Remember that you can attend a resume workshop or have your resume critiqued at the career center of your college or university.

2.3.1 WHAT IS A RESUME?

Depending on whom you ask, a resume may be viewed as the single most important vehicle to securing your next job, or it may be viewed as an unnecessary nuisance.

In actuality, a resume is a professional introduction meant to encourage a one-on-one interview situation; an opportunity for communication that can lead to a job offer.

It is a rare candidate who is hired by his or her resume alone. It is just as rare to be offered an interview without one.

A resume is often the first line of contact. It establishes a first impression of a potential job candidate's skills, background and hiring value. If written well, this impression can be a positive one, offering the reader a sense of the candidate's "fit" for the position and company being targeted. If written really well, it may convince the reader that the job candidate is the person most ideally suited for the job. When coupled with an effective cover letter, the resume can be a very strong marketing tool.

Preparing a resume may be seen as a nuisance, but having a well-constructed, well-designed resume is an important part of your job search. Consider that for each available job opening there may be as many as 100 to 1000 resumes submitted. If your resume fails to adequately represent your qualifications (for the specific position), fails to establish your hiring value over competing candidates, or is difficult to follow, your ability to compete against those other 100 to 1000 professionals vying for the same position will be greatly diminished.

If your resume secures an interview, then it has done its job. If it sets you ahead of the competition in the mind of your interviewer, then it has given you a distinct advantage and gone beyond its main objective. Good job, because that should be your goal.

A great resume does what all good marketing pieces do: it sells the "consumer" (the potential employer or hiring manager) on the "product" (you).

Like it or not, the act of looking for employment is a function of sales and marketing. The product you are "selling" is you, and the "customer" (the person you hope will "buy" the product) has unique needs and interests. This customer (potential employer) needs to be sold on the fact that you have what it takes to get the job done, that you will meet or exceed the needs and expectations of the position, and you will be worth the compensation.

The reader of your resume is going to want to know how you are going to solve his or her problems, and they are going to give your resume a whopping 15 seconds, or less, to sell you. 15 seconds is the average time a hiring manager will spend "reading" a new resume - before giving it a potential "yes" or "no" response.

2.3.2 PREPARATION IS KEY

In preparing your resume, the more you know about the position you are targeting, the better. If you know the company's missions and goals, if you understand the needs and expectations of the position, if you recognize the target company's "concerns," if you understand who comprises the company's customer base or target market... and you (and your unique skills and experience) can meet these needs and expectations (you have accurately assessed your own value and are able to communicate how your skills, experience and contributions have benefited employers in the past), then you will have the material necessary to create an effective marketing piece.

As in any type of marketing collateral, it is important to present the information so that it captures your reader's interest quickly. Your goal is to encourage the reader to stay with your document as long as possible. Your chance for a more detailed reading increases when you give the reader information which he or she most wants to secure, early in the document.

One of the best ways to accomplish this is to create a Summary Section at the beginning of your resume. A Summary Section highlights for your reader those personal and professional skills you possess that are relevant and valuable to the position you are targeting and allow you to excel in your chosen field and position.

Items and skills of greatest importance (from your readers' viewpoint) should be listed in priority, supporting an impression of both "fit" and potential success. In addition, these should be aspects of your background that set you apart from your competing candidates, particularly candidates with skill sets similar to your own.

You are, in effect, showing your reader how you will solve their problems - better than the competition - and why interviewing you will be a worthwhile expenditure of their time.

2.3.3 FOR WHOM YOU ARE WRITING?

First, let us be very clear about one important fact: you are not writing a career autobiography. This is not about you, seriously. It is about how you can meet the needs, interests and expectations of your reader and this particular position, at this particular company. It is all about them: about what they need, what their hopes and expectations are, and how what you bring to the table will meet these expectations. It is all about how you will benefit them.

The interview stage will be your first opportunity to negotiate; when you will get a chance to discuss what you hope to get out of the deal. But right now, the only person who matters is your reader. They hold all the marbles.

When writing your resume, keep in mind what your reader needs to know. Listing information that will be of no value or benefit to the position you are targeting or the company in question, is just a waste of time and space.

And not only does the information have to have value (from your reader's point-of-view), but it should be interesting, so that your reader wants to keep reading. If the information or dialogue feels repetitive or lacks flow; you will quickly lose your reader's attention.

Check for redundancy in your statements. If the positions you have held are similar, then repeating the same functions, over and over, in ad nauseam detail, will lose your reader's interest (heard it, got it). However, never short-change your accomplishments.

Your potential employer is most interested in seeing how hiring you will benefit the company. But keep this in mind, as well: if it were your job to fill this position, how important would it be to you to hire the best person possible, knowing this decision will reflect back upon your own capabilities?

If you are dealing with a hiring manager or Human Resource (HR) director, you can bet this person has a lot riding on the fact that, if you are hired, you are the right person for the job. It is extremely expensive to recruit, interview, hire and train, only to let an employee go and start the whole process over again. It is the HR director's job to make sure the right person is hired the first time.

All parties involved want to know the right hiring decision is being made. Make it your job to assure them that hiring you is a very good idea. The most effective way to achieve this is by identifying how your efforts and contributions have benefited employers in the past. Take credit for your participation and accomplishments. Know the quantitative results of your efforts (numbers, figures, dollar amounts, and percentages) wherever possible. While aspects of your background may seem minor or of little value to you, they may be seen as a valuable asset to those looking to fill a need.

2.3.4 THE LAYOUT OF YOUR RESUME

The layout of your resume is extremely important. Your resume needs to maintain a "clean" and professional appearance (remember, it is representing you!). It should allow the reader to access the information quickly, even at a glance.

Neat margins, adequate "white space" between groupings, and indenting to highlight text all aid ease of reference and retention of the material. Use bolding and italics sparingly. Overuse of these features can actually diminish their effectiveness of promoting the material they are intended highlight, and can also reduce overall readability.

Your contact information (how the reader can reach you) is essentially the most important information in the entire document. Make certain your name, address, phone number, and e-mail address are clearly visible and at the top of your document (from habit, this is where your reader will look for this information - do not make them search for it).

If your resume is more than one page in length, be certain that your name is on these secondary pages, in case the sheets become separated.

The standards for resume length have changed. It used to be typical for resumes to be no more than one-page in length. For candidates with years of experience, having held multiple positions, or having worked with multiple companies, or who have outstanding achievements to present, this one-page restriction can result in a document that is unreadable, looks "squashed," or utilizes a font size so small that the reader is forced to squint (no, they won't bother). The one-page standard no longer holds true.

Use as much space as you need to concisely, accurately, and effectively communicate your skills, history, achievements, and accomplishments - as these relate to the position and company being targeted. A two-page document, if presented well, will not diminish the effectiveness of your marketing strategy, as long as the information you provide is relevant and valuable to your reader's needs, goals and interests.

A three-page resume is requiring much of your reader's time (and patience), and may not be as effective as a more concise presentation. In fact, your reader may wonder if you have difficulty conveying your value and are unable to create a concise and powerful presentation.

In academic fields and European markets, it may be necessary to go over two pages in length, because additional detail and information is required. But only provide this much information if you feel it will be beneficial and if you are certain your reader will agree with you.

An overly long presentation may leave the reader wondering if you believe their time is not valuable. Remember, by creating something in writing, you are demanding the reader's time and attention. This is fine – just do not waste their time.

Document, **in detail**, the most recent 10 to15 years of your employment and/or experience. Longer if the most recent position extends back 10 years or more. Be certain to highlight growth and advancement in any company where multiple positions were held, including identification of promotions and increases in responsibility.

List prior positions in decreasing detail, unless a previous position more effectively represents your skills and experience relevant to the position and company you are currently targeting.

You want to entice you reader into wanting to meet you (the interview) **to learn more**. Current history and recently utilized skills will hold the most value.

Remember, you will have an opportunity to expand on the information provided in your resume during the interview. So, in your résumé: establish your qualifications, indicate the benefits of hiring you, and entice your reader to want to learn more, through a one-on-one interview.

2.3.5 PHOTOCOPY, FAX, AND SCAN

You can never be certain what your recipient may do with your resume once he or she is in receipt of it. Therefore, you want to make sure your resume can hold up to various processes such as faxing, scanning or photocopying.

Because of this, it is also a good idea to bring along fresh copies of your resume to each interview. Many interview sessions are held by multiple interviewers, and each interviewer should have a clean copy of your resume presentation (not a photocopied version).

Having a clean copy of your resume with you can also help if you if you are required to complete a job application or formal company documents.

A resume will not, typically, get you a job (well, it has happened, but it is extremely rare), but it can secure your chances of being seen and interviewed for a position or company that interests you - just as it can cause you to be passed over in favor of a candidate who offers a better presentation of what he or she has to offer.

It is often your first opportunity to make a company aware of you and all you have to offer.

As with any type of marketing campaign, use your resume as one tool in your job search. Continue to network, improve your interviewing skills, and use every avenue available to you to better your chances and opportunities.

And, when you have secured that next position, do this all over again. Always be prepared for the next opportunity. Keep your resume up-to-date and stay career fit.

2.3.6 TYPES OF RESUME

The format for a **chronological resume** is by far the most common form of resume in use today. The chronological resume is best suited for entry-level job-seekers or those who have stayed in the same field. Occasionally, alumni who are changing careers or re-entering the work force after a prolonged absence, or job-seekers with varied work experiences and accomplishments may find that a **functional resume** is more appropriate. A functional resume is one that is not job specific. In other words, you can write up a resume with your name, address, contact information, your goals, education, previous employers and personal references and use this resume.

2.3.6.1 THE CHRONOLOGICAL RESUME

Here are the key components of a standard chronological resume:

Identification

It is essential that a potential employer can reach you. This section should include your name, address, phone number(s), and e-mail address. If a college student, this section might also include a school address and a permanent home address.

Job Objective

A job objective is optional and should only be included for new college grads and those changing careers. Otherwise, use your cover letter to show your career interests and job objective. If you do use an objective, make sure your objective explains the kind of work you want to do, and keep it between two to four typed lines.

Key Accomplishments

Some resume experts are suggesting adding a section that highlights your key accomplishments and achievements. Think of this section as an executive summary of your resume; identify key accomplishments that will grab the attention of an employer.

This section should summarize (using nouns as keywords and descriptors) your major accomplishments and qualifications.

This section can also be labeled "Professional Profile," "Summary of Accomplishments," "Key Skills," "Summary of Qualifications," "Qualifications Summary," or "Qualifications."

Education

For new college grads, this entry should be your next. For others with full-time work experience, this section should follow your experience section.

This section should include school(s) attended (including years of attendance), majors/minors, degrees, and honors and awards received.

For new grads only: There appears to be a growing trend of employers wanting your GPA in this section. If you decide to do so, make sure to use the GPA that puts you in the best light -- either overall GPA, school or college GPA, or major GPA.

Professional Experience

This section can also be labeled "Experience, "Work History," or "Employment." Using experience is especially good for new college grads because experience is broader than work history, allowing you to include major school projects that showcase your skills and abilities.

This section should include company name, your job title, dates of employment, and major accomplishments. List experiences in reverse chronological order, starting with your most current experience.

List your accomplishments in bullet format (rather than paragraph format). Avoid discussing job duties or responsibilities.

If you don't have a lot of career-related job experience, consider using transferable skills to better highlight your work experience.

Finally, make sure to make use of action verbs when describing your accomplishments.

Affiliations/Interests

This section is optional; include only if you have room on your resume for it. Items from this section are often used as an ice-breaker by interviewers looking to start an interview on an informal basis.

This section should only include professional memberships and non-controversial activities/interests.

References

Many experts say this section is optional, but if you have room, include it. If nothing else, this section signals the end of your resume.

This section should only include a statement saying references are available upon request.

Do **not** include the names of your references on your resume.

2.3.6.2 THE FUNCTIONAL RESUME

Among jobseekers who should consider a functional format:

- Those with very diverse experiences that don't add up to a clear-cut career path
- College students with minimal experience and/or experience unrelated to their chosen career field.
- Career-changers who wish to enter a field very different from what all their previous experience points to.
- Those with gaps in their work history, such as homemakers who took time to raise and family and now wish to return to the workplace. For them, a chronological format can draw undue attention to those gaps, while a functional resume enables them to portray transferable skills attained through such activities as domestic management and volunteer work.
- Military transitioners entering a different field from the work they did in the military.
- Job-seekers whose predominate or most relevant experience has been unpaid, such as volunteer work or college activities (coursework, class projects, extracurricular organizations, and sports).
- Those who performed very similar activities throughout their past jobs who want to avoid repeating those activities in a chronological job listing.
- Job-seekers looking for a position for which a chronological listing would make them look "overqualified."
- Older workers seeking to deemphasize a lengthy job history.

If you can look at a chronological resume without a stated career objective and know exactly what field the jobseeker is headed toward and would be good at, then the chronological format probably is working just fine. But if you can't guess what the jobseeker wants to do and would be good at by looking at the chronology of past jobs, a functional format may be indicated.

The functional format also can work well for college students because it allows skills attained from experiences other than paid employment to be listed within the skills clusters. For example, one student chose leadership as one of her skills clusters, and she listed the following supporting experiences, none of them paid employment:

EXAMPLE 2: An example of leadership on a resume.

Leadership

- o Selected as president-elect of Omicron Delta Kappa honorary and vice president of Phi Eta Sigma honorary
- o Acquainted new students with campus as orientation leader
- o Serve as president of residence hall on Residence Hall Council
- o Function as vice president for intellectual development and assistant recruitment chair for social sorority

It's true that functional formats have been the subject of some employer backlash in recent years. Some employers are unaccustomed to the functional format, and they may become confused or even irritated by functional resumes. Recruiters/headhunters particularly disdain functional formats, so this approach should never be used if you are primarily targeting recruiters with your job search. Employers in conservative fields, such as banking, finance, and law are not big fans of functional formats, nor are international employers. Functional formats also are not acceptable on many online job boards.

Some employers like to know what you did in each job. One solution is to structure your resume in a mostly functional format but include a bare-bones work history in reverse chronological order, creating what is variously known as a chrono-functional, hybrid, or combination format. Such a work-history section need include only job title, name and location of employer, and dates of employment. You don't need to list what you did in each job because that information already is listed in your functional section.

To make your functional resume as reader-friendly as possible for employers, include as much context as you can within each functional description. That way, the employer has a better idea of which skill aligns with which job. In the above leadership-skills example, for instance, the student tells where she demonstrated each skill, thus making helping the employer connect her skills with the experience that produced those skills.

If you're unsure whether a functional resume is right for you, try it both ways and show the two formats to people in the field you wish to enter. See which one they feel presents your skills more effectively.

2.3.6.3 SAMPLE RESUME

SAMPLE CHRONOLOGICAL RESUME A

YOUR NAME

yourname@bc.edu (no hyperlink/line), 617-656-0000
Your Boston College address here, Chestnut Hill, MA 02467
Your home address here, Any Town, CA 01000

EDUCATION
Boston College   Chestnut Hill, MA
College of Arts and Sciences (optional *full, formal* name of school you are in)
Bachelor of Arts /Science in Major Minor (if you have one)   anticipated May 201x
GPA 3.xx (incl. GPA if > 3.00, do NOT round up)

Honors/Awards: Dean's List, Golden Key, AHANA Honor Roll
Relevant courses (optional) (if applicable - no more than 4-5 upper level classes)

Abroad University, City, Country Spring   Semester, 201x
Studied (courses/subjects included)
EXPERIENCE
Name of Organization City, State   Start date - end date
Job title
- Describe any accomplishments that you achieved at your job
- Explain what you did, how you did it, why you did it, and what the results were
- Whenever possible, quantify the number of people/items/data that you worked with
  (Use present tense for verbs describing jobs that you are currently performing)

Name of Organization City, State   Start date - end date
Job title
- Describing Accomplishments: Result + Action + Problem/Project = good bullet point
- **Sample vague bullet point**: Assisted with general upkeep and organization of homeless shelter
- **Sample good bullet points:** Prepared and served meals to 50 homeless male residents; Maintained organization of supply closet and distributed resources to residents as needed; Acted as a liaison between program participants and staff members.

VOLUNTEER EXPERIENCE and/or ACTIVITIES
Name of first Organization City, State   Start date - end date
Title
- Focus on a few key skills that your industry is looking for, and demonstrate how you used those skills through the description of the tasks/projects you accomplished at your job.

Name of Second Organization (brief description if necessary) City, State Start Date - end date
Title
- Remember to be consistent; punctuation at the end of the phrases is not necessary unless you are using paragraph formatting.

ACTIVITIES Section: List each organization (add an action verb phrase describing an acquired skill if you have space)

SKILLS

> **Computers**: Microsoft Excel, PowerPoint, Word, and any other relevant computer skills or languages
>
> **Language:** List all languages you are fluent or proficient in or currently studying, if listed as fluent, should be able to conduct interview in that language.

Christopher O'Connell
coconnell@bc.edu · (cell) 617-656-1234

Boston College, Hardy House   14 Clark Street
Newton Centre, MA 02462
                                                                   Bayside, NY 13790

EDUCATION
Boston College, College of Arts and Sciences; Chestnut Hill, MA
Bachelor of Science in Psychology, May 2010
Honors Program; plan to research and write a thesis, complete focused program coursework

Benjamin Cardoza High School; Bayside, NY
High School Diploma, June 2006
Captain, Varsity Men's Crew

WORK EXPERIENCE
Benjamin Cardoza High School; Bayside, NY

Bookkeeper   Summer 2006
- Maintained account records of 4,000 student body school, including general ledger, accounts payable/receivable; prepared 370 bi-weekly payroll checks along with school accountant
- Analyzed class selections and times data to create 4,000 individual daily schedules for Students

Long Island Medical Group; Garden City, NY
Administrative Assistant   June 2005 - May 2006
- Verified and scheduled patient appointments for seven doctors; screened emergency situations to determine if visit was needed in order to keep doctor on schedule as much as possible
- Maintained over 5,000 patient files for doctor review before patient appointment; filed incoming lab results and notified doctor of any unusual reports

ACTIVITIES
- BC Men's Crew Team; devote 20 hours per week to practice during height of season
- 4Boston; volunteered four hours per week at the Jackson Mann Community Center Pre-school Program; acted as an aide for lead teacher
- Campus School Volunteer; spend five hours bi-weekly with a moderate special needs student

SKILLS
PC and Mac; Microsoft Word, Excel

INTERESTS
Mountain biking, cross country skiing, travel to Ireland, chess

67

SAMPLE CHRONOLOGICAL RESUME C

Mark Stomato   32 Frasure Ave., Malvern, PA 10324 (610) 552-0056

Boston College, Edmunds Room 122, Chestnut Hill, MA 02467 (617) 656-6601 stomato@bc.edu

OBJECTIVE
A Web design position within a Research and Design Division in a major consumer electronics organization.

EDUCATION
Boston College, Wallace E. Carroll School of Management; Chestnut Hill, MA
Bachelor of Science in Information Systems, May 2004
GPA 3.4, Dean's List First Honors

EXPERIENCE
General Electric Capital; Philadelphia, PA
Assistant Web Administrator   Summer 2003
- Created and implemented process to allow multiple groups and users to publish documents to a single source for an Intranet audience; increased lines of communication across 10 departments
- Designed Intranet database to record and track employee Total Quality Management practices; trained staff on usage of TQM reporting process, which also streamlined the entire process
- Constructed a database, for the Real Estate Department, to provide an organized method to track and contact
  commercial developers and owners as part of Six Sigma quality project; raised awareness of business
- regional coverage and ensured targeting of only top players

Undergraduate Government at Boston College (UGBC), Boston College; Chestnut Hill, MA
Senator, Community Service Committee   Fall 2002 - Spring 2003
- Organized logistics of a clothing drive for a homeless shelter and created a Web page off the main UGBC site, advertising the drive; obtained donations from the campus; raised over 500 lbs. of clothing, which
- surpassed student government's goal by 100 lbs.
  Supervised a committee of 11 students to publicize the event on campus

Advent International; Newtown, PA
Network Administration Intern   Summer 2002
- Configured, upgraded, and supported PC hardware and software in a networked environment of over 200 PC's
- Provided help desk and on site support to over 100 employees at national headquarters

Westchester Field Club; Westchester, PA
Swim Instructor, Counselor   Summer 2001
- Managed and scheduled eight swim instructors to teach basic swimming skills to a camp of 70 children, ages 5-8; designed daily learning activities to meet a variety of abilities
- Formed partnerships with three other local clubs to coordinate bi-monthly swim meets and water-polo matches

ACTIVITIES
- Information Technology Club
- Student Interviewer, Boston College Office of Admissions

SKILLS
- PC; Word, Excel, PowerPoint, Access, HTML, UNIX operating systems, JavaScript, SQL, Dreamweaver, Flash, Photoshop, Serena Collage
- Conversant in Italian

INTERESTS

- Learning new computer applications (C++), skiing, swimming

CHRIS ATTWATER
567 Rosewood Lane
Colorado Springs, CO 81207
(960) 555-1212
cattw@somedomain.com

OBJECTIVE

Executive assistant position allowing for parlay of demonstrated organization, customer service, communication and project management skills proven by 13 years of successful, profitable self-employment.

PROFILE

Motivated, personable business professional with multiple college degrees and a successful 13-year track record of profitable small business ownership. Talent for quickly mastering technology -- recently completed Microsoft Office Suite certificate course. Diplomatic and tactful with professionals and nonprofessionals at all levels. Accustomed to handling sensitive, confidential records. Demonstrated history of producing accurate, timely reports meeting stringent HMO and insurance guidelines.

Flexible and versatile -- able to maintain a sense of humor under pressure. Poised and competent with demonstrated ability to easily transcend cultural differences. Thrive in deadline-driven environments. Excellent team-building skills.

SKILLS SUMMARY

• Project Management • Report Preparation • Written Correspondence • General Office Skills	• Computer Savvy • Customer Service • Scheduling • Marketing & Sales	• Insurance Billing • Accounting/Bookkeeping • Front-Office Operations • Professional Presentations

---

PROFESSIONAL EXPERIENCE

Communication: Reports/Presentations/Technology

- Prepare complex reports for managed-care organizations and insurance companies, ensuring full compliance with agency requirements and tight deadlines.
- Author professional correspondence to customers and vendors.
- Design and deliver series of classes for local businesses and associations, providing ergonomic counseling and educating employees on proper lifting techniques to avoid injury.
- Conduct small-group sessions on meditation/relaxation techniques.
- Communicate medical concepts to patients using layman's terms to facilitate understanding.
- Rapidly learn and master varied computer programs; recently completed Microsoft Office Suite certificate course.

Customer Service/Marketing/Problem Solving

- Oversee front-office operations and provide impeccable customer service:
  --Built a clientele supported by 60% referral business.

- Develop and implement strategic marketing plan for business:
  -- Launched a thriving private practice, building revenue from $0 to over $72K in first three years with minimal overhead.
  -- Create special promotions, write/design print and outdoor advertising and coordinate all media buying.

- Won over a highly skeptical medical community as the first chiropractor to target MDs for informative in-service demonstrations, classes and booths:
  -- Presentations resulted in standing-room-only crowds of 50+.
  -- Four MDs subsequently became patients and referred family members as well.
  -- Increased client base by one-third resulting from MD referrals.

Detail Mastery & Organization

- Manage all aspects of day-to-day operations as multisite owner and practitioner of Attwater Chiropractic:
  -- Facility rental/maintenance.
  -- Patient scheduling for busy office averaging 52 appointments weekly.
  -- Finances: accounts payable/receivable, invoicing, insurance billing, budgeting.
  -- Supervision of a total of eight medical receptionist interns.
  -- Compliance with all healthcare facility, HMO and insurance requirements.

EMPLOYMENT HISTORY

ATTWATER CHIROPRACTIC -- Colorado Springs, CO; Pueblo, CO; Cheyenne, WY
Owner/Operator, 1997 to Present

LAKEVIEW RESTAURANT & CAFÉ -- Minneapolis, MN
Waitress, 1994 to 1997

EDUCATION

NORTHWESTERN COLLEGE OF CHIROPRACTIC -- Minneapolis, MN
Doctor of Chiropractic Degree, 1997

- Four-year advanced degree requiring 30-34 credit hrs. per quarter.
- GPA: 3.89/4.0
- Licensed to practice chiropractic in Colorado, Minnesota, Wyoming and Montana.

BARTON COUNTY COMMUNITY COLLEGE -- Great Bend, KS
Associate's Degree in Pre-chiropractic, 1993

- GPA: 4.0/4.0

COMPUTER SKILLS

• Microsoft Word • Microsoft Excel • Microsoft PowerPoint	• Visio • Microsoft Access • Medisoft (Insurance Billing Software)

Available for relocation
567 Rosewood Lane | Colorado Springs, CO 81207 | (960) 555-1212 |
cattw@somedomain.com

2.3.7 THE CURRICULUM VITAE

The primary differences between a resume and curriculum Vitae (CV) are the length, what is included and what each is used for. A resume is a one or two page summary of your skills, experience and education. While a resume is brief and concise - no more than a page or two, a curriculum vitae is a longer (at least two page) and more detailed synopsis.

A curriculum vitae includes a summary of your educational and academic backgrounds as well as teaching and research experience, publications, presentations, awards, honors, affiliations and other details. In Europe, the Middle East, Africa, or Asia, employers may expect to receive a curriculum vitae.

In the United States, a curriculum vitae is used primarily when applying for academic, education, scientific or research positions. It is also applicable when applying for fellowships or grants.

2.4 THE INTERVIEW

Before you go on your interview, you should realize there are several common types of job interviews. You will definitely want to inquire what type of job interview you will be going on beforehand so you can best prepare for it. Don't be afraid to ask your recruiter what type of job interview will be conducted, as it serves both of you and the interviewer to know.

2.4.1 SIX TYPES OF INTERVIEWS

1) Traditional one on one job interview:

The traditional one on one interview is where you are interviewed by one representative of the company, most likely the manager of the position you are applying for. Because you will be working with this person directly, if you get the job; he or she will want to get a feel for who you are and if your skills match those of the job requirements.

You may be asked questions about the experience on your resume, what you can offer to the company or position. Many times the interviewer will ask you questions such as "Why would you be good for this job?" or "Tell me about yourself." The one on one interview is by far, one of the most common types of job interviews.

2) Panel interview:

FIGURE 2.10

In a panel interview, you will be interviewed by a panel of interviewers. The panel may consist of different representatives of the company such as human resources, management, and employees. The reason why some companies conduct panel interviews is to save time or to get the collective opinion of panel regarding the candidate. Each member of the panel may be responsible for asking you questions that represent relevancy from their position.

3) Behavioral interview:

In a behavioral interview, the interviewer will ask you questions based on common situations of the job you are applying for. The logic behind the behavioral interview is that your future performance will be based on a past performance of a similar situation. You should expect questions that inquire about what you did when you were in a particular situation and how did you dealt with it. In a behavioral interview, the interviewer wants to see how you deal with certain problems and what you do to solve them.

4) Group interview:

Many times companies will conduct a group interview to quickly prescreen candidates for the job opening as well as give the candidates the chance to quickly learn about the company to see if they want to work there. Many times, a group interview will begin with a short presentation about the company. After that, they may speak to each candidate individually and ask them a few questions.

One of the most important things the employer is observing during a group interview is how you interact with the other candidates. Are you emerging as a leader or are you more likely to complete tasks that are asked of you? Neither is necessarily better than the other, it just depends on what type of personality works best for the position that needs to be filled.

5) Phone interview:

A phone interview may be for a position where the candidate is not local or for an initial prescreening call to see if they want to invite you in for an in-person interview. You may be asked typical questions or behavioral questions.

Most of the time, you will schedule an appointment for a phone interview. If the interviewer calls unexpectedly, it's ok to ask them politely to schedule an appointment. On a phone interview, make sure your call waiting is turned off, you are in a quiet room, and you are not eating, drinking or chewing gum.

6) Lunch interview:

Many times lunch interviews are conducted as a second interview. The company will invite you to lunch with additional members of the team to further get to know you and see how you fit in. This is a great time to ask any questions you may have about the company or position as well, so make sure you prepare your questions in advance.

Although you are being treated to a meal, the interview is not about the food. Don't order anything that is too expensive or messy to eat. Never take your leftovers home in a doggy bag either. You want to have your best table manners and be as neat as possible. You don't need to offer to pay, it is never expected for a candidate to pay at a lunch interview.
Chew quietly and in small bites so you don't get caught with a mouthful of food when the recruiter asks you a question.

So, now you have an idea of these six common types of job interviews. However, no matter what type of job interview you go on, always do your best to prepare for it the best you can ahead of time so you can do your best and show them the best of who you are.

2.4.2 PREPARATION FOR THE INTERVIEWING PROCESS

When you submit a job application or enquiry, you - the applicant - are in control. Normally *you* select the information to include in your resume or curriculum vita and *you* decide where to put the emphasis. There is usually time to deliberate on each individual item and the opportunity to enlist the help of friends and colleagues.

If your application is successful you may then be invited for an interview. From this point on the employer is in control. *The employer* determines the format of the interview and *the employer* sets the questions. *You* must answer the questions in real-time without consulting friends or colleagues. A great resume may get you an interview - but you need to follow-through at the interview to win the job.

Interviews divide into two categories: the screening interview and the hiring or selection interview. **Screening interviews** are used to qualify a candidate before he or she meets with a hiring authority for possible selection. The **hiring or selection interview** can take on many different forms. Screening interviews are the normal process for companies to weed out candidates for a single job opportunity. These interviews are usually quick, efficient and low cost strategies that result in a short list of qualified candidates. These interviews save time and money by eliminating unqualified candidates.

If invited to a face to face screening interview, it will usually be with a third party recruiter or someone from the Human Resources department. These are considered the gatekeepers for a company. They are typically experienced and professional interviewers who are skilled at interviewing and screening candidates. These interviewers should be effective at judging character, intelligence, and if the candidate is a good fit for the company culture. They also should be good at identifying potential red flags or problem areas in the candidate's work background and general qualifications. Some examples of screening interviews include the telephone interview, the computer interview, the videoconference interview and the structured interview.

2.4.3 PREPARING FOR THE INITIAL INTERVIEW [SCREENING INTERVIEW]

A typical hiring process consists of a screening, or initial, interview and one or more "callback" interviews. All of the strategies you used to succeed in your first interview apply to subsequent interviews—but more so. The callback interview involves more people, more time, more scrutiny and more pressure.

The initial interview screens out candidates who clearly don't have the requisite skill and fit; subsequent interviews dig deeper. At a callback interview, you are introduced to additional members of the team. This usually includes technical and or managerial members of the company. Each interviewer will have a slightly different style and perspective.

You will be evaluated on how well you fit into the firm culture and what skills, experience, and opportunities you have to offer the prospective employer. The assessment continues from the moment you arrive until you leave, many hours later, including while you are walking from one office to the next, speaking with support staff, and while at lunch. At the same time, this is your chance to determine whether the opportunity is a good fit for you, as well.

Callback interviews can take a variety of forms including meeting with a group of people at one time, dining with one or more persons, or interviewing with several individuals consecutively. Interviews with decision-makers in far-flung offices can be via videoconference or telephone. Each of these settings requires different strategies and techniques.

Those conducting first interviews often are trained in interviewing techniques. The array of people you see during subsequent meetings may include some less skilled as interviewers or who practice in an unrelated area. You may have to take the initiative to communicate what you want the interviewer to know about you and your qualifications.

Callback interviews may last from several hours to an entire day. Ask beforehand how long the interview is expected to take. It may extend longer than anticipated, so plan accordingly. Request a list of people you are expected to meet, and research their backgrounds ahead of time.

Bring several copies of your resume, transcript, writing sample, business plan, and other relevant documents– enough for everyone you are meeting and extras, in case others are added to your schedule. Be prepared to provide references shortly after your callback, if requested. You can stipulate that they not be contacted without your authorization.

Each meeting represents a fresh beginning. There is no such thing as a "rubber stamp" interview. Therefore, don't coast on the success of earlier interviews. Review your performance in the previous interview. Note any questions or situations that caused you difficulty and practice how to handle them better. Consider what made you shine, and plan to do more of the same. Take another look at the job posting, if there was one. Your responses to all questions should attempt to demonstrate that you possess the attributes the employer is seeking.

Brainstorm fresh information you can bring into a callback interview—new accomplishments, different examples, and more knowledge about the prospective employer. Keep abreast of developments relevant to the prospective employer by reviewing its website, trade publications and other sources. Consider conducting informational interviews with members of your extended network who may have valuable insights. Make a list of questions to ask your interviewers during the callback that will demonstrate your knowledge of the prospective employer's operations and challenges, and fill in any gaps in your understanding of the opportunity.

Be ready to discuss—but do not introduce—your compensation requirements and other deal points, such as willingness to travel or relocate. Do any market research necessary to prepare to negotiate if an interviewer raises the subject. The best time to discuss these topics is when the prospective employer has indicated that they are ready to make you an offer. However, you do not want to be caught unawares if they bring it up beforehand.

Moreover, you must be physically prepared to maintain focus and energy throughout the possibly lengthy callback interview. Get a good night's sleep the night before and eat a decent breakfast. Don't take the red eye and head right to your interview. If you are tired you might let your guard down or misspeak. Dress professionally but comfortably as you may be moving around their offices and walking to and from lunch. Don't wear something that will wrinkle or wilt by the end of a long day. You might want to toss a small snack into your briefcase or purse in case there is no lunch break.

Depending upon the recruiting practices of the prospective employer, their ability to schedule you with all of the appropriate interviewers, and the number of candidates under consideration, you may be asked back for several callback interviews. You also may be asked to come back for further interviews if there is some question regarding your cultural fit or skill set, or if there is a difference of opinion among the various interviewers. It is typical for finalists to be asked back one more time so that the prospective employer can evaluate all such candidates on a level playing field before a final decision is made. With some thought and advance preparation before each subsequent interview, you increase your chances of being the candidate selected to receive an offer.

2.4.4 PREPARING FOR THE ON-SITE INTERVIEW
[HIRING OR SELECTION INTERVIEW]

To prepare for the on-site interview, you should know the company's products and services, financial picture, geographical locations and culture. You should take the time to find out if alumni from your institution are working there. If so, interview them about the kinds of positions that are available and the environment or workplace culture. Others in the workplace can provide firsthand knowledge about the pros and cons of working for the company. Successful interviews are those in which you, the candidate, and interviewer both leave the room with a feeling that they know and understand each other.

FIGURE 2.11

In the interview, the employer has three objectives: (1) to gather relevant information about your qualifications; (2) to assess how your qualifications match the requirements of the job; and (3) to present the organization to you in a positive way.

Your objective as a candidate should be to communicate information about yourself and your qualifications clearly and accurately, and to seek relevant information about the particular job, position, and employer.

Most interviews can be successful for you if you prepare for the expected and unexpected. This is usually a six-part process:

1. Preparation
2. Establishing rapport
3. Talking about yourself
4. Talking about the organization
5. Close-Out
6. Evaluation

You are involved in the first five segments; the sixth typically takes place while you are on site or shortly after you leave the premises.

When you travel to the interview city, you will most likely arrive the evening before the interview is scheduled. Be sure you are comfortable with knowing exactly where you are going for the interview. Plan on arriving at least 30-45 minutes before the actual interview. This allows you time to unwind, make sure that you are well groomed and have time to relax.

Most on-site interviews will put you before a panel or group, or you may be in a one-on-one setting. Be sure that your handshake is firm, and keep eye contact with each individual as you are introduced. Let the interviewer invite you to be seated. Your eye contact is very important because often it is the believability concept that sells what you are saying. Your body language also sends a message of confidence and sincerity. In addition to the firm handshake and eye contact, be sure to have well-balanced posture, an open, relaxed facial expression, a firm voice, and use appropriate gestures when emphasizing key words.

The first 30 seconds to five minutes of the interview are very important. The first impression is next to impossible to change. You never get a second chance to make a first impression. Your appearance and dress are critical in that you should fit into the culture of the workplace by dressing appropriately. You should wear conservative colors and avoid excessive jewelry, flashy colors, excessive makeup, strong perfumes or colognes.

Be sure that you have practiced your 30 second or 3-5 minute infomercial. The strong lead tells the interviewer about yourself, what your assets and strengths are and the value you can bring to their organization. Be prepared to give examples of a time when you exemplified leadership, a time when things were not going well and you turned them around. Also be prepared to discuss your involvement in professional societies, civic organizations and summer or part-time employment. Be able to describe a time when you experienced failure and the lessons that came from that experience.

Be yourself during the interview. Bear in mind that the organization chose to interview you. Let the knowledge and your interview preparation bolsters your confidence. During the interview, take notes. Inform the interviewer(s) at the beginning of the interview that you would like to take some notes to help in the questioning and answering session at the end of the interview.

The competencies that will be evaluated during the interview are skills that you have polished during your education, extracurricular involvement, internships, co-op and summer experiences. The areas that will be evaluated are adaptability, communication, initiative, interpersonal acumen, planning and organization, accountability, resourcefulness, work orientation, and negotiation skills among others. Be a good listener but not reticent about asking penetrating questions.

Some routine questions that will be asked of you during the interview are listed below:

- Tell me about yourself. What do you look for in a job? What are your special abilities? How do you perform under pressure?
- Why did you choose your particular field of study and work? What do you perceive as the advantages of your chosen field?
- What makes you think that you could be successful with our organization? What do you know about our organization?
- What types of positions are you most interested in?
- Are you willing to relocate multiple times?
- What have you learned from some of the jobs that you have held?
- Is your GPA indicative of your ability?
- What leadership positions have you held in college and in your community?
- Are you very creative? Give some examples.
- What is your philosophy of management?
- Why should we hire you?

In answering all questions, be specific, concise, and give examples that show your ability to provide direction, allocate resources, that you can execute with quality, and have a passion to succeed. Exemplify that your value system is one of fairness, truth telling, promise keeping, and respect for all individuals.

Be prepared for the unexpected by writing down five questions that you hope no one would ever ask you in the interview. Take some time and thoughtfully answer those questions. Once you master how you would answer those questions on site, your comfort level will come naturally.

Some routine questions that you may want to ask the interviewer are:

- If hired, would I be filling a newly created position, or would I be replacing someone?
- Would you describe a typical work day and the things that I would be responsible for and accountable for?
- What are the most critical duties of the job?
- How will I get feedback on my performance?
- What is the career path from this position to the top of the organization?
- How does this position contribute to the bottom line of the organization?
- What is the diversity mix of your management, the organization and the area in which you will be working?

Do not ask about salary. Let the organization bring up the subject.

During the interview, sell yourself, show what you can do for the organization, show that you are a team player, ask for the job, and never apologize for any areas where you need growth. Present those areas from a positive viewpoint if they must be discussed. Project confidence and never imply that you can work miracles. You should not discuss religion, politics or race, although, as stated above, you may ask about the company's diversity.

Be sure that you never lose your personal touch, and give the interviewer(s) a true sense of the value that you can bring to their organization by letting your unique qualities come out.

Consult a dining etiquette book or website to be sure that you are prepared in case part of the interview takes place in a restaurant or company dining room.

Be clear, as you end the day, on what the next steps in the process are for moving forward. If an offer is made on the spot, thank the organization and take some time to ponder in order to make an informed decision. Send a personal handwritten thank-you note to those who interviewed you in the process.

It is important that you feel valued, challenged, and have an excellent compensation package, training for personal and professional development, and clearly defined career progression.

2.4.5 PREPARING FOR VIDEO CONFERENCE, COMPUTER AND PHONE INTERVIEWS

As companies continue to look for ways to trim costs, video, computer and telephone conferences are quickly becoming an initial first step for interviewing non-local candidates. The telephone interview is the most common way to perform an initial screening interview. This helps the interviewer and the candidate get a general sense if they are mutually interested in pursuing a discussion beyond the first interview. This type of interviewing also saves time and money. They may be tape recorded for the review of other interviewers. The goal, for the candidate during the phone interview, is to arrange a face to face meeting.

To prepare for a telephone interview:

- Minimize distracting background noise prior to the call's start. Barking dogs, television noise and flushing toilets can blow it.
- If the call is unexpected, ask to reschedule for a time when you'll have had a chance to prepare yourself and your environment.
- If the interview is scheduled, keep your résumé and notes close for reference.
- Like a video interview, avoid checking your blackberry or e-mail, and pay close attention to the conversation. Phone interviewers judge candidates by what they say and how they say it. Lulls in conversation can indicate a lack of focus or knowledge on a subject.

FIGURE 2.12

Therefore a few additional preparation tips should be kept in mind for phone interviews:

- Turn call-waiting off so your call isn't interrupted.

- Clear the room of other people and pets. Turn off the stereo, TV and close the door.

- Keep your resume in clear view, on the top of your desk, so it's at your fingertips when you need to answer questions.

- Don't eat or drink during the interview.

- Smile, as it will change the tone of your voice.

- Speak slowly and enunciate clearly.

- Don't interrupt the interviewer.

- Take your time - it's perfectly acceptable to take a moment or two to collect your thoughts.

- Give concise answers.

The computer interview involves answering a series of multiple-choice questions for a potential job interview or simply for the submission of a resume. Some of these interviews are done through the telephone or by accessing a web site. One type is done with pushing the appropriate buttons on the telephone for the answer you are submitting. Wal-Mart uses this method for screening cashiers, stockers, and customer service representatives.

Another type of **computer interview** is provided by **accessing a website** while using a computer keyboard and a mouse. Lowes Home Improvement uses this type of screening. Some of the questions on both of these types of interviews are related to ethics. As an example, "If you see a fellow co-worker take a candy bar and eat it, do you a. Confront co-worker, b. Tell the supervisor, c. Do nothing."

82

Face-to-face interviews are the preferred selection tool for recruiters, but this may be changing as videoconference technology becomes more available and easy to use. It doesn't hurt that videoconference interviews take up less resources in terms of people, time, money, and environmental impact. They allow companies to broaden their applicant pool in a world that's becoming more globally competitive. More than half of the largest U.S. companies do videoconference interviews. The Modern Language Association (MLA) has increased their use of videoconference interviews from 12% to 18%, and any college career center worth its salt includes tips and advice on preparing for a videoconference interview. Chapman and Webster in 2003 anticipated that 10% of companies would be hiring purely from videoconference interviews.

Videophone and Video Conferencing interviews provide the transfer of audio and video between remote sites. More than half of the largest U.S. companies already utilize videoconferencing. It is a convenient communication method and an alternative to the more costly face-to-face meetings. Anyone, anywhere in the world can perform videoconferencing with the use of a microphone, camera and compatible software. Videoconferencing is available on the Internet. Its continual drop in cost is making it a popular resource for businesses as well as for home use.

Although telephone interviews save a lot of money and resources in the recruitment process, few companies are rash enough to actually hire someone based on phone interviews. There's something about needing to "see it in order to believe it." For better or for worse, nonverbal cues such as eye contact, smiling, body orientation, gestures all influence a person's perception and ability to trust in another person, which you can't get over the phone.

For those of you who are concerned about how applicants perceive videoconference interviews. An informal poll on Microsoft's Job Blog reported that 88% of poll participants preferred videoconference to telephone interviews. In an early 1997 study by Kroeck and Magnusen, a remarkable 54% of applicants rated videoconference interviews the same or preferable to a traditional face-to-face interview. While applicants have a harder time reading how a videoconference interview went, applicants definitely feel they are better able monitor themselves, respond to questions, and know their interviewer(s). Of course, it's also good to take into consider the impression a phone or videoconference interview may give about your company, after all, not everyone is a videoconference fan.

Here are several tips on how to prepare for your video interview:

- Dress as you would for a face-to-face interview - from head to toe. Even though the camera may catch you from waist-up at your desk, don't take the chance being viewed in shorts.
- Try to maintain eye contact with remote viewers and avoid frequently looking away, which could create an impression that you're distracted.
- DON'T CHECK YOUR BLACKBERRY.
- Speak clearly and pay close attention to the interviewer's conversation with you, even if the interview is being simultaneously broadcast to multiple offices.

- When emphasizing something important, lean in slightly toward the camera. If you're a small person in a large chair, sit on the edge of your seat to maintain a strong visual presence.

Take Away Points:

- videoconference interviews can be used not only to screen applicants but to hire applicants
- applicants like being able to see and respond to interviewers although they have a harder time knowing if they did well on an interview
- technical problems will probably come up–how an organization handles technical problems rather than detract from the experience can reveal what a group is really like
- if you're at home, remember to lock up your dog before going into the interview–oh, and don't sneeze or make fast hand movements

FIGURE 2.13

Tips for a successful videoconference interview:

Appearance:

- Pastel shirts and interesting ties that are not too busy in pattern are best. Pastel shades work well
- on television, as do bright blues, pinks, fuchsia and green.

- Avoid large areas of red, bright whites, black and navy, as well as plaid, stripes and overly busy
- patterns.

- High gloss lips and glittery jewelry will catch the light and be distracting.

Body Language:

- Look straight into the monitor at the interviewer. It will give the impression that you are looking into their eyes.

- Most people find that it only takes a few minutes to get comfortable in a videoconference interview. Focus on the person you are talking to and soon you will forget the camera is running. Avoid excessive motion. Rocking in your chair or rapid arm movements will appear as a blur to the other person. Don't be unnaturally stiff however. Relax just as you would if you were speaking to someone in person.

- Speak naturally. The microphones will pick up your audio without you having to raise your voice. There is no need to shout.

- Show your energy and enthusiasm. Remember that the camera will stay static. Image and voices are all you have to make yourself interesting and stand out. Don't forget to smile!

Set-up:

- Arrive at the videoconference site early enough to get comfortable with the equipment. You want to make sure that everything is working properly and that the table, chair, and microphone are set up to your advantage. Position yourself so that you are looking into the camera, not at the monitor, to give the impression of eye contact. Have the camera as close to eye level as possible so that you are not looking up or down at the interviewers. It is best to position the camera and the monitor so that you can glance at the other participants in the monitor briefly, without breaking your gaze at the camera too often.

- Center yourself in the screen and at a medium distance rather than at the end of a long conference table. You should appear from about the middle of your upper arms and have an excess of screen space above your head. Sit up straight; do not slouch or lean to the side. Leaning forward slightly towards the camera helps increase eye contact. Conversely, leaning back can create a feeling of distance.

- Set up your notes, pen, water, and reading glasses so that they are accessible but out of camera range. Remember to refrain from shuffling papers or tapping a pen during the interview, however, as that will be picked up on the microphone.

- If possible, arrange the lighting so that you are not in unflattering shadows or washed out, and your coloring is as lifelike as possible. Watch for reflection from your glasses. Don't forget, however, that the camera catches everything while it is on. Therefore, do not use it as a mirror to fix your hair or makeup before the interview. Likewise, do not relax or comment inappropriately after the interview until you are sure the camera is off.

Etiquette:

- Hesitate slightly: Be prepared for a very slight delay in receiving the audio and video. This takes a few moments to get used to. Try and get into the habit of hesitating slightly before speaking to assure that the other person has finished speaking, and again when you complete what you have to say so that other participants know that you are done .

- Speak clearly and listen carefully.

- Each participant in the videoconference should introduce themselves, and state their location if there are various offices involved, at the beginning of the interview or anytime a new participant joins the session. Jot down this information so you can use your interviewers' names during the interview, and address your questions and comments as appropriate.

- Videoconference interviews also differ from in-person meetings in that there is no opportunity for a handshake to begin or end the session. Therefore, to wrap things up, summarize your main points, thank the interviewers for their time, let them know you are interested in the job, and ask about next steps. Pay attention to the time without obviously glancing at your watch and follow the interviewer's cues that the session is drawing to a close.

- Rehearse: A dry run with a friend is critical for you to have an idea of what to do and where to look as well as any potential hiccups.

For both telephone and video conference interviews, it helps to practice. You can practice in the mirror or even by recording yourself. Additionally, it's nice to send a follow-up thank you that reiterates your top selling points. Be sure to proofread, though.

2.4.6 DEADLY MISTAKES MADE IN JOB INTERVIEWS

There are three main reasons why interviews may go wrong:

a) You can't articulate yourself and communicate exactly why you are the perfect fit for the job.

b) You are unprepared; you can't give the right answer to the tough question behavioral questions.

c) You are too nervous; you can't control your nerves and unfortunately lose control during the interview.

Since no two interviews are alike, it is difficult to be prepared for what lies ahead, but you can focus on your presentation skills, which may be even more important than what you have to say. Three areas of performance, which should be considered dangerous and deadly, are worth spending some time thinking about before your next interview.

1. Poor Non-verbal Communication Image

It's about demonstrating confidence.

- Stand straight, and make good eye contact.
- Connect with a good, firm handshake.
- Sit erect and lean forward in the chair, appearing interested and attentive.

That first impression can be a great beginning, or a quick ending to your interview.

2. Poor Verbal Communication Skills

Your interviewer is giving you information, either directly or indirectly.

- Good communication skills include listening and letting the person know you heard what they said.

- Observe your interviewer's style and pace and match that style, adjusting your style and pace to match.

- Use appropriate language. Beware of using slang words or references to age, race, religion, politics, or sexual preferences, these topics could get the door slammed very quickly.

- Telling the interviewer more than they need to know could be a fatal mistake. Too much information, particularly personal information, could get into some areas that are best not discussed in an interview.

3. Not Asking Questions

It is extremely important to ask questions.

- When asked, "Do you have any questions?" if you answer "No," it is the WRONG answer!

- Asking questions gives you the opportunity to show your interest. The best questions come from listening to what is said and asked during the interview. Ask for additional information.

- Asking questions gives you the opportunity to find out if this is the right place for you. Your interview is your chance to find out what goes on in the company.

The job market is very competitive and the competition is fierce. Give yourself every advantage by preparing and practicing before the interview. Be aware of your verbal and non-verbal performance and the messages you are sending. It could make the difference between a job offer or not.

2.4.7 THE TONE OF YOUR VOICE DURING INTERVIEW

Often, your **tone of voice** says more than your words do. You can say that you know how to perform the job duties, but if it doesn't sound like you do, you won't inspire much confidence in the hiring manager. In addition, avoid saying anything offensive or vulgar! (Absolutely no swear words/cussing!) Avoid using any of the following words or phrases:

Bling	Hater	Jacked Up	Nerd
Beast	Shorty	Like	Props
Bomb (Da Bomb)	Snap (Oh Snap)	Ill	Yo
Bro	Trick (Trick Out)	Word	Sucks
Busted	Yeah Right	Sup	Sweet
Chill (Chill Out)	Whatever	Tight	OMG
Dawg	Salty	Score	Sick
Dude	Homie	Head	Juiced
Fiending	Hook (Off the Hook)	Hell	Emo
Frontin	Bum	Bogus	Crispy
Geek	Duh	Freak Out	Blitz
Ghetto	Cool	Crunk	Cop Out
Hick	Fed Up	Bounce	Fly
My bad	As If	Ballin	Chick

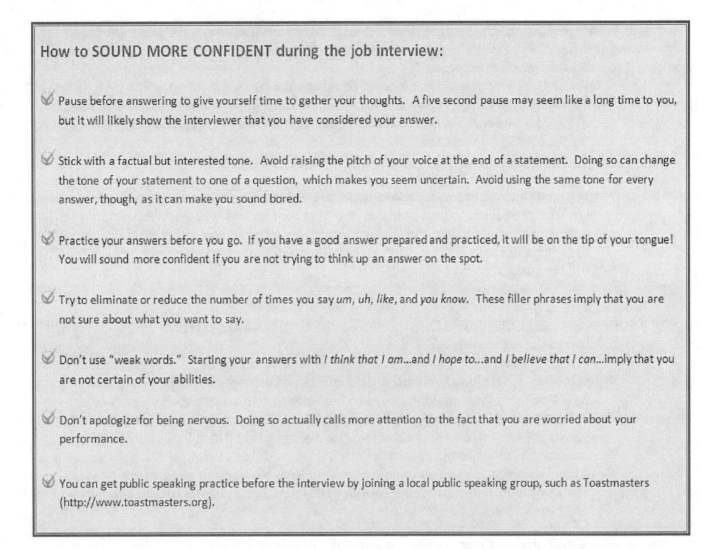

Figure 2.14

2.4.8 TOUGH JOB INTERVIEW QUESTIONS

This section contains twenty of the toughest interview questions with sample answers.

1. How would you describe yourself?

Sample excellent response:

My background to date has been centered around preparing myself to become the very best financial consultant I can become. Let me tell you specifically how I've prepared myself. I am an undergraduate student in finance and accounting at _____ University. My past experiences have been in retail and higher education. Both aspects have prepared me well for this career.

2. What specific goals, including those related to your occupation, have you established for your life?

Sample excellent response 1:

I want to be working for an excellent company like yours in a job in which I am managing information. I plan to contribute my leadership, interpersonal, and technical skills. My long-range career goal is to be the best information systems technician I can be for the company I work for.

Sample excellent response 2:

My goals include becoming a Certified Financial Advisor so I can obtain a better working knowledge of financial research analysis. That background would enable me contribute to my client base as a better financial consultant since I would have that extra insight into the companies they seek to invest in. I could then be a portfolio manager or even branch office manager.

3. How has your college experience prepared you for a business career?

Sample excellent response:

I have prepared myself to transition into the work force through real-world experience involving travel abroad, internship, and entrepreneurial opportunities. While interning with a private organization in Ecuador, I developed a 15-page marketing plan composed in Spanish that recommended more effective ways the company could promote its services. I also traveled abroad on two other occasions in which I researched the indigenous culture of the Mayan Indians in Todos Santos, Guatemala, and participated in a total-language-immersion program in Costa Rica. As you can see from my academic, extracurricular, and experiential background, I have unconditionally committed myself to success as a marketing professional.

4. Please describe the ideal job for you following graduation.

Sample excellent response (equates ideal job with job he's interviewing for):

My ideal job is one that incorporates both my education and practical work skills to be the best I can be. Namely combining my education in finance with my working knowledge of customer-service operations, entrepreneurial abilities, computer skills, and administrative skills. I want to utilize my analytical expertise to help people meet their financial goals. This is exactly why I am convinced that I would be a very valuable member of the Merrill Lynch team.

5. What influenced you to choose this career?

Sample excellent response:

My past experiences have shown me that I enjoy facing and overcoming the challenge of making a sale. Without a doubt, once I have practiced my presentation and prepared myself for objections, I feel very confident approaching people I don't know and convincing them that they need my product. Lastly, I like sales because my potential for success is limited only by how much of myself I dedicate toward my goal. If any profession is founded on self-determinism, it surely must be sales.

6. What will it take to attain your goals, and what steps have you taken toward attaining them?

Sample excellent response:

I've already done some research on other workers at Merrill Edge to see how they achieved similar goals. I know that Merrill Edge encourages the pursuit of a graduate degree and will reimburse for tuition. I plan to pursue an MBA to give me an even more extensive knowledge of business and financial analysis.

7. How do you determine or evaluate success? Give me an example of one of your successful accomplishments.

Sample excellent response:

Last semester I was hired by my university's Council for Student Activities. The group negotiates contracts of entertainers, sets up sound equipment, markets the entertainers to students, and generally decides what kind of programming should be done. When I got hired, I didn't know the first thing about how fill any of those responsibilities. I decided, however, that I wasn't going to fail. Four months later, I have become the Webmaster for the group. I also write our campus newsletter and created Game Night, a student competition of table games. That event yielded the biggest audience ever for a non-concert event.

8. Explain why you have, above all others applying for this position, the qualifications and personal characteristics necessary for success in this position?

Sample excellent response:

I believe I have a combination of qualities to be successful in this career. First, I have a strong interest, backed by a solid, well-rounded, state-of-the-art education, especially in a career that is technically oriented. This basic ingredient, backed by love of learning, problem-solving skills, well-rounded interests, determination to succeed and excel, strong communication skills, and the ability to work hard, are the most important qualities that will help me succeed in this career. To succeed, you also need a natural curiosity about how systems work -- the kind of curiosity I demonstrated when I upgraded my two computers recently. Technology is constantly changing, so you must a fast learner just to keep up, or you will be overwhelmed. All of these traits combine to create a solid team member in the ever-changing field of information systems. I am convinced that I possess these characteristics and am ready to be a successful team member for your firm.

9. Are you more energized by working with data or by collaborating with other individuals?

Sample excellent response:

I like the validity of information and also like the energy that comes with working with people. The best thing about working in a group is combining the great minds from different perspectives and coming up with something extremely great, compared with when you're working alone. At the same time, information can generate vitality in the project you're working on. No matter how many heads you've got together, without information, you can't go very far. The perfect situation would be a combination of working with information and people, and I'm confident of my abilities in both areas.

10. By providing examples, convince me that you can adapt to a wide variety of people, situations and environments.

Sample excellent response:

I've shown my ability to adapt by successfully working in several very different jobs. For example, I lived with a native family in Costa Rica. I worked as a nanny for a famous writer in Cape Cod. I was responsible for dealing with Drug Court participants. And I catered to elite country-club clientele. I did it all well and had no trouble adapting.

11. Describe a time when you were faced with problems or stresses that tested your coping skills.

Sample excellent response:

Arriving at the language school I was attending in Costa Rica in the middle of the night with very minimal Spanish-language skills, I found my way to a very small town with no street addresses or names and found my temporary residence. I was scared, but I handled the situation very well, very calmly. In very stressful situations, I am always the one in the group to stay calm and focused. My friends, family, and professors have always said that I am an oasis of calm in a storm.

12. Give an example of how you applied knowledge from previous coursework to a project in another class.

Sample excellent response:

Last semester I was taking a microeconomics and a statistics course. One of the microeconomics projects dealt with showing the relationship between the probability that customers would stop buying a product if the price was raised a certain amount. Through what I learned in statistics I could find the median where the price was the highest and still kept most of the customers happy.

13. Describe an instance when you had to think on your feet to extricate yourself from a difficult situation.

Sample excellent response:

When I was a resident assistant at my college, a student I did not know asked me if he could use my phone to call another room. Although I did not know the student, I allowed him into my room. He used the phone and in the course of this conversation, he stated that he had just come from a fraternity party and was high from taking some drugs. Well after his conversation, I had to enforce the student conduct code by writing him up. He became very hostile toward me and would not give me any identification or information. I stood in the doorway to prevent him from leaving. I noted the serial numbers on his keys, so when the situation got to the point where I felt unsafe, I allowed him to leave. I still preformed my job without jeopardizing my or his physical welfare.

14. Describe a situation in which you were able to use persuasion to successfully convince someone to see things your way?

Sample excellent response:

Recently my company asked for bids on a phone system for our new college campus. Two companies came in very close with their bids, and most of my department wanted to go with a vendor that we have used in the past. After I looked over the proposals, it was clear that this was the wrong decision. So, I talked individually with each member of our staff and succeeded in changing their minds and get the best product that would save money and provide the highest quality.

15. Tell me about the salary range you're seeking.

Sample excellent response 1:

I am sure that I am the candidate you are looking for. If you feel the same, then I'm sure your offer will be fair and commensurate with the value I can bring the company.

Sample excellent response 2:

I am not depending on money to make me happy. What makes me happy is having a satisfying job that provides challenge and new situations daily.

Sample excellent response 3:

A salary commensurate with my experience and skills is important, but it's only one piece of the package. Many other elements go into making up a compensation package, but more importantly, it's critical to me to enjoy what I'm doing, fit into the corporate culture, and feel I'm making a genuine contribution.

16. Do you have a geographic preference?

Sample excellent response:

Although I would prefer to stay in the Mid-Atlantic area, I would not rule out other possibilities.

17. Would it be a problem for you to relocate?

Sample excellent response:

I'm open to opportunities within the company; if those opportunities involve relocation, I would certainly consider it.

18. Tell me what you know about our company.

Sample excellent response:

You're large and respected worldwide. You're both a clinical and teaching hospital. Over the last 60 to 70 years you've produced award-winning research. In reviewing your Web site, I've familiarized myself with many of your corporate goals and objectives.

19. Why did you decide to seek a position in this company?

Sample excellent response:

I am convinced that there would be no better place to work than Accenture. You are the top consulting firm in the United States. You provide your employees with the tools they need to stay competitive and sharpen their skills while working in an open, team-based environment. I am also aware that you provide a mentor for all new employees, and I would embrace any opportunity to work with a mentor and eventually become one myself.

20. What personal weakness has caused you the greatest difficulty in school or on a job?
Sample excellent response (shows how he recognized his weakness and worked to improve):
My greatest weakness used to be delegation. To improve my workers' efficiency, I would take it upon myself to do many small projects throughout my shift as a manager that could have been done by others. Once I realized that I was doing more work than the other assistant managers, and they were achieving better results, I reevaluated what I was doing. I quickly realized that if I assigned each person just one small project at the beginning of the shift, clearly state expectations for the project, and then follow up, everything would get done, and I could manage much more efficiently and actually accomplish much more.

2.5 SUMMER INTERNSHIP & CO-OP EXPERIENCE

Internships are usually, but not always, one term. Internships are usually, but not always, in summer. Co-ops are usually, but not always, multi-term; e.g. you might work fall semester, go to school in spring semester, work summer, go to school in fall, and work the next spring semester. Schedules vary depending on when you need to be in school and when the employer needs you to work

Internships can be either part-time or full-time; depends on employers' needs and the way each employer chooses to structure an intern program. Some internship programs are very formal and structured, while others offer more flexibility to negotiate terms. Co-ops are always full-time positions.

Internships can be paid or unpaid; this depends on employers' preferences and on the career field and on the job market supply and demand conditions which exist. Co-op positions are always paid.

The compensation for co-op and internship positions varies greatly among employers and geographic locations. You will have to do a salary research for salaries in your field. Be aware that in some career fields, unpaid internships are common and are the best way to get career-related experience.

Most institutions consider an "internship" just a summer job, with no academic credit earned. However, for internships and co-ops, the authority to grant academic credit is entirely determined by each academic department; that is, some absolutely never do, some commonly do; with some it might be negotiable. Ask in the department of your academic major. If your department allows this, academic credit is usually earned by registering for a Field Study or something similar, and usually requires you to submit academic work, such as reports, to a faculty member, in addition to the employer's on-the-job requirements. Some departments offer internship seminars or courses, in which they assist you with internships. Again, this is entirely up to the individual academic department.

Internships are not always in the summer. You will find the majority of internships offered in summer, but some employers offer internships year 'round, including fall semester or spring semester terms. Some employers (such as tax preparers or political campaigns) may have a busy season during the year when they employ interns — and therefore offer non-summer internships.

If you work only in the summer, this is typically referred to as an internship (although some employers may call this a co-op). However, some employers do not offer summer-only programs. Be aware of the requirements of each employer as you search for your job.

If you intend to do an internship during the Fall or Spring semester then first check with your academic department (the department which offers your major) to find out what affect leaving campus for a semester will have on your academic standing and your ability to get the courses you need in the appropriate sequence. If you are receiving scholarships or financial aid, inquire in those offices what affect leaving campus for a semester will have on your scholarship or financial aid. Determine whether or not you need to be formally enrolled as a student during your internship to meet the employer's requirements or for other reasons. If so, inquire about your academic department's policy to see if it offers or allows (or requires) academic credit for an internship. Only academic departments may grant academic credit.

You can search for a job in a particular location, but you are advised to look at all opportunities. You should be aware of the job market for your skills and take that into consideration — some career fields offer more opportunity and you may be able to be more selective about location. Other career fields are more competitive and you may need to go where the employers have needs. Some employers may assist with relocation and living expenses.

Only a very few employers provide housing; some rent-free; some require you to pay rent. Some employers provide assistance finding housing. Some provide some financial assistance or allowance for moving and/or housing. If you get a job offer and the employer hasn't explained exactly what help they provide, you should ask.

No student is guaranteed an internship or co-op job. Applying for a co-op or internship position is competitive. Employers evaluate your resume and compare you to your peers at your institution and possibly at other institutions.

For summer internships, start in fall and keeping looking through spring — until you get a position. Use school breaks (Thanksgiving, winter & spring breaks) to make contacts at home, if "home" is where you would like to be located for your internship. For co-op positions, begin looking at least one semester before you hope to begin work. Be aware that if an employer requires a security clearance, it may take up to six months between the time the employer begins considering you and the time you can begin work.

Benefits of hiring co-op students:

- Provides an excellent pool of well-prepared employees.
- Improves personnel selection process by using actual on-the-job performance as a basis for permanent hiring decisions.
- Increases cost-effectiveness of recruitment and training. Studies show employers save money by using co-op to identify and train personnel.
- Improves workforce diversity through access to minority students for permanent employment.
- Increases retention rates among permanent employees recruited and hired through a co-op program. Both students and employers have the time to try out the position and ensure that the fit is the most productive and effective for both.
- Enhances human resource flexibility with effective short-term employees.
- Strengthens company relations with colleges and students. Through evaluations, advisory boards and other means, employers can work with colleges to ensure an effective curriculum.

Employers' responsibilities of the co-op student:

- Provide the student with paid, challenging work experience in an area specifically related to the student's academic field of study.
- In multiple co-op assignments, the work should be progressive in nature.
- Evaluate the co-op student twice during the co-op assignment with the forms provided by Career Services at the institution (at mid-point and at the end of the assignment), and return them to Career Services in a timely manner.
- Read the student's completed technical report and sign the required statement on the first page, verifying the report does not contain proprietary material and may be forwarded on to the appropriate academic department at the institution for grading.

The basic requirements of most co-op programs:

1. Endorsement and support of the supervisor and management. It is crucial that management be actively supportive of a co-op program to 1) ensure participation from their employees; 2) acknowledge the co-op's credibility and 3) make sure the co-op is not being relegated solely to "back-burner" projects.
2. Active and supportive mentor at the company. Whether the supervisor also plays a role as mentor, or another person is asked to take on this part, the mentor is essential in the real-life development of the student's abilities, work habits and interpersonal skills.
3. The co-op benefits from active mentor interaction in the following areas:

- Learning by experience
- Improving self-confidence
- Getting career advice
- Gaining a sense of value to the company
- Learning the ropes of the company (culture, values, presentation skills, where power lies, etc.)
- Experiencing the day-to-day management process

4. Strong communication between the supervisor and co-op.
5. Successful supervisors:
    - Take a strong interest and concern in developing the co-op
    - Have a broad base understanding of the industry and organization
    - Getting career advice
    - Have relevant areas of expertise
    - Are easily accessible to the co-op
    - Offer mutual respect
    - Teach and encourage the co-op
    - Evaluate the co-op fairly and honestly
    - Provide constructive suggestions for improvement.
6. Appropriate training/orientation. To ensure a smooth transition period for co-op students and the company, an orientation session in the company is very helpful.
7. Acquaint the co-op with the work site, company expectations, and areas of responsibility.

The Career Services at most institutions offers numerous options for recruiting students for internships and co-op positions. Their services range from on-campus interviews, mock interviews and job fairs, to video conferencing and general job postings.

CHAPTER 3
Student Success

CHAPTER 3
STUDENT SUCCESS

6.1 WHAT IS STUDENT SUCCESS?

Students' persistence to completion of their educational goals is a key gauge of student success and therefore institutional success. Two most frequently cited statistics in connections with student success are the freshman-to-sophomore retention rate, or first-year annual return rate and the cohort graduation rate. The freshman-to-sophomore retention rate measures the percentage of first-time, full-time students enrolled at the university the following fall semester. The cohort graduation rate is defined as the percentage of an entering class that graduates within three years with an associate's degree, and within four, five, or six years with a baccalaureate degree. Since the annual return rate of students as they progress through a program is directly related to their degree/certificate completion, the concept of retention usually includes year-by-year retention or persistence rates as well as graduation rates. Together, these statistics represent student success. These student success statistics are commonly regarded as primary indicators of institutional performance. They have come to reflect the overall quality of student learning and intellectual involvement; how well integrated students are in campus life; and how effectively a campus delivers what students expect and need.

Student success is beneficial to society because students:

- understand the rights and responsibilities that allow them to function as contributing members of our democracy.

- cooperate and collaborate with others in work, social, and family settings.

- make independent decisions based on reasoning and supported by facts.

- relate in a positive and constructive manner with family members and other members of the world community.

- take responsibility for their own actions and act supportively and compassionately toward others.

6.2 DESIRABLE OUTCOMES OF STUDENT SUCCESS

The following desirable outcomes have been the most frequently cited indicators of student success in higher education.

Student Retention: Entering college students remain, re-enroll, and continue their undergraduate education. Alternatively, student retention is an institutional goal of keeping students enrolled for consecutive semesters until degree completion. (For example, first-year students return for their sophomore year.)

Student Persistence: individual goal of a student reaching his or her *specific educational attainment*.

Educational Attainment: entering students persist to completion and attainment of their degree, program, or educational goal. (For example, 2-year college students persist to completion of the associate degree, and 4-year college students persist to completion of the baccalaureate degree).

Academic Achievement: students achieve satisfactory or superior levels of academic performance as they progress through and complete their college experience. (For example, students avoid academic probation or qualify for academic honors.)

Student Advancement: students proceed to and succeed at subsequent educational and occupational endeavors for which their college degree or program was designed to prepare them. (For example, 2-year college students continue their education at a 4-year college, or 4-year college students are accepted at graduate schools or enter gainful careers after completing their baccalaureate degree.)

Holistic Development: students develop as "whole persons" as they progress through and complete their college experience. This outcome consists of multiple dimensions, which may be defined or described as follows:

- *Intellectual* Development: developing skills for acquiring and communicating knowledge, learning how to learn, and how to think deeply.

- *Emotional* Development: developing skills for understanding, controlling, and expressing emotions.

- *Social* Development: enhancing the quality and depth of interpersonal relationships, leadership skills and civic engagement.

- *Ethical* Development: formulating a clear value system that guides life choices and demonstrates personal character.

- *Physical* Development: acquiring and applying knowledge about the human body to prevent disease, maintain wellness, and promote peak performance.

- *Spiritual* Development: appreciating the search for personal meaning, the purpose of human existence and questions that transcend the material or physical world.

Colleges and universities retain students, while students persist to a goal. The assumption underlying retention is *retention to degree from original institution*. Individual students' goals are different from institutions' goals. A student may successfully persist to his or her individual goal(s) without being retained to graduation. "Educational attainment" captures the variability of students' goals and disentangles retention and persistence.

6.3 SEVEN CENTRAL PRINCIPLES OF STUDENT SUCCESS

The critical first step toward promoting student success is to define it, i.e., to identify positive student outcomes that represent concrete indicators of student success. Step two is to identify the key, research-based principles or processes that are most likely to promote student success and lead to positive student outcomes. Serendipitously, the same success-promoting principles serve to promote three key student outcomes simultaneously: a) student retention / persistence, b) student learning (academic achievement), and c) personal development (holistic outcomes). This serendipity supports the long-held contention among student retention scholars that "successful retention is nothing more than successful education"

The following seven processes are offered as the most potent principles of student success because they are well supported by higher education scholarship and are firmly grounded in research and theory:

1. personal validation
2. self-efficacy
3. sense of purpose
4. active involvement
5. reflective thinking
6. social integration
7. self-awareness

6.3.1 PERSONEL VALIDATION

Student success is more likely to be realized when students feel personally *significant*—i.e., when they feel *welcomed*, recognized as *individuals*, and that they *matter* to the institution. In contrast, student success is sabotaged by college practices or policies that depersonalize or marginalize students. Students are more likely to become committed to the institution and, therefore stay, when they come to understand that the institution is committed to them. Programs cannot replace the absence of high quality, caring and concerned faculty and staff.

6.3.2 SELF-EFFICACY

Student success is more likely to take place when students believe that their individual effort matters, i.e., when they believe they can exert significant influence or control over their academic and personal success. Conversely, the likelihood of student success is reduced when students feel hopeless or helpless. Meta-analysis research indicates that academic self-efficacy is the best predictor for student retention and academic achievement. Personal traits such as self-efficacy, self-esteem, and internal locus of control are among the best predictors of job performance and job satisfaction.

6.3.3 SENSE OF PURPOSE

Student success is more probable when students find meaning or purpose in their college experience—i.e., when they perceive relevant connections between what they're learning in college and their current life or future goals. In contrast, lack of personal goals for the college experience and perceived irrelevance of the college curriculum are major causes of student attrition.

When students are provided with a personally relevant context for a new concept, they continue to think about that concept longer than if they learn it without reference to a personally relevant context and the more relevant the academic content is to students, the more likely they are to engage in higher-level thinking with respect to it.

6.3.4 ACTIVE INVOLVEMENT

The probability of student success increases commensurately with the degree or depth of student engagement in the learning process, i.e., the amount of time and energy that students invest in the college experience—both inside and outside the classroom. In contrast, student persistence and academic achievement is sabotaged by student passivity and disengagement.

The greater the student's involvement or engagement in academic work or in the academic experience of college, the greater his or her level of knowledge acquisition and general cognitive development. Research also indicates that student involvement outside the classroom is a potent predictor of student retention. For instance, students who utilize such support services, and interact with the professionals involved with the provision of such services, are more likely to persist to college completion.

6.3.5 REFLECTIVE THINKING

Students are more likely to experience success when they engage in reflective thinking about what they are learning and elaborate on it, transforming it into a form that relates to what they already know or have previously experienced. Successful learning requires not only action, but also reflection. Such reflection or thoughtful review is the flip side of active involvement. Brain research also shows that active involvement and reflective thinking involve two distinct mental states of consciousness, the former characterized by faster, low-amplitude brain waves and the latter by slower, higher-amplitude brain waves. Both mental processes are needed for learning to be complete. Active involvement is necessary for engaging student attention—which enables learners to initially get information into the brain, and reflection is necessary for consolidation—keeping that information in the brain, by locking it into long-term memory.

6.3.6 SOCIAL INTEGRATION

Student success is enhanced by human interaction, collaboration, and formation of interpersonal connections between the student and other members of the college community—peers, faculty, staff, and administrators. In contrast, feelings of isolation or alienation are likely to contribute to student attrition. Students who have become "socially integrated" or "connected" with other members of the college or university are much more likely to complete their first-year of college and continue on to complete their college degree. The importance of social integration and interpersonal interaction for learning is also supported by the epistemological theory of social constructivism; according to this theory, human thinking is shaped by social interaction and conversation, whereas an individual's thought process is largely an internalization of these external dialogues.

6.3.7 SELF AWARENESS

Student success is promoted when students gain greater awareness of their own thinking, learning styles, and learning habits, i.e., when they engage in meta-cognition—when they think about their thinking, when they self-monitor or check their comprehension, and when they self-regulate or accommodate their learning strategies to meet the demands of the learning task at hand. Research demonstrates that high-achieving college students tend to reflect on their thought processes during learning and are aware of the cognitive strategies they use. Successful college students also "self-monitor" their academic performance, that is, they maintain awareness of whether or not they are actually learning what they are attempting to learn and they self-regulate or adjust their learning strategies in a way that best meets the specific demands of the subject matter they are trying to learn. Lastly, self-awareness has been found to be a critical element of any effective self-management and self-improvement plan whether it is the management of time, money, or health.

6.4 FACTORS THAT INFLUENCE STUDENTS' SUCCESS IN COLLEGE

Although academic success means that a student has fulfilled the requirements for his course of study, more goes into doing well in college than just concentrating on grades. Although academic factors account for 68 percent of success in school, other things influence a student's academic success as well. Students who fully prepare for their upcoming tasks and who tap into the resources in their environment stand the best chance of doing well in college.

FIGURE 6.1

Family Influences

A student's family exerts a large influence on how well he or she does in school. Having parents and siblings who concern themselves with the student's academic well-being gives him or her necessary support to handle the stress of college. Additionally, the family should have realistic expectations of how university life will affect the student. It's not unusual for parents to receive frequent texts and emails about homesickness and other difficulties. Knowing about some of these eventualities helps the family and the student cope with school, particularly if he or she is a first-generation student.

The Student's Role

College students' success rests just as much on themselves as it does on the support of their family. Students with good self-discipline, emotional self-control and academic self-confidence stand the best chance of moving successfully into college life. These qualities allow students to involve themselves in the academic environment without becoming overwhelmed by the obstacles that arise from it.

Aside from these intangible factors, a strong GPA in high school often represents the most accurate indicator of students' future success. If they didn't keep up on grades, attend class regularly and develop solid study habits in high school, their chances of succeeding at college are hampered considerably.

Academic Goals

College students' goals work in tandem with factors such as grades and self-discipline in determining how well they'll meet the challenges of college. Once students decide what their goals are, research suggests that they make friends with similarly minded people. Friends who have incompatible goals can knock a student off course. For example, a student serious about academic success who has very social, party-oriented friends may find it difficult to keep up a high GPA if he or she frequently attends social events.

On-Campus Help

An academic advisor can help guide students toward college success if they meet with the advisor regularly. This on-campus resource helps students stay on track by explaining the particulars of their degree and what classes they need to meet the academic requirements of their major. The advisor also provides the student with a more realistic understanding of how much work is required to succeed in college. They may offer pointers about seeking help from professors and other on-campus resources and amenities.

6.5 ADJUSTING TO COLLEGE

Attending college is one of the first major life transitions for many young adults. Some students are excited to take on the new experiences of campus life, while others feel apprehensive about making this change. Regardless of your outlook when beginning your first year of college, you may benefit from talking with others who have already made that transition.

Making the Transition

What are some of the most common changes you can expect in the first year on campus?

- **New environment and relationships.** First year students must adapt to an unfamiliar environment, adjust to different living arrangements, and develop new relationships. Living with roommates may be the first 'test' freshmen experience. Students face the challenge of adjusting to roommates who may have very different boundaries and individual needs than family and friends from home. Roommates may or may not develop close friendships, but communication and compromise can build a smoother transition. College brings a unique opportunity to interact and live with students from various backgrounds and cultures. Expanding your worldview by learning about each other's differences and similarities will likely enhance your college experience.

- **Greater personal freedom.** Living on your own for the first time means that you will gain independence and take charge of the many choices and decisions that your parents and teachers made for you in the past. While this new found freedom can be exciting, it may also feel overwhelming and less predictable than what you are accustomed to. The freedom to manage your daily life is a learning process, but one that can be very satisfying.

- **Added responsibility.** First-year students must manage the important daily responsibilities that accompany their increased personal freedom. Students must manage basic tasks such as eating, sleeping, exercising, and going to class. New students must also address more complex responsibilities such as balancing studying and socializing, participating in clubs and activities, and handling finances. Managing time is a demand that all first-year students experience. A typical day in college is less structured than high school, and there is more reading and studying that is required outside of class. Some students may feel as if they have no free time to do anything but schoolwork, while others feel like they have too much free time outside of the classroom.

- **Changing relationships.** While there are many changes occurring in your new campus life, there will also be changes in your relationships. New students often face challenges such as best friends going to other universities, beginning new romantic relationships or maintaining existing ones, and juggling newly formed relationships with already established ones. Students must balance a sense of connectedness and separation while at college. Some freshmen feel the need to call or e-mail home several times a week in the first few months away, while others require less frequent communication with their family and friends.

Common Stressors

The first year of college is a new and exciting adventure, but one that may come with a few challenges along the way. Below are most common stressors that first-year students experience.

- **Time Management.** Now that you are in college, there are no more eight hour school days like those in many high schools. You may have class for six, three, or even zero hours a day. The rest of your time must be negotiated between homework, clubs and activities, work, socializing, and self-care. College students often feel as if there is just not enough time to do everything that needs to be done. Using a schedule and some organizational skills will help you to effectively manage your hectic and changing life.

- **Academic Performance.** By nature, college coursework is challenging, and it can be hard to keep up with the increased academic demands. Some students undergo pressure from both themselves and their parents. There may be requirements for scholarships and graduate school admission that you have not previously experienced. In order to manage the increased demands and expectations, it is important to attend class regularly, keep up with readings and assignments, and ask for help when you need it. Professors and teaching assistants are there to assist you, and want you to succeed. If you need additional help, various organizations on campus offer tutoring services, many of which are free.

- **Roommate Conflict.** Learning to live with someone new can be one of the most challenging aspects of going to college. Different living habits are the most common source of roommate conflict (i.e. neat vs. messy; quiet vs. noisy; early-to-bed vs. up-all-night). Failure to communicate your expectations about living together can lead to tension and eventually conflict. To avoid "roommate fallout" you should communicate your needs and expectations respectfully, while recognizing your own habits and quirks that might affect your relationship. If conflict does escalate you should take it to a Resident Advisor, Resident Director, or a Counselor to determine a course of action.

- **Long Distance Dating Relationships.** It is not uncommon for first-year students to begin college in a long distance dating relationship. Where at one time this relationship may have helped you cope with everyday stress, it could now be a source of distress due to the distance between you and your partner. Uncertainty in what the future holds for the relationship is one of the most common stressors experienced by college students in long distance dating relationships. There are a few key efforts that each partner can make to lessen the sting of separation. Verbal communication, openness, and assurance of one another can reduce stress associated with being separated. It is also essential for each partner to seek social support from others and remain active in their individual lives while apart.

- **Body Image.** Many college students also struggle with body image. Our culture pays a great deal of attention to the appearance of our bodies, particularly during young adulthood. Media representations of the ideal body, messages from peers, and other cultural factors shape what we perceive as "normal" or "good". It can be difficult to have a clear, healthy perspective on ourselves and our bodies when our culture sends so many confusing, conflicting, and sometimes unhealthy messages. This can be stressful at a time when many are trying to "fit in" with others and make new, exciting relationships. If you find yourself preoccupied with how you look or become distressed about your body, discussing your concerns and ideas with someone can be extremely helpful in creating, developing, and maintaining a body image that is healthful and fulfilling.

Recommendations for First-Year College Students

What steps can you take to have a great first year of college?

- **Be patient.** While campus may seem new and overwhelming for new students, it becomes more familiar with time. Refer to the many resources available to assist you in navigating your surroundings. Maps, your Resident Advisor (R.A.), upper-classman, and the university Websites are all useful tools to get you through the initial transition to campus.

- **Connect with other students.** If you talk to other students, you are likely to discover that they share similar questions and concerns. Your R.A. is an excellent person to go to when issues arise. She or he is equipped to help you solve problems and refer you to appropriate resources.

- **Get involved.** Student organizations are a fun way to interact with other students and faculty. Meeting people with similar interests and goals is an exciting way to make friends and participate in social activities.

- **Utilize resources.** There are numerous resources on campus designed to create a rewarding college experience. In addition there are numerous sources of support such as the Office of Dean of Students, the Counseling Center, the Career Center, your Academic Advisor, financial aid programs, and mentoring/tutoring programs offered to address various student needs. Some colleges and universities have cultural programs such as (Lesbian, Gay, Bisexual, Transgender, Queer/Questioning) LGBTQ to assist the diverse campus's needs.

- **Care for yourself.** The foundation for a productive college career is a healthy lifestyle. Take the necessary steps for nurturance, getting adequate rest, socializing, and physical activity. Campus Recreation offers several resources that students can utilize to work towards wellness. The Anti-Virus Research Center (ARC), Continuing Respiratory Care Education (CRCE), and the Wellness Center are just a few campus facilities that strive to promote healthy practices and to educate the campus community on various health topics.

6.6 STUDENT TIME MANAGEMENT

Student time management is one of the most important skills for students to manage their study and get good grades.

The following scenarios are a good indication of poor time management:

1. feel stressed and overwhelmed by a lack of time.

2. are studying at hours when you are not fresh and productive.

3. procrastinating on that must-do homework.

4. cramming the night before.

5. not getting assignments in on time.

The demands of school, work, and social life can mean that you leave things to the night before or forget to hand in that important assignment. Good time management helps you juggle your busy life. The next five sections offer advice to help students manage their time better in college.

6.6.1 GET A HELICOPTER VIEW OF YOUR SCHEDULE

As a student, one of the first things you want to do is to get an academic planner. An academic plan highlights any bottle necks of intense periods of assignments and assessments. This lets you know when 'all hands should be on deck.'

In your academic planner put:

- Assignment due dates and other assessment due
- Exam dates
- Social functions that need to attend, such as a family birthday or regular sporting events.

6.6.2 CREATE A MASTER TO-DO LIST

Student life can be overwhelming! With assignments to hand in, assessments to complete, and exams to sit, it is easy to feel overwhelmed and stressed.

One of the best things that you can do is to list all the things that you need to do.

The very act of writing things down and getting them out of your head and onto paper reduces your stress and gives you a clear idea of what you need to do.

Make sure that some of your master to-do list is aligned with your specific goals as a student.

6.6.3 USE A WEEKLY PLAN

By planning your work and then working your plan, you avoid the trap of last minute cramming sessions and stressful write-ups of assignments the night before.

An efficient use of time management will help students to reduce stress, increase the quality of studying and will improve your grades. But the benefits extend beyond college and study as time management is a transferable skill that is valued by employers. The best way to set up a short-term time management plan is to develop a weekly plan that reflects the natural ebb-and-flow of most people's short-term horizons.

Using a student planner tool of your work and then working your plan is essential for student success. Good planning involves identifying what is important to you and then protecting your time for those things.

6.6.4 WORK YOUR PLAN

One of the biggest problems for students is not the plan; it is putting the plan into action.

Some of the common barriers to student time management are:

1. Procrastination. Facebook...Internet...even washing the dirty dishes - all have been used as a form of procrastination when there is a need to do some study. One research study quoted that 80% of students procrastinate on important assignments and study.

2. Lack of focus. Everywhere you look there are distractions....Facebook, TV, surfing the Net. All of this can mean that you spend less time focusing on school work.

3. Poor prioritization. With too much to do and not enough time you are going to have prioritize your work. Keep a daily time management to-do-list to prioritize your work like a professional.

Whether you are:

- an elite athlete,
- a top business professional or
- a great student,

.....any success started with small steps and then building on those successes.

6.6.5 IMPROVE YOUR STUDY TECHNIQUES

Studying effectively is not an all-night cram session the day before the exam. Nor is it chaining yourself to a desk for 12 hours straight. Being a student involves readings, attending lectures and tutorials, and participating throughout the semester. One important student time management tip is being able to plan and manage the new information. This involves keeping up-to-date with readings and being an active contributor to your learning experience. One part of academic performance is being able to connect and relate facts with larger patterns of knowledge, and then communicating them in your own words.

6.6.6 TIME MANAGEMENT COLLEGE ACTIVITY: BIG ROCK LITTLE ROCK STORY

The 'Big Rocks Little Rocks' story starts with a professor who stands in front of a class holding a glass jar, into which he places a number of large rocks.

FIGURE 6.2

After filling the jar with large rocks the professor asks the students, "Is the jar full yet?"

Most of the class replied, "Yes!"

Then he reaches into his pocket and pulls out a number of smaller rocks and puts them into jar with the big rocks.

After which he says, "Is the jar full yet?"

Still many in the class reply "Yes!"

From the other pocket the professor pulls out a bag of sand and proceeds to fill the glass jar.

The sand fills the gaps between the big and small rocks.

Again he asks, "Is the jar full yet?"

Some of the class replies guardedly, "Yes it's now full."

The professor now produces a glass of water and proceeds to pour the water into the jar. The water seeps into the sand and finally fills the jar.

What is the moral of the story?" the professor asks.

One girl replied "That no matter how full the jar, you can always fit more into it".

However the professor shook his head. "No No No…"

"The moral of the story" said the professor, "is that you need to get the big rocks of your day or life out of the way first or all the other small stuff will get in the way and take up space"

If the professor had first filled his jar with sand and small rocks then he never would be able to put the big rocks into the jar.

This story highlights that it is important to get the big rocks of your life, those high impact activities, into the jar before the smaller stuff crowds it out. Are you getting your big rocks done at college and in your life? To know what your big rocks are you need to be able to figure out what it is about college life that you want. What is important to you? Do you want good grades? Are you a student who believes that anything higher than a pass is wasted effort? Are you a student who wants to genuinely learn his or her art and good grades is just a by-product? In essence - what drives you as a student?

By having a vision of what you want to achieve, whether it is good grades or a dream job, knowing how you will achieve your vision is the essence of student goal setting. Student goal setting keeps you motivated, gives you confidence, and helps you to persist when the last thing you want to do is to sit at the desk and study.

6.5 STRATEGIES FOR STUDENT RECRUITMENT AND SUCCESS

Recruitment Strategies

Common strategies for recruitment include community outreach, high school outreach, financial aid, and climate and inclusion for undergraduates and graduate student recruitment for graduate students. Figure 6.3 shows an estimator or profile for predicting the likelihood of students who will graduate from two- or four institutions.

Community Outreach

- Promote programs which bring residents from the surrounding communities to campus. Pay attention to community outreach, with particular emphasis on underrepresented populations.

- Create a multicultural recruitment day to bring under-represented groups to introduce students to the University.

- Recruit community college students and other transfer students. A sizeable number of underrepresented and low-income students are enrolled at community colleges. Forming partnerships with these institutions is a strategy for recruiting underrepresented students.

- Recruit and develop cooperative programs with institutions that enroll large numbers of students from racial and ethnic minority groups (e.g. HBCU's).

- Collaborate with pre-college programs and high schools to identify prospective recruits.

High School Outreach

- Host workshops and orientations for middle and high school students. College Prep Day for middle and high school students that includes workshops, student panels, campus tours, and information about application process. Host a Minority Scholars Weekend or a three day orientation for high school students to stay in residence halls and attend classes.

- Visit racially diverse high schools and college fairs where diverse students are represented.

- Enhance bridge programs to develop a smooth pipeline from K-12 to college, with particular emphasis on underrepresented groups. These programs must include components that reach out to potential students, families of potential students, guidance counselors, K-12 school administrators, and community organizations. The intent is to better inform and better prepare potential students for pursuing a college education.

- Offer summer programs that expose high school students to science, engineering, technology, and mathematics.

- Monitor the participation of students enrolled in institutionally-sponsored pre-college programs.

- Include guidance counselors from high schools in the area, especially those from racially and ethnically diverse high schools, in a campus orientation.

- Fund support programs for area schools.

Financial Aid

- Provide advising and outreach about financial aid opportunities to low-income and other underrepresented groups.

- Support University development efforts that prioritize resources for need and merit-based financial aid.

Climate and Inclusion

- Involve currently enrolled students, faculty, and staff in recruitment initiatives.

  1) Multicultural Student Recruitment Committees: Faculty and staff join committee to aid the Admissions in staying connected to multicultural communities and suggesting recruitment ideas for those communities.

  2) Multicultural Student Receptions to introduce newly admitted minority students to the campus community and expose the students and their families to multicultural student organizations, student support services and alumni of the University.

- Personalized the recruitment of underrepresented students.

  1) Parent-to-Parent Letter: Letter from the parent of a currently enrolled minority student to the parents of admitted students. The letter discusses the transition to college and the great opportunities that their child and the family have participated in and how much they love the college or university.

- Disseminate information about campus diversity to prospective students and their families.

  1) Create a Diversity website to direct prospective students to resources and support.

  2) Send multicultural newsletters to all admitted students.

  3) Develop foreign language websites of key information for the admission process and university information.

- Ensure that images and messages in publications, office buildings, webpages, etc. indicate a welcoming environment.

Graduate Student Recruitment

- Recruit at graduate school fairs and conferences.

- Establish relationships with faculty at other institutions to facilitate referral of potential graduate students.

- Host campus visits and information sessions for prospective graduate students.

- Encourage underrepresented undergraduate students to pursue graduate education.

- Develop baccalaureate to master's transition enhancement programs.

- Create opportunities for participation in undergraduate research with efforts to encourage participation of underrepresented students.

- Establish mentoring programs for advising and supporting graduate students.

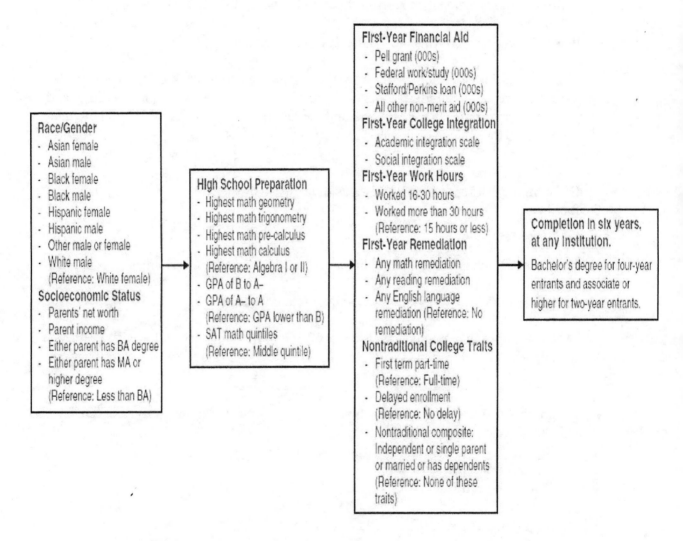

FIGURE 6.3

6.6 MODELING STUDENT SUCCESS [RETENTION & PROGRESSION]

The following seven variables can be used to model retention and progression. They are:

1) Learner characteristics
2) Learner behaviors
3) Academic integration
4) Social-psychological integration
5) Other learner support
6) Course/program characteristics
7) Instructor behaviors

Figure 6.4 is a black diagram of the seven variables

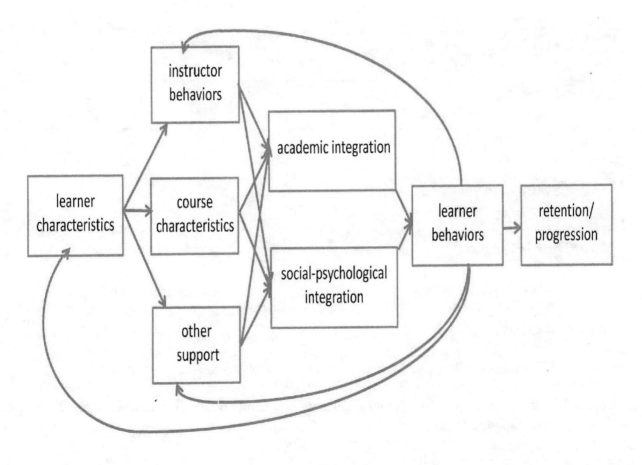

FIGURE 6.4

Table 6.1 is a matrix for modeling retention and progression. Example 6.1 is a sample matrix for modeling student success.

TABLE 6.1

PREDICTOR CATEGORY *italics* = research literature regular = partner experience **bold**=PAR Framework findings —limited list of predictors below each category—	CONNECTION application to enrollment (advising to enrollment)	ENTRY completion of gatekeeper courses (beginning of class)	PROGRESS entry into program to 75% of classes complete (middle of class)	COMPLETION of course of study & credential w/ market value (end of class)
LEARNER CHARACTERISTICS *prior GPA; achievement beliefs; content Knowledge & skills; ...* **1st time in college**				
LEARNER BEHAVIORS *attendance/log ins; participation in orientation programs; withdrawals;...engagement*				
ACADEMIC INTEGRATION *participation in student learning communities; peer mentoring;...specialized program coordinators*				
SOCIAL/PSYCHOLOGICAL INTEGRATION *perceived social presence; participation in freshmen interest groups;...specialized program coordinators*				
OTHER LEARNER SUPPORT *ongoing student support services...*				
COURSE/PROGRAM CHARACTERISTICS *perceived interactivity; ...perceived utility*				
INSTRUCTOR BEHAVIORS/CHARACTERISTICS *faculty responsiveness;...perceived social presence*				

Targeted Focus [T] • General Focus [G]

"In a national sample, approximately 59% of Bachelor of Arts recipients graduated from a different college than the first institution they attended" (National Center for Education Statistics [NCES], 2003).

Implication: Institutions will fail to "retain" students most of the time.

Interventions targeted toward the following items will have the greatest numerical potential for improving completion rates:

• *preventing* delayed entry to college
• *increasing* part-timers' level of enrollment
• *boosting* financial aid in colleges
• *reducing* students' work hours

Example 6.1

Interpret what particular groups of students who can be targeted with this student success model.

PREDICTORS *italics* = research literature regular = partner experience **bold** = POC findings	CONNECTION application to enrollment (advising to enrollment)	ENTRY completion of gatekeeper courses (beginning of class)	PROGRESS entry into program to 75% of requirements complete (middle of class)	COMPLETION of course of study & credential w/ market value (end of class)
learner characteristics *prior GPA(1)* *self-motivation(2) . . .* *attitudes towards tech (10)* *content knowledge & skills (11)* **being net new/no prior college** **Need Dev-Ed/Take DevEd** **#prior courses with C or better**	New Student Orientation (UIS)	Services for students with disabilities (UIS) Technology Helpdesk (UIS) Tutoring (UIS) Referrals to Counseling (UIS)	Services for students with disabilities (UIS) Technology Helpdesk (UIS) Tutoring (UIS) Referrals to Counseling (UIS)	Services for students with disabilities (UIS)
learner behaviors *easy access to a computer (13)* *participation in tutorials (14) . . .* **too many concurrent courses**		Tutoring (UIS) Referrals to Counseling (UIS)	Tutoring (UIS) Referrals to Counseling (UIS)	
academic integration *participation in tutorials (14)* *peer mentoring (17)* *student learning communities (20)* *orientation programs (21)* *freshman interest groups (22)* *program coordinators (24)*	Online program coordinators (UIS)	Online program coordinators (UIS) Writing center (UIS) Social media groups (UIS) Honors Program (UIS) Work study (UIS)	Online program coordinators (UIS) Writing center (, UIS) Social media groups (UIS) Honors Program (UIS) Work study (UIS)	Online program coordinators (UIS)
social/psychological **integration . . .**	Online program coordinators (UIS)	Online program coordinators (UIS)	Online program coordinators (UIS)	Online program coordinators (UIS)
other learner support . . .	Financial Aid (UIS)	Financial Aid (UIS)	Financial Aid (UIS)	
course/program **characteristics . . .**		QM reviews for some classes (UIS)	QM reviews for some classes (UIS)	
instructor **characteristics/** **behaviors** *perceived social presence (15)* *perceived interactivity (16) . . .*		Community of Practice for E-Learning (UIS) Center for Online Learning Research & Service Fellows (UIS)	Community of Practice for E-Learning (UIS) Center for Online Learning Research & Service Fellows (UIS)	

general focus – institution wide   targeted focus – targets particular groups of students or programs

6.7 SHARED RESPONSIBILITY

First and foremost all people associated with the college or university show be attentive on student success. All administrators, support staff, and faculty should know the university or college and know its students. Student success should be everyone's business. Mission statements and institutional leadership should focus on student success.

Universities and colleges should specify the path to student success. Draw an accurate map; 'distribute' it widely and follow it consistently. Implement a comprehensive network of early warning systems and safety nets. If something works, consider requiring it. Conduct ongoing outcomes assessment and use the results. Do more of what you know works for student success; do less of what you know doesn't work or can't demonstrate that it does. Review and revise time commitments and priorities. Align the reward system with the institutional mission, values, and priorities. Invest in student learning and activities that contribute to student success. Invest in faculty and staff members who are doing the right things. Make every student residence a learning community. Build and renovate spaces to reflect commitment to student engagement.

CHAPTER 4
Effective Communication Skills

CHAPTER 4
EFFECTIVE COMMUNICATION SKILLS

4.1 INTRODUCTION – EFFECTIVE COMMUNICATION SKILLS

4.1.1 THE IMPORTANCE OF COMMUNICATION

In a survey conducted by the Katz Business School at the University of Pittsburgh, organizations rated communication skills as the most important factor used in selecting their management staff. The study found that oral and written communication skills were important in predicting job success, as was the ability to communicate well with others in the workplace.

> A University of Pittsburgh study found that the most important factor in selecting managers is communication skills.

This makes sense when you think about it. If you can communicate well, you can get your message across to others in an effective way and they then have accurate instructions to complete their assigned tasks. If you are not able to communicate well, the messages you send get lost in translation. Communication breakdowns result in barriers against your ability to develop both professionally and personally.

Even though communication skills are so important to success in the workplace, there are many individuals who find these skills to be a stumbling block to their progress. They struggle to convey their thoughts and ideas in an accurate manner, making it difficult to progress and nearly impossible to lead well.

However, there is hope for anyone who finds communicating to be difficult. These skills can be practiced and learned. It takes learning about how communication works, how to communicate exactly what it is you want to say, what mode of communication is best, and what factors are influencing the ability for you to send and receive messages with acumen.

4.1.2 WHAT IS COMMUNICATION?

When asked to define communication, how would you respond? Most people will relate to the forms of communication – talking or listening. But communication goes beyond that. Communication involves getting information from one person to the other person. Yet even this is not a complete definition because communicating effectively involves having that information relayed while retaining the same in content and context. If I tell you one thing and you hear another, have I communicated effectively?

> Communication is the art and process of creating and
> sharing ideas. Effective communication depends on the
> richness of those ideas.

So if we look at communication from another angle, it involves the perception of the information as much as the delivery of that information. In other words, we can define communication as the art and process of creating and sharing ideas. Effective communication depends on the richness of those ideas. In order to be effective at communicating, there are a number of skills that you can rely. Which skill you choose will depend upon your situation, the recipient of your communication, and the information that you need to convey.

4.1.3 WHAT ARE COMMUNICATION SKILLS?

Imagine you are on one side of a wall and the person you want to communicate with is on the other side of the wall. But there's more than the wall in the way. The wall is surrounded by a moat that is filled with crocodiles and edged by quicksand. These barriers could be things like different cultures, different expectations, different experiences, different perspectives, or different communication styles, stereotypes, to name just a few.

> Communication skills are the tools that we use to remove the
> barriers to effective communication.

You might experience only one of these barriers at a time, or you might find yourself facing them all. Getting your message to the other person requires that you recognize these barriers exist between you, and that you then apply the proper tools, or communication skills, to remove those barriers preventing your message from getting through.

Of course, communication is a two-way street. The person on the other side of those barriers will also try to send messages back to you. Your ability to understand them clearly could be left to a dependence on their ability to use communication skills. But that's leaving the success of the communication to chance. Instead, you can also use your own communication skills to ensure that you receive messages clearly as well.

Finally, there isn't only one point in your communication with another person at which you have to watch out for barriers. To be successful at communicating, it's important to recognize that these barriers to communication can occur at multiple points in the communication process.

4.1.4 THE COMMUNICATION PROCESS

The communication process involves multiple parts and stages. These are:

> The communication process is composed of several stages, each of which offers potential barriers to successful communication.

- Source
- Message
- Encoding
- Channel
- Decoding
- Receiver
- Feedback
- Context

At each of these stages, there is the potential for barriers to be formed or problems to arise. As we look at ways to limit the barriers to communicating effectively, remember that you may have to apply them at more than one occasion during your communication process. The steps in the process are represented in Figure 4.1 and explained further in the chapter.

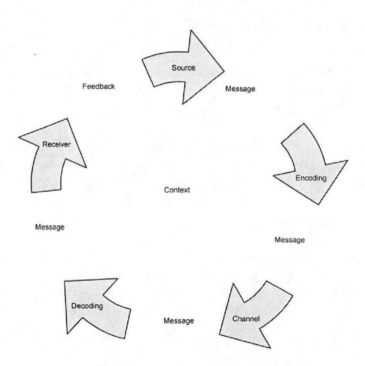

Figure 4.1 The Communication Process

4.1.4.1 SOURCE

The source of the communication is the sender, or for our purposes, you. In order to be a good source, you need to be clear about the message that you are sending. Do you know exactly what it is that you want to communicate? You'll also want to be sure you know why it is that you are communicating. What result is it that you expect? If you cannot answer these questions, you will be starting the communication process with a high chance of failure.

> The source of the message is the sender. The sender must know why the communication is necessary and what result is needed.

4.1.4.2 MESSAGE

The message is simply the information that you want to communicate. Without a message, there is no cause for communicating. If you cannot summarize the information that you need to share, you aren't ready to begin the process of communication.

4.1.4.3 ENCODING

Encoding is the process of taking your message and transferring it into a format that can be shared with another party. It's sort of like how messages are sent via a fax. The information on the paper has to be encoded or prepared, before it can be sent to the other party. It has to be sent in a format that the other party has the ability to decode or the message will not be delivered.

In order to encode a message properly, you have to think about what the other person will need in order to understand, or decode, the message. Are you sharing all the information that is necessary to get the full picture? Have you made assumptions that may not be correct? Are you using the best form of sending it in order to ensure the best chance of the message being properly received? Are there cultural, environmental, or language differences between you and the other party cause miscommunication?

> Encoding is the process of taking your message and transferring it into the proper format for sharing it with your audience. It requires knowing your audience and ensuring that your message provides all of the information that they need.

Of course, to encode a message properly, you have to know who your audience is. You need to have an understanding of what they know and what they need to know in order to send a complete message. You need to use language they will understand and a context that is familiar.

One simple example of how you can do this is being sure to spell out acronyms. We sometimes forget that not everyone is familiar with the acronyms that we may use on a regular basis.

4.1.4.4 CHANNEL

The channel is the method or methods that you use to convey your message. The type of message you have will help to determine the channel that you should use. Channels include face-to-face conversations, telephone calls or videoconferences, and written communication like emails and memos.

> The Channel is the method of communication that you choose such as face-to-face, by telephone, or via email.

Each channel has its advantages and disadvantages. For example, you will find it difficult to give complex, technical information or instructions by using just the telephone. Or you may get bad results if you try to give criticism via email.

4.1.4.5 DECODING

Decoding happens when you receive the message that has been sent. The communication skills required to decode a message successfully include the ability to read and comprehend, listen actively, or ask clarifying questions when needed.

> Decoding is the process of receiving the message accurately and requires that your audience has the means to understand the information you are sharing.

If the person you are attempting to communicate with seems to be lacking the skills to decode your message, you will need to either resend it in a different way or assist them in understanding it by supplying clarifying information.

4.1.4.6 RECEIVER

Since you have thought out your message, you've certainly also thought about what you want the desired result to be on the part of your listener. But it's important to realize that each person who receives your message will be listening to it through their own individual expectations, opinions, and perspectives. Their individual experiences will influence how your messages is received.

> You have expectations for a response from the receiver when you send a message. You can increase the chances of getting this result by addressing your audience's concerns or addressing specific benefits as part of your communication.

While you can't always address each person's individual concerns in a message, part of planning for your communication is to think ahead of time about what some of their thoughts or experiences might be. For example, if you are releasing a new product and want to convince customers to try it, you would want to be certain to address the specific benefits to the customer, or what improvements have been made since the last version was released.

4.1.4.7 FEEDBACK

No matter what channel you have used to convey your message, you can use feedback to help determine how successful your communications was. If you are face-to-face with your audience, you can read body language and ask questions to ensure understanding. If you have communicated via writing, you can gauge the success of your communication by the response that you get or by seeing if the result you wanted is delivered.

> Feedback lets you gauge how successful you were at communicating. It also offers a chance to adjust your communication process for the future.

In any case, feedback is invaluable for helping you to improve your communication skills. You can learn what worked well and what didn't so that you can be even more efficient the next time you communicate with that person or the next time you need to communicate a similar message.

4.1.4.8 CONTEXT

The context is the situation in which you are communicating. It involves the environment that you are in and that in which your audience is in, the culture of your organization(s), and elements such as the relationship between you and your audience. Your communication process will not look the same when you are communicating with your boss as it will when you are communicating with a friend. The context helps determine the tone and style of your communication.

> Context involves things such as your relationship with your audience, the culture of your organization and your general environment.

4.2 PERSPECTIVES IN COMMUNICATION

4.2.1 INTRODUCTION

We all come to each communication exchange with our own "filter" through which we see the world, the person we are communicating with, and the situation or topic we are communicating about. These filters mean that we don't always start with the same perspective as the person we are communicating with.

> Our individual perceptions are the 'filter' through which we communicate with others.

4.2.2 VISUAL PERCEPTION

These filters can be visual, as in the famous example in Figure 4.2. What do you see when you look at the picture? A young woman or an old crone? Both perspectives are possible, and both are valid.

Figure 4.2: Young Woman & Crone

Figure 4.3 reveals the two perspectives. Both of the perspectives represented in the young and old woman are valid- they are simply two different ways of seeing the same thing. We cannot decide that one does not exist just because we don't see it. We have to recognize that there is more than one way to perceive the picture, just like there is usually more than one way to see any situation we encounter.

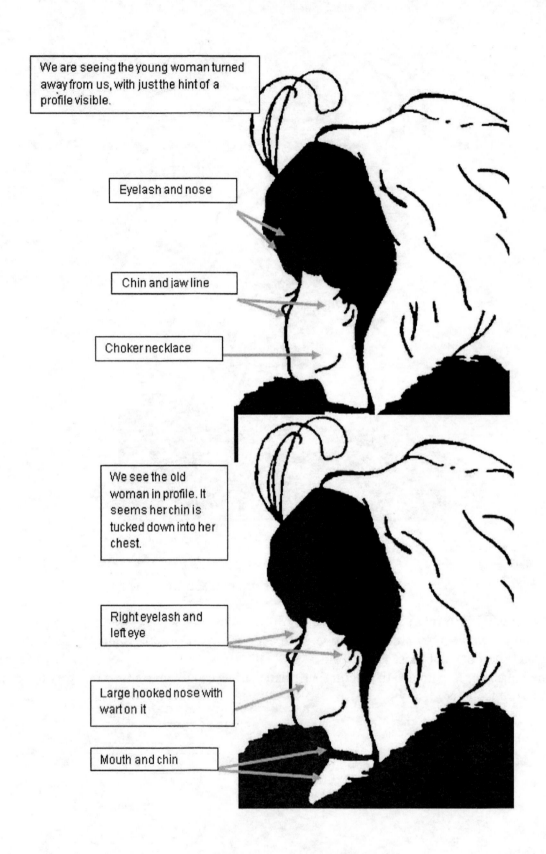

Figure 4.3 The Two Perspectives

4.3 LANGUAGE

The different perspectives we experience can be with language as well. How many times have you received an email that seemed to have a certain "tone to it," and that perception of tone colored the way that you might have responded?

> The same words can have very different meanings depending on how we interpret them.

Here's another example. What is the meaning of the following phrase?

A woman without her man is nothing.

Sounds pretty bad at first glance, doesn't it? Look again. If you add punctuation or change the word emphasis, how does the meaning change?

A woman. Without her, man is nothing.

The words were the same in both cases. But the meaning has now changed completely. So although we think our meaning may be clear when we use specific words in a certain order, we can't always be certain that the other person will read or hear them in that way.

"Effective listeners remember that "words have no meaning-people have meaning." The assignment of meaning to a term is an internal process; meaning comes from inside us. And although our experiences, knowledge and attitudes differ, we often misinterpret each other's messages while under the illusion that a common understanding has been achieved." – Larry Barker.

4.4 OTHER FACTORS AFFECTING OUR PERSPECTIVE

There are a multitude of other factors that can affect our perspective, thereby affecting how we communicate with another person. Some of these factors come from our past experiences, our prejudices, our feelings, and our environment. Some of these will be discussed in greater detail in later sections.

4.4.1 PAST EXPERIENCES

Imagine that you are in a meeting where you will be discussing changes in your personnel policies at work. What will you be bringing to that conversation? You might have examples of other company's personnel policies. You might have examples from your own time in the company that demonstrate why you feel that certain changes might need to be made. Or you might come to the table empty-handed, with just a pad of paper and a pen in order to take notes.

What influences you to do any of these things? Your past experience. You would bring outside information because you have learned in the past that comparing situations can be helpful in decision-making. You bring examples of your own experience because you have learned in the past that examples can be powerful ways to make your case. Or you come to the table empty-handed because in the past you have felt that your input wasn't valued or you have no past experience in this topic and so you are clean-slate information wise.

In every one of these situations, your communication is being affected by your past experience. You enter a situation, a meeting, or a conversation, with certain expectations of what will happen in that scenario, and you behave accordingly.

Of course, sometimes you want your past experiences to influence your future communications. For example, when your team responded positively to the sales tactics you put in place, those similar tactics can certainly be successful again.

It's when our negative past experiences stifle our communication or alter our full potential for communicating that we need to be aware. Further examples of how your past experience could influence your communication are given in Figure 4.4. Note that not all of them are negative – our past experiences can reaffirm our communication as well.

Past Experience	Resulting Effect on Communication
Your boss has reacted negatively when you have discussed this topic in the past	You hesitate to discuss the topic even when it is necessary for your work
Your co-worker has forgotten important information multiple times in the past	You assume he or she will forget the information this time and so you overload him or her with reminders
Your boss ignored your idea in the last meeting	You don't bring up another idea that could have made an impact
You got nervous the last time you gave a presentation	You start out even more nervous on your next presentation
The group reacted well to your last sales pitch	You use a similar style for your next sales pitch
The last twenty customers rejected your new product	You fail to offer that product to the 21st customer and beyond, some of whom may have wanted the product
The last email you received from a colleague was rude (you perceived it as rude!)	You send a rude email in return
Your subordinate was disagreeable the last time you asked him to work overtime	You don't ask him this time, even though he would have agreed

Figure 4.4 Past Experiences Influencing Communication

4.4.2 PREJUDICES

We all have prejudices. They occur when we take our past experiences with a person and assume that the same type of experience will happen with all people who are similar to the first. Prejudices are partly due to culture and partly due to personal preference or experience. Not all prejudices involve a negative characteristic either; for example, you could consider all of one group to be smart.

The problem with prejudices is when they start to influence how or to whom we communicate. To get an idea of how this could be happening in your workplace, consider how you might complete the phrases below. If you can't think of a way to complete it from your own experience, complete each phrase with a stereotype that you might have heard in the past:

- Women in the workplace are….
- Young people in the workplace are….
- Seniors in the workplace are….
- Working mothers in the workplace are…
- Supervisors at work are…..
- The lowest job level workers are….
- Blacks, whites, or (fill in a race) in the workplace are….
- Homosexuals in the workplace are….
- Christians, Muslims, or (fill in a religion) in the workplace are…
- Disabled people in the workplace are….

> Prejudices occur when we take an isolated experience with one 'type' of person and then act as if all encounters in the future with people of the same 'type' or with the same characteristics will result in the same experience.

When we categorized people like this, we eliminate their individuality. If you are communicating to a person through a perceived prejudice or stereotype, at the very least you are greatly limiting the chances of your communication being successful or producing the desired result. At the most, you are alienating or insulting someone with whom you are trying to build a working relationship.

Your goal should be to see each person as an individual that is separate from any preconceived notions you might have about them. It takes practice, but wouldn't you like to be seen and communicated with as an individual and not as a sum of different labels that can be placed on you?

4.4.3 FEELINGS

For this area of influence, there are actually two ways in which your feelings can influence your communication with another person. The first step simply refers to the way that you feel on a given day; if you feel well, you'll communicate in one way and if you feel ill you'll communicate in another. Since your well-being fluctuates, it makes sense that the way you communicate will change somewhat with how well you are feeling. If you find yourself experiencing difficulty in communicating due to an illness or other physical stressor, recognizing and acknowledging it, when appropriate, can be very helpful when others might interpret the change in your communication as having something to do with them.

The second aspect related to feelings refers to how you feel about a specific person. When you genuinely like someone, the way you communicate is going to show it. Unfortunately, the same can be said for when you don't like someone. However, as you continue learning about effective communication skills in the following sections, you will find some tools to help you be as effective as possible in communicating, even when it's with someone that you dislike.

The last area of influence on your communication is your environment. All of us communicate differently in different environments. This is simple enough to observe in everyday life. Do you speak to your colleagues the same way that you do to your friends? Do you talk to strangers with more or less formality than people you know well? Do you talk to your subordinates the same way when your own boss is there as you do when she or he is not there? As you go through your workday, notice where you are, what is going on and who else is present may be impacting the way you communicate.

Recognizing how the environment might be affecting others you communicate with is a skill that can come in handy for you, particularly when you perceive that the environment is having a negative impact on your ability to communicate effectively with someone. This skill will help you perceive why someone might be communicating in the way that they are. It will also give you a factor that you can alter in order to make the person more comfortable or to establish a level of formality that you feel is important in a particular situation.

"Precision of communication is important, more important than ever, in our era of hair trigger balances, when a false or misunderstood word may create as much disaster as a sudden thoughtless act." – James Thurber

4.5 ELEMENTS OF COMMUNICATION

4.5.1 INTRODUCTION

What does it takes to communicate with another person? How are we communicating even when we aren't using words? When you begin studying communication, you'll find that we communicate with much more than our words. In face-to-face communication, our words are only part of the message.

The balance of the message, and in fact, the largest part of the message that we are sending to others is made up of non-verbal information. It is composed of our body language and our tone of voice. Figure 4.5 below demonstrates this fact.

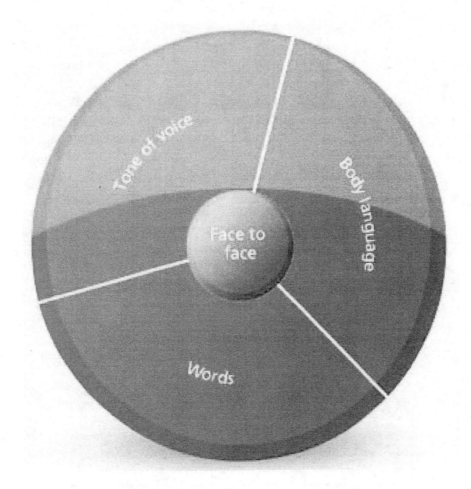

Figure 4.5: Face-to-Face Communication

4.5.2 FACE-TO-FACE COMMUNICATION

Albert Mehrabian's work on verbal and non-verbal communication in the 1960s and early 1970s is still considered a valid model today. He posed that the non-verbal aspects of communication such as tone of voice and non-verbal gestures communicate a great deal more than the words that are spoken. He also found that people are more likely to believe your non-verbal communication than your verbal communication if the two are contradictory. In other words, you are most believable and most effectively communicating when all three elements of face-to-face communication are aligned with each other.

> Over half of the information we send to others is through non-verbal methods.

4.5.2.1 TONE OF VOICE

According to Mehrabian, the tone of voice we use is responsible for about 35-40 percent of the message we are sending. Tone involves the volume you use, the level and type of emotion that you communicate and the emphasis that you place on the words that you choose. To see how this works, try saying the sentences in Figure 4.6, with the emphasis each time on the word in bold.

I didn't say he borrowed my book.
I **didn't** say he borrowed my book.
I didn't **say** he borrowed my book.
I didn't say **he** borrowed my book.
I didn't say he **borrowed** my book.
I didn't say he borrowed **my** book.
I didn't say he borrowed my **book**.

Figure 4.6: Impact of Tone of Voice

> The same sentence can have multiple meaning depending on which word is emphasized. The emphasis on a particular word implies additional information than what the words say.

Notice that the meaning of the sentence changes each time, even though the words are the same. The emphasis you place on the word draws the listener's attention, indicating that the word is important somehow. In this case, the emphasis indicates that the word is an error. So in the first example, **I** didn't say he borrowed my book, the phrase includes the message that someone else said it. The implied information continues to change in each sentence, despite the words remaining the same each time.

4.5.2.2 BODY LANGUAGE

Over half of the message that we are sending to others is non-verbal, according to Mehrabian. This means that we receive more than half of what a person is communicating through the subconscious messages they are sending with body language.

Examples of body language include:

- Facial expressions
- The way they are standing or sitting
- Any swaying or other movement
- Gestures with their arms or hands
- Eye contact (or lack thereof)
- Breathing rate
- Swallowing or coughing
- Blushing
- Fidgeting

Basically, body language includes anything they are doing with their body besides speaking. We recognize this communication instinctively, without having to be told what it means. The following examples will good you a good idea of what a person's body language is telling you.

> We instinctively recognize what body language is telling us.

- Mike is sitting with his arms crossed over his chest. His head is tilted down and away from you. His finger is tapping his arm in a fast, erratic manner.

- Jane is sitting back in her chair with her arms crossed behind her heads. She is smiling at you and nodding her head from time-to-time as you speak.

- Dave is standing close to you at an angle. He is speaking just above a whisper and in a strained voice. He makes quick, sharp movements with his hands.

- Marci is presenting to the marketing team. She is swaying back and forth, her hands keep changing positions, and she seems to keep absent-mindedly touching her hair.

- Regina is sitting at the conference table in a meeting. Her legs are crossed and the leg that is on the floor is bouncing up and down at a rapid pace. She is sitting forward in her chair with her pen tapping on the table.

> It's not what you say, it's how you say it that matters the most in relaying your message.

We can picture these people and their behaviors from the short description here and without hearing a word from them, we have a pretty good idea of how they are feeling about the situation or about what we are saying to them.

There is another reason to understand body language besides being able to read what another is saying to you subconsciously. You can use it to communicate intentionally that you are on the same wavelength as another person. Next time you are in a conversation that you are enjoying or with whom it is important to you to make a good impression, notice their body language. Now notice yours. Chances are, you have subconsciously mimicked their body language. If they lean forward, you will lean forward. If they cross one foot over the knee, you do the same. This is our automatic response to someone that we want to establish a positive connection with- and it's one you can use to your advantage.

> Body language is a useful tool that you can learn to use.
>
> You can mimic another's body language when you want to express support for them.
>
> You can use a person's body language to realize that your message is incomplete – there is more to say or there are questions to be answered.

When you are in a situation where you want to convey your support of another person, you can intentionally mimic their body language. If you are standing in the hallway and they lean to one side, mirror their action. If they sit back and relax, do the same. You are sending subconscious signals that you are on their side, even if the topic that you are discussing is one where there may be disagreement. It reaffirms that you are part of the same team, no matter what else might be going on.

You can also use this tool to gauge whether or not others are buying in on what you are saying. Are they using words that express agreement, but sitting all wound up with crossed arms and legs? Unless they just happen to be cold, chances are that there is some matter still unresolved in their mind. You can use this signal as information to you that you still need to do some explaining or ask some additional questions.

4.5.2.3 VERBAL COMMUNICATION

The third communication element is verbal communication. Believe it or not, it is actually the least impactful element in face-to-face communication. The old adage is true – it's not what you say, it's how you say it that counts.

Of course, this is a bit simplified. We do want to use verbal communications, the words we choose, to our best advantage. You would definitely make a different impression if you curse during your presentation than if you don't. Choosing our words carefully is a way to enhance our message, but we should remember that it is not the most important part of the message. We should not neglect to pay attention to the other non-verbal elements.

What about when we are limited to using only verbal communication? Given that we know that face-to-face communication delivers the most complete message, we know that verbal communication alone can be challenging in creating effective communication.

You might think that talking on the telephone or sending off a quick email is an excellent time saver. There are times when this is true. For example, when confirming specific facts or asking simple questions. But for many communication needs, verbal communication only is rarely going to suffice.

As an example, imagine trying to give someone verbal instructions on how to draw the string of shapes shown in Figure 4.7.

How could you give someone directions on drawing the string of shapes in Figure 7 by only using verbal communication? What would be challenging about doing so?

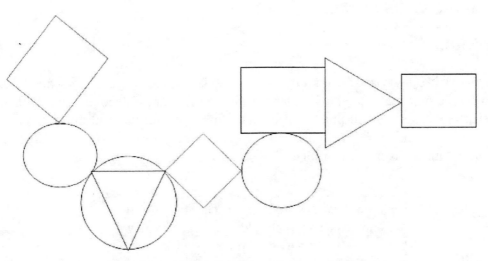

Figure 4.7: Describing a String of Shapes

How would you start? Would you give a general description of the string of shapes first? Would you tell them to be prepared to use rectangles, circles, triangles, and squares? Would you attempt to use measurements to give the other person the general idea of the size of each shape? Or would you just give directions as to the general area to start and say "draw a rectangle?"

If you do try this with another person, chances are you will feel the strong desire to show them the picture or to use your hands to indicate the shapes and their position to one another. That's because in this case, you instinctually know that there are better ways to deliver this type of communication.

Notice that each of these ways of communicating the information is valid. They may end up with slightly different results with the same person, but your challenge is in the fact that you are very limited in how you communicate the information. Using only words, you are likely to end up with as many different versions of the drawing as there are people drawing it. We'll spend more time on improving your verbal communications in later sections.

4.6 PHYSICAL COMMUNICATION

Although it is less used in a business scenario, there is one last element of communication that all of us use on a regular basis – physical communication. At work you might use it – to pat someone on the back or to give them a slight tap on the shoulder to get their attention. When it is used, it is more effective than verbal communication.

To clarify this point, imagine doing the exercise on the shapes in the last section, but this time, instead of words, you are able to put your hand of the person doing the drawing and direct the motion of their pen physically. You will end up with something much closer to the actual picture than by verbal instruction alone.

4.7 COMMUNICATION STYLES

4.7.1 INTRODUCTION

Each one of us has a style of communicating that is unique. Some of us are talkative and extroverted while others are quiet and reserved. Some of us are outspoken while others are less likely to share their opinions in public. Still others of us are formal and direct while others are informal and like to take our time getting to the main point. So how do these different styles of communication impact us in the workplace?

> Communication style refers to the choices we tend to make when communicating to others. It involves two basic dimensions: the assertiveness level of our communication and the emotiveness level of our communication. We also use different styles depending on with whom we are communicating.
>
> Differences in communication style can lead to barriers in communication success.

When you work with someone who has a decidedly different communication style from your own, that difference can act as one of the barriers to effective communication. You may feel that someone is being aloof and cold while they feel that they are being quick and business-like. Or you might feel that someone is being too analytical and detailed, while they feel that you aren't recognizing the importance of the small things that can make a big difference.

There is a way to overcome these differences, however. It involves learning the basic characteristics of the different communication styles and how they influence the context in which your communication is happening. If you can learn to understand the other's person communication style and how it is manifesting itself in the way they communicate you are learning your audience and what they need in order to understand your message. You can then encode your message in a way that they will be more likely to be able to decode it, thereby increasing the chance that your message will be delivered successfully.

To put it another way, imagine that you are in a foreign country. You can stumble about, using your own words for things and trying to communicate, with the result being that one or both parties may become frustrated – and with very little chance that you will get the result that you want.

But if you speak the language of the person you want to speak with, suddenly you can communicate. You can ask for what you need, give them the information they need, and hopefully achieve the result that is the original aim to communicate to your audience in their "native tongue."

So how do you start? You begin by studying the four basic communication styles and how they relate to each other. You identify your own personal communication style and what particular barriers you might face when communicating with the other styles. Then you learn some simple tools you can use to enhance your communication with others, no matter what communication style they are.

4.7.2 THE COMMUNICATION STYLES MATRIX

There are many different models that describe the ways in which we communicate. But one very useful model is based on the work of Dr. Eileen Russo. Her matrix is displayed in Figure 4.8. It shows that there are two different dimensions in communication styles: the level of expressiveness and the level of assertiveness.

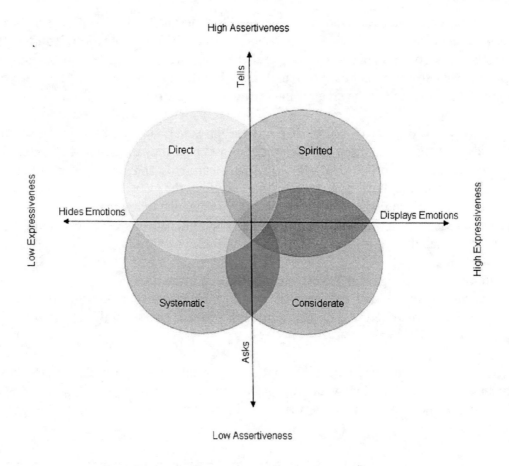

Figure 4.8: The Communication Styles Matrix

Each quadrant in Figure 4.8 represents a different communication style. People can fall anywhere within each quadrant, becoming more uniformly one style over the others as they move further from the center.

> The assertive communication styles tell others what to do while the less assertive styles ask others what should be done.
>
> The more expressive styles show emotion while the less expressive styles refrain from showing it.

Notice that the more sensitive communication styles tend to "tell" others what to do. The less assertive communication styles tend to "ask" others what should be done. The more expressive communication styles tend to show their emotions in their face, speech and tone. The less expressive styles will either not express their emotions or will work to hide them. The resulting four basic communication styles are shown in Figure 4.9. In the following sections, we'll look at the basic characteristics of each communication styles and some things you can do to help you communicate well with each type.

Low Expressiveness + Low Assertiveness = Systematic

Low Expressiveness + High Assertiveness = Direct

High Expressiveness + High Assertiveness = Spirited

High Expressiveness + Low Assertiveness = Considerate

Figure 4.9: The Four Basic Communication Styles

4.7.2.1 DIRECT COMMUNICATION STYLE

As indicated in the communication style matrix, people with the direct communication style are highly assertive and not expressive. They tend to tell others what to do instead of asking others what they think should be done, and they will not easily show emotions in their communications with others. Their communication style is meant to be expedient, though others may not always see it that way. They may appear terse and cold to others, who might take their style of communicating personally.

> People with direct communication styles are the 'go-getters' in the group. They will work hard and fast and will brook few questions or distractions.
>
> These people need to use caution to avoid appearing dictatorial or cold.
>
> If you are a direct style, you could probably use some practice with listening skills.

Direct communicators will try to tell you as little as possible before moving on to the next topic – not because they are trying to be evasive, but because they are trying to save time. They won't always stop to listen to others, even if the others have something valuable to contribute. They may seem impatient and overbearing at times, but it's not meant to be personal. They are attempting to focus on results rather than emotions. They will speak their minds, even if it could be off-putting to others. Don't expect them to talk about their personal lives – they like to keep business and personal issues separate. They don't back down from conflict, and at times could be seen as being aggressive rather than assertive in the way that they express their opinions. Figure 4.10 give tips if you are a direct style, while Figure 4.11 gives you tips for working with others who are the direct style.

Tips for Communicating if You Have a Direct Communication Style

- Make an effort to listen fully to others and avoid interrupting

- Allow time for "chatting" at the beginning of a meeting

- Recognize that others may feel the need to express their emotions about topics

- Recognize that brainstorming can be helpful and not just a "waste of time"

- Try to communicate your expectations for how a meeting will go – the length of time, the topics to be covered, and the expected results – before a meeting occurs

- Take the time to show your appreciation for others' contributions

- Don't use email for sensitive or complicated topics

- Allow time in your schedule for questions and feedback

Figure 4.10: Tips for Communicating if You have a Direct Communication Style

Tips for Communicating with People with a Direct Communication Style

- Ask if they have time to talk before jumping in

- Get to the point quickly – don't bore them with lots of background information

- Limit "chatting" or conversation that is off-topic

- Use short, direct sentences

- Ask for a specific call to action or make a specific request

- Do not speak in abstract

- Only promise what you are certain you can deliver

- Don't give or ask for information about personal issues unless they initiate it

- Don't sugar coat things – speak plainly

Figure 4.11: Tips for Communicating with People Who have a Direct Communication Style

4.7.2.2 SPIRITED COMMUNICATION STYLE

People with the spirited communication style are very interested in the "big picture." They are the dreamers, the inventors, and the innovators in the group. Their communication may be full of grand ideas and hyperboles that tend to be very persuasive to others at first.

> People with the spirited communication style love to flesh out ideas, brainstorm, and talk about the big picture – as long as they get to do a lot of the talking!
>
> Spirited people can have a hard time nailing down the details in their wonderful ideas. They may also have a hard time sticking to an agenda or to one topic.

However, they are not always very good at discussing the details or the exact steps in the process. They will tend to go off on tangents in their conversations, and like to interject anecdotes into their dialogues in order to demonstrate or drive home a point.

Keeping to an agenda is sometimes a challenge for those with the spirited communication style since both time management and remaining focused are challenges for this group. Their written or verbal communication may tend towards the dramatic. While they can be very entertaining, getting them to communicate clearly on specific topics may take the assistance of someone else to guide them through a conversation and keep them on track by bringing them back to the subject at hand. See Figures 4.12 and 4.13 for tips on communicating as or with a person with a spirited communication style.

Tips for Communicating if you have a Spirited Communication Style

- When considering new ideas to share, also consider whether or not you have suggestions on how to put those ideas into action.

- Request agreed-upon agendas and time limits when in meetings

- Try to limit your sharing of personal anecdotes that take the group off-topic

- Make sure you are allowing others to contribute their ideas and suggestions – and that you are listening.

- Be certain any requests you make are clear and that you convey the reason for asking

- Communicate your appreciation for others' work and input

Figure 4.12: Tips for Communicating if you have a Spirited Communication Style

Tips for Communicating with People Who have a Spirited Communication Style

- Use an agenda with time limits for each topic

- Praise them in front of other people

- Learn to gently redirect the conversation back to the topic at hand

- Understand that they may exaggerate

- Challenge them to break down their "big ideas" into specific outcomes and steps

- Reaffirm with them what they have agreed to do

- Use checklists or other written reminders as a way to help communicate what needs to be done

Figure 4.13: Tips for Communicating with People Who have a Spirited Communication Style

4.7.2.3 SYSTEMATIC COMMUNICATION STYLE

Those with a systematic communication style like to focus on facts and details rather opinions and possibilities. Expect to use and appreciate logic when you communicate with a systematic. They will appreciate facts and analysis rather than ideas that have not yet been proved useful.

> People with a systematic communication style will focus on facts over opinions. Communication with tangible evidence is best for systematic. They will likely be uncomfortable expressing feelings and will tend to avoid confrontation.

Those with a systematic style are uncomfortable with expressing their feelings about things and do not like conflict. They may tend to shut down communication rather than dealing with emotional or confrontational situations. If you give them directions, then you will need to be very thorough and precise in relaying them.

The more information you can give them, the happier they will be – as long as the information is relevant to the current discussion or is relevant background information. Figures 4.14 and 4.15 give you tips for communicating if you have a systematic communication style or if you are speaking with someone with a systematic communication style.

Tips for Communicating if you have a Systematic Communication Style

- Recognize that not everyone follows linear thought processes and decision-making

- Realize that for good working relationships, consideration for others' feelings is important

- Learn to ask qualifying questions that will help you get the information you need

- Ask others about themselves if you want to build rapport

- Make sure you understand the scope of a project so that you don't waste time collecting information that is not going to be needed

- If you need to ask for more time for analyst, be able to explain the benefit of the information you are working on

Figure 4.14: Tips for Communicating if you have a Systematic Communication Style

Tips for Communicating with People Who have a Systematic Communication Style

- Focus on the facts of the situation rather than individuals' opinions

- Speak with precision and accuracy rather than generalizations

- Be organized, on time, and on topic when you communicate with them

- Give logical reasons for your actions and for what you ask of them

- Allow them time for research and analysis before decision-making

- Avoid personal topics unless they open the conversation

Figure 4.15: Tips for Communicating with People Who have a Systematic Communication Style

4.7.2.4 CONSIDERATE COMMUNICATION STYLE

Those with the considerate communication style are very concerned about the feelings of others. They want to please other people and to be included in their peer group. They like to work with others, help others, and connect to others on a personnel level. If there is conflict in your group, they will be the ones to attempt to mediate it. They want everyone to have a chance to speak their minds, have their turns, and receive recognition for their contribution. They are natural trainers and counselors, and enjoy helping others to succeed. They will encourage group collaboration and communication, though they are not always inclined to speak their own minds.

> People with a considerate communication style will be very interested in listening and in finding out how you and others are doing. They will want everyone to have a chance to speak, but might refrain from expressing their own opinions if they think it will displease others.

This is the major communication challenge for those with the considerate personality style – they may be reluctant to share an opposing opinion, even if it's important information, because they are concerned about keeping the peace and being liked.

They are also inclined to take direct communication as a personal matter. It's difficult for them to separate other peoples' opinions about a topic from the opinions about them, and so may feel that an opposing opinion is due to not liking them. There is also the possibility that they will be talked into something in order to preserve the peace rather than standing their ground. Figure 4.16 offers tips for communicating if you have a considerate communication style, and Figure 4.17 offers advice if you are speaking with someone with a considerate communication style.

Tips for Communicating if you have a Considerate Communication Style

- Recognize that other people's opinions about a topic are separate from their opinions about you

- Realize that not everyone is comfortable discussing personal topics with work colleagues: allow others to open personal topics before asking questions

- Respect your own opinion as you respect others' opinions

- Recognize that you don't have to be friends with everyone, but you should treat others and be treated professionally

Figure 4.16: Tips for Communicating if you have a Considerate Communication Style

Tips for Communicating with People Who have a Considerate Communication Style

- When possible, reassure them that your opinions are not personal

- Express a sincere interest in their feelings, thoughts, and personal life

- Encourage them to ask questions and share their opinions

- Let them know that you appreciate their help

- Resolve any conflicts quickly

Figure 4.17: Tips for Communicating with People Who have a Considerate Communication Style

4.8 EXAMPLES OF COMMUNICATION FOR EACH STYLE

It will take some time and practice to learn exactly what will work in communicating with the people in your work group. Hopefully you recognized the people in your office in the descriptions of the different communication styles in the last section. If not, you can pay more attention to how they communicate with you as a sign of their main communication style. Remember too that not everyone fits neatly into a category; some people will bridge more than one style, depending on with whom they are communicating. You may need to do some experimenting to determine which communication style works best with them.

It will also take practice for you to become comfortable in altering your own communication style or methods in order to best communicate with others. You will still be inclined to your natural communication style, which is to be expected. It will also be easier to do at first when you have the time to think about your communication ahead of time, such as when writing an email. However, over time, you will find that you can adjust faster and employ the tools that you need without thinking it out ahead of time.

4.8.1 DIRECT STYLE

When communicating with someone who has the direct communication style, the key is to get to the main point of your communication as soon as possible, and to do so in as efficient manner as possible. The first example below shows the type of communication that will not work with someone who has a direct communication style. In this example, Jane is the one with the direct communication style.

Hi Jane,

I heard from Alex that you landed a new business account yesterday. He said that you did an excellent job in explaining the company's benefits to the customer and that you were very professional.

Alex also said that the customer asked for a quote on a new phone system for his existing offices. Have you thought about how you will proceed? Let me know if I can help you get the quote together or if you need any ideas on the configuration. I'd like to get the quote to them later this week if you think you can manage it. That way we would have a good chance of getting the order in for this month's numbers.

Thanks again, and hope you are having a blessed Tuesday!

Anne!

What is the main point of the communication? What is the requested action? How much of the communication is superfluous information?

A person with a direct communication style will not necessarily glean what you want them to do or by when. They will appreciate the accolade, but they won't appreciate the personal references or information.

Jane,

Great job on the new account. I'd like to meet for 10-15 minutes tomorrow to discuss strategy and timing. Please let me know if you'd prefer to meet at 1:00, 1:30, or 2:00 pm.

Thank you,

Anne

See the difference? The first one does eventually get around to the point, but it is too personal-sounding and doesn't give a clear request for the direct person to respond to. The second one still communicates approval and makes a request, but it does so in a much clearer way. If it seems curt to you, don't worry the direct style person will appreciate it. It's a perfect professional communication and there is much less chance for misunderstanding.

4.8.2 SPIRITED STYLE

When communicating with someone who is spirited, it might be hard to even pin them down for communication in the first place. And once you have their attention, keeping it is another matter entirely. You will find that consistency is important in communicating with people who are spirited. If you can get them used to a particular format or method of communication, it will be easier to keep them communicating. This doesn't mean always choosing email or always choosing telephone. But it does mean always using follow-up questions or checking in on a regular basis to see if you are both still on the same page.

Also remember that a person with a spirited style may need more time to brainstorm and discuss ideas than the other communication styles. If you want them to come to the table with decisions already made, be sure to get their buy-in-beforehand. Otherwise they may still find the need to discuss something that you already felt was decided.

Finally, you can go a long way towards relationship-building with a spirited style person if you give them the opportunity to shine. Does your team need to make a presentation? Let the spirited person know that you think they would be a good choice to lead. Complimenting them in a public arena is a good choice as well. Here's an example of a good written communication to a spirited person.

Hi Sally!

I thought your presentation yesterday was fantastic! I enjoyed the way that you had the audience participating in the session.

I think you would be a great choice for the educational component at our next board meeting. The Board of Directors needs some information about local economic trends, but in a way that is not too boring or complicated.

Would you like to have lunch to discuss it? I'm free on Thursday or Friday this week. Let me know if either of those days will work for you.

Thanks so much!

George

Why would this communication work for a spirited person? It is enthusiastic, complimentary, and would be flattering to Sally. Sally will be pleased that you noticed her first presentation and more pleased that you would like her to repeat it.

Of course, you're sure to have a very excited person on your hands at lunch. So be prepared. You could bring an outline of the topics you want to cover at the presentation. Ask her input and make sure you've planned enough time to let her give it. Then help her narrow the ideas down and note them down for her. Sending a follow-up email or note will help ensure that you are both on the same page as well. Remember, the spirited person is very valuable for all their talents and enthusiasm – so with a little structure around your communications you can be successful in communicating without stifling the very qualities they bring to the table.

4.8.3 SYSTEMATIC STYLE

When you need to communicate with a person who has the systematic communication style, remember that facts are what to emphasize. Opinions are not going to be very effective. Use logical, linear thinking and communicate in the same way. Step them through your thinking – don't jump ahead of any steps. It will save you time in the long run if you take the time to explain your argument or thoughts through the first time.

If you need a systematic to make a decision, let data do the talking for you as much as possible. Have charts? Know some trends? Have examples to show how something works? All of these can be useful in communicating with a systematic person. If you are attempting to encourage a systematic to support an idea that is not supported by the data, you will be in for a bit of a challenge. However, you can still get their help if you can logically explain your position.

Remember too that systematic types are not prone to sharing personal information with work colleagues. You shouldn't take this personally – it's simply what they prefer. Yet if they do broach a personal subject with you, you can usually take it as a sign that they feel more comfortable with you than others.

The example of how not to communicate with a direct communication style person is a good example of how not to communicate with someone of a systematic style as well. You could also avoid phrases like:

- It's my opinion that …
- I believe that….
- I feel that…

Instead, try using phrases like:

- The data shows that…
- The trends show that…
- The results of the test show…

Figure 4.18 gives more suggestions for language that will work better with systematics.

Instead of...	Use...
Some, many, the majority of	20%, three out of five, an average of 2.7
Next week	Thursday at 3:00 p.m.
ASAP	By tomorrow at noon
In a timely manner	Within two weeks
They	Gail, Amy, and Wes
An upward trend	An increase of 12% over five years
Eventually	When the following conditions have been met:

Figure 4.18: Suggestions for Language to Use with Systematics

4.8.4 CONSIDERATE STYLE

To best communicate with someone who is a considerate communication style, remember that the person's feelings are going to be important. They will listen best when you make them feel as if their feelings are important to you, their opinion is important to you, and that you value them as a team member and a contributor. This doesn't mean that you have to become very emotionally expressive yourself, but showing an interest in them as a an individual will go a long way. Why not start your communication with an inquiry into how their child is doing, or how their last vacation was? The small investment of your time can be a great return.

If you have something to communicate that will perhaps be perceived as a critical, you will need to tread cautiously in order to be effective. Let the person know that you appreciate their work, and name the aspects that you find valuable and good. Then note the changes that need to be made, explaining the reason for the changes as much as you can. Smile, and use open body language to let them now that there is nothing personal in what is being said. Whenever possible, use requests instead of imperatives in discussing the needed changes.

For considerate style people, the example of how not to speak to a direct style person is actually a good one to use for a considerate style person. It builds to the point easily, it shows care for the other person, and it makes a request in a friendly, personal manner.

4.9 BASIC LISTENING SKILLS

"The basic building block of good communications is the feeling that every human being is unique and of value." –Author Unknown

4.9.1 INTRODUCTION

Good listeners are rare these days. Studies have shown that most listeners retain less than 50% of what they hear. Imagine what that means when it comes to a conversation that you might have with your boss, a colleague, or a customer. If you speak for ten minutes, chances are that you have only heard about half of that conversation – and so have they. No wonder miscommunications happen so frequently!

Yet listening is one of the most vital skills that you need if you want to communicate effectively. Listening allows you to "decode" the messages that you are receiving, but it also allows you to help others communicate better. When you aren't certain of the message that you have heard the first time, listening well allows you to ask questions that will clarify the message.

Of course, listening is important in more arenas than in the work place. We listen for multiple reasons:

- To build relationships
- To understand others
- To be entertained
- To learn
- To show empathy
- To gather information

With as much as listening can do for us, it's obvious that we can all benefit from improving our listening skills. We can become more productive at work, more connected in our relationships, and more efficient in everything that we do. But listening also helps us to persuade and negotiate with others. It can help us avoid misunderstandings and can just make life more conflict-free in general. All of these are very good reasons for learning more about how to be a better listener.

4.9.2 SELF-AWARENESS

An important tool for becoming a good listener is becoming aware of your own behavior, feelings, and habits when listening. Do you know whether or not you are a good listener? Are you only a good listener in certain situations, like when listening to a friend who is upset? Or can you also listen in a tense situation when you have to communicate with someone who is angry, stressed, or expressing an opposing opinion to your own?

Take time to become aware of your own listening behavior in different scenarios. At work, at home, with friends, with strangers, or with other groups that you communicate with, notice the following:

- Your body language –how are you standing or sitting? Are you tense or relaxed? In an open position or a closed one?

- Do you make eye contact? Do you keep it? Or do you look away, look down, or turn your eyes to other people or things in your environment?

- Are you following every word? Could you repeat what was just said verbatim? Or is your mind wandering off to lunch, that email you need to write, or that phone call you just had?

- Are you planning what you will say in return?

All of these behaviors make it difficult to be a good listener. You may be sending the message to the speaker that their message is unimportant – or worse, that they are unimportant. As you practice better listening skills, you'll need to be able to recognize when you're straying back to these old behaviors. Being self-aware will let you self-correct and get better and better at listening to others.

4.9.3 ACTIVE LISTENING

"You cannot truly listen to anyone and do anything else at the same time."—M. Scott Peck

Becoming a better listener requires improving your active listening skills. What is meant by active listening skills? Most of us spend at least part of the time that we are listening waiting for the person to stop so that we can have our next turn. This is particularly true when a conversation is heated or when the information we are trying to convey is very important.

Active listening occurs when you are attentive during the times that you are listening as when you are speaking. You must learn to be consciously attentive to the words that are being said, but in addition, to the whole message that the other person is attempting to relay to you. In order to do this you must pay close attention to the speaker.

This requires concentration and practice. It means being certain that you either eliminate or ignore the distractions surrounding you, and that you don't spend the whole time coming up with your response to what they are saying. This may sound difficult, but there are some simple tools you can use to make Active Listening a regular habit.

4.9.4 BECOMING AN ACTIVE LISTENER

There are five key aspects of becoming an active listener. You will probably already be employing some of them, but may need to practice others. However, once you are using these tools over time, you will find that they get easier and easier. Plus, you'll learn so much about others and have such better conversations that you will be positively reinforced each time you practice.

1. **Pay close attention.**

With each step, you learn to give the speaker your undivided attention. But you also let the speaker know that you are listening by using acknowledgements—types of verbal and non-verbal tools that help add proof that you are truly listening.

- Look the speaker in the eyes

- Stop any mental chatter

- Don't start preparing your response or rebuttal while the other person is talking

- Make sure your environment doesn't distract you

- Notice the speaker's body language and tone of voice – what are the non-verbal messages telling you?

- If you are in a group, avoid side conversations

- Avoid using cell phone or any other electronics that will distract you from concentrating on what is being said

2. **Demonstrate physically that you are listening.**

Use non-verbal and verbal signals that you are listening to the speaker attentively.

- Nod from time-to-time when appropriate

- Use appropriate facial expression

- Monitor your own body language. Be sure you remain open and relaxed rather than closed and tense.

- Use small comments like uh-huh, yes, right.

3. **Check for understanding.**

As we learned in previous sections, our personal experiences, our perceptions, and our feelings can all influence the way that we hear. It is possible for the message to get mistranslated or misinterpreted, so that we hear a message that was not intended. Before responding, it's important to check for understanding using these tools.

- Use reflecting and paraphrasing. Check that you heard the message correctly by saying things like "what I hear you saying is..." or "If I'm hearing you correctly, you're saying... "or "I think you're talking about...".

- Ask questions that will help clarify the speaker's meaning. Suggestions include things like, Can you tell me more about..." or "What did you mean when you said...?" or "I think you're saying...is that right?"

- Summarize what you've heard occasionally—don't wait until the end or you might not remember exactly what was said.

4. **Don't interrupt.**

There is nothing good that comes from interrupting the speaker. You will only be limiting your chance of understanding the message because you won't hear it all—and because the speaker will get frustrated!

5. **Respond Appropriately.**

When you are actively listening, you are showing your respect for the speaker, as well as gaining the information that you need to form your response. Once you have the information and have clarified it, it's time to form your reply. When expressing your thoughts:

- Be honest and open
- Be respectful
- Be thorough

Remember too that you are modeling excellent behavior for others when you use active listening. Don't be surprised to hear others start to use clarifying or reflecting phrases as well—which would be a good thing for everyone concerned!

4.10 LISTENING IN DIFFICULT SITUATIONS

Listening is particularly difficult when you are in a heated or emotionally charged situation. In order for your communication to be successful and productive, you may need to employ some additional tools in order to listen to others and to allow for the exchange of information despite your feelings.

Some tips include:

If possible, suggest that you move the discussion to a private location with no distractions.

- If tension is high, start by agreeing on what your goal of the discussion will be. Are you resolving a problem? Learning about what happened in a difficult situation? Deciding roles in an important project? Determining how to proceed in order to reach a deadline? Come up with a common goal that you can both agree to work toward and that you can both refer back to should the conversation go off-topic.

- If you need to, set ground rules. These could include agreeing that you won't bring up old events again, that you will keep personal comments out of the discussion, or that you will both keep your voices down.

- While listening, remind yourself of the active listening guidelines. Breathe slowly in and out in order to remain calm.

- If you can't seem to pay attention, try repeating to yourself in your mind every word that the other person says. Then you are "hearing" the message twice and it has a better chance of getting through.

4.11 EFFECTIVE WRITTEN COMMUNICATION

"Regardless of the changes in technology, the market for well-crafted messages will always have an audience."—Steve Burnett

4.11.1 INTRODUCTION

In today's world of rapid-fast communication via texts and emails, most of us would rather shoot off a written message than make a phone call. It's fast, efficient, when used properly, and it provides a nice document trail for our work records. Written communication is more important than ever, yet very few people know when writing is the right—or wrong -- form of communication, and fewer still can write well. Of course, like all other communication skills, good writing skills can be learned.

4.11.2 WHEN AND WHEN NOT TO USE WRITTEN COMMUNICATION

Sure, sending an email is easy. How many of us haven't written one while on hold with another call or in those few moments between one meeting and the next? Tests are even easier – and let you send information from virtually anywhere.

Yet when is written communication most effective, and when is it not? There are a number of factors that can help you make that choice.

4.11.2.1 COMPLEXITY OF THE TOPIC

Using written communication is an excellent choice for sharing information that is easily organized and easily understood by the independent reader. This means that the reader can read the communication and get the message clearly without additional information from you or other sources. Meeting notices, answers to quick questions, or quick clarifications are all easy to complete with written communication.

> Highly complex topics or lengthy explanations are not good choices for normal written communication. Written communication should 'stand alone' for the reader.

However, there is a point at which written communication becomes inefficient for one of several reasons. The information may be too complex to organize in a manner that will be intelligible to your reader without further assistance. The amount of explanation required to make the information intelligible might be cumbersome, leading to misinterpretation or lack of understanding. In the long run, you'll end up answering so many follow-up emails or phone calls that in these cases you would have been better off having a face-to-face meeting or in a formal training session.

4.11.2.2 AMOUNT OF DISCUSSION REQUIRED

> Lengthy discussions by written communication (email) are not efficient, and each exchange risks meaning getting lost.

If the topic is complex or involved enough that there will need to be a long exchange of discussion-type emails, the longer you allow the exchange to continue in writing, the more you are risking that someone will misunderstand. Furthermore, you can't be assured that everyone who received the email has actually had the chance to participate in the discussion unless you are able to track the receipt of others' emails or require everyone to respond one way or the other. Therefore, decision making, long, involved explanations or conversations, or controversial subjects are not usually good topics for written communication.

4.11.2.3 SHADES OF MEANING

We've learned from previous sections in this chapter that non-verbal communication is the most important form of communication in getting your message delivered. When you are writing, you are left to the small portion of communication that is possible through words alone in getting your message through to the reader. So the more intense the emotions around a topic or the more important the message is, the less likely writing will be a successful form of communicating.

> Written communication alone does not allow for non-verbal communication – the most important aspect of getting your meaning across.

For example, it can be difficult to convey tone of voice, humor, sarcasm, or other shades of meaning in writing alone. Don't risk offending someone or causing confusion by someone not understanding your true meaning by trusting written communication with the task of conveying highly emotional or important information.

4.11.2.4 FORMAL COMMUNICATION

Although there are exceptions, written communication is still the common choice when the level of formality between two parties is high. For example, think about your customers or clients. Chances are that formal communication such as contract terms, sales agreements, account information, or other legal or administrative information will be transmitted in written form. This gives you both the information in a format that you can pass on as needed, and gives you both the reference material to help you in continuing your communication. As the level of formality decreases in the relationship, you are more likely to move from paper documentation to email communication as well.

> The higher the level of formality of communication, the more likely you will use written communication. Plus, you will usually employ email more as the level of formality decreases.

4.11.3 WRITING EFFECTIVELY

Although some of the following information relates to either email or paper communication, it is mainly geared towards email since so much of our work involves email. However, you can apply most of the advice to paper communication as well.

4.11.3.1 SUBJECT LINES

When you are writing a letter or an email, the subject line of the communication is like the headline in a newspaper. It calls your attention to the communication and should also let you know what it is about. The best subject lines will also tell you what needs to be done—and will let the recipient prioritize which emails to open first and which ones to ignore for later (or altogether!)

What do these subject lines tell you about the information that will follow?

- Response to Your Email
- Question
- Hello
- Meeting
- Information for you

By these subject lines, can you tell any information about what will follow? Sure, the first one could be clear if the receiver has only written one email that day. But most of us handle dozens, if not hundreds, of emails every week. It's unlikely the receiver will remember exactly what you are responding to.

The other subject lines are too general. They don't specify what information will be contained or what action the recipient needs to take. If there is important or urgent information included, this might go unread –or opened, scanned, and dismissed.

Instead, try subject lines such as:

- Information on Open House Tuesday June 22, 2010 – Please RSVO
- Question Regarding the Change in Health Benefits – Response Needed
- Meeting Requested on New Website Design—Please Confirm Availability
- URGENT! Change in On-Call Schedule for Memorial Day Weekend
- Response to Your Question on the Marketing Plan for 3rd Quarter

Each of these tells the reader what information they will find when they open the email, and also tells them whether or not they need to take action. The reader can decide which of these is most important and process the incoming emails in the best order.

4.11.3.2 PUT THE MAIN POINT FIRST

When you write your communication, you need to know exactly what, why, and to whom you are writing. Are you simply giving information, asking for information, or requesting the other person to take an action? If you can't narrow down the point, you either aren't ready to write or writing isn't the right choice of communication formats to use.

Once you know what the main point of your email is, you should put that first in the communication. We all tend to scan written communication to save time, focusing more at the top of the information than the bottom. Putting your main information at the top of the communication pulls the reader's attention to the main topic, request or instruction. You can follow with background information after you've stated the reason for writing – but if you start with the background information, you risk your reader missing the point of the communication.

Here's a bad example:

Subject Line: Widget Super Deluxe

Dear Tom,

I spent some time with Joan this morning reviewing the numbers from last quarter's sales results. I was concerned to see that there seems to be a downward trend in sales of the Widget Deluxe, which is significantly different from what we forecasted. I am concerned that this might have an impact on our launch of the Widget Super Deluxe planned for next quarter. I think we should meet with the marketing team and the sales team to see if we can identify any possible issues with the sales and fulfillment process that we could influence. Would you let me know when you are available this week?

Thanks,

Julie

Notice the subject Line? Again, it is not precise. Then the writer doesn't get to the point of the communication until the last line. If the reader is scanning for information, he or she might not even get to the last line before moving on to the next email. If that happens, you'll have to write another communication or follow-up with a phone call – which is a waste of your time.

Now read this version:

Subject: Request to Meet with You Regarding Sales Process – Please Respond

Dear Tom,

I'd like to meet with you, the sales team, and the marketing team this week to discuss the impact of the latest sales trends on the launch of Widget Super Deluxe. Would you be available on Monday at 3:00 pm for about an hour?

I spent some time with Joan this morning reviewing the numbers from last quarter's sales results. I was concerned to see that there seems to be a downward trend in sales of the Widget Deluxe, which is significantly different from what we forecasted. I think we should attempt to identify any possible issues with the sales and fulfillment process.

Thanks,

Julie

See the difference? The second email has a clear subject line that asks for a response. It gets to the point in the first paragraph. Even if the reader is scanning the information, he or she will have a better chance of getting the message.

4.11.3.3 KNOW YOUR AUDIENCE

When you are writing a communication, you need to be able to identify to whom you are writing. Sure, you could be writing to the "world" of your organization or the "world" of all of your customers, but you need to know what it is that they will gain from your communication. Is it just information for everyone, or are there particular unidentified members of the audience who need to receive your communication, recognize the information that is important to them, and then take a specific action?

For example, say you are changing the healthcare plan at the office so that domestic partners are now eligible for coverage. You might be sending the communication to everyone in your organization, but your true audience is employees that have domestic partners. In thinking about those people, what information do they need? What choices do they need to make? What concerns might they have in acting on the information? How can you handle those concerns in your communication? Identifying your audience helps you target and fine tune the communication in order to make it as effective as possible.

Another aspect of knowing your audience is being aware of what they don't know. Most of us have a "lingo" that we use in the day-to-day operations of our work. They might be technical terms, references to internal structures or teams, or acronyms that are shared among peers. However, you need to be certain that every member of your audience would understand that lingo or acronym before using it – and that every person they might forward your communication to would also understand it. When in doubt, add a brief explanation or spell it out.

4.11.3.4 ORGANIZATION OF THE MESSAGE

Perhaps your communication has more than one request or call to action. If the actions are unrelated to each other, the best choice is to send a separate email for each one. That requires your reader to see each topic in the subject line and then to respond accordingly.

However, you might have situations where you have several requests or several important facts for the reader. In that case, you need to organize the information in a way that increases the chance that the reader will give you all of the information or take all of the actions that you request. You can do this by using topic headings that still put the main topic of the communication at the top such as: Response Needed, Background, Concerns, Or RSVP Requested, Instructions, Directions, FAQs. You could also use the bullets or numbers for each subtopic. You could consider using bold or colored font to highlight requested actions. One word of caution – avoid using all capital letters, which can be interpreted as "yelling."

Your job is to make it easy and fool-proof for your reader to get the message. Use whatever tools you can employ to ensure that the message is delivered fully, as long as they are still professional and appropriate for your audience.

CHAPTER 5
Leadership and Diversity

CHAPTER 5
LEADERSHIP AND DIVERSITY

5.1 LEADERSHIP DEFINED

"Leadership is the art of getting someone else to do something you want done because he wants to do it." ~ Dwight D. Eisenhower

Leadership is the process of directing the behavior of others toward the accomplishment of some common objectives. A leader should be an individual of character whose actions and words are not constricted by negative pressures from those around him or her. A leader sets positive examples through his or her actions and can bring in those people who are around him or her. Leaders demonstrate performance character and moral character in one's actions, and the cultivation of this character in others both of which are consistent, purposeful and recognizable.

Figure 5.1

Leadership ability cannot be acquired by reading a textbook or listening to a lecture. Leadership skills are developed from interactive and challenging activities and opportunities that allow potential leaders to develop qualities such as determination, focus, decisiveness, time management, social confidence and self-discipline. These outward characteristics or qualities are crucial to developing leadership skills.

The embracement of diversity is very important characteristic for leaders and future leaders. Leaders must support and institutionalize respect and have an appreciation of diversity. Too often, differences make group members anxious and/or a likelihood of becoming isolated. Given that teaching and learning rests on relationships, how leaders understand, manage and celebrate diversity matters.

Four "Musts" for an Ethical Culture:

- Relationships
- Modeling
- Empowerment
- Purpose/Meaning "Magic Glue"

Necessary components for an environment to support growth and initiation of leadership:

- A sense of connectedness
- A vision (purpose) for the group's benefit
- The will to motivate a group toward the vision
- The skills to motivate and influence others to participate with effort

5.2 LEADERSHIP ATTRIBUTES

Leadership attributes are the inner or personal qualities that constitute effective leadership. These attributes include a large array of characteristics such as values, character, motives, habits, traits, motives, style, behaviors, and skills. Furthermore, leadership is a process of engagement which moves people to understanding and action in an environment inspired by trust. Leadership involves more than simply getting others to act. Alternatively, leadership can be defined as a collaborative, relationship-building, and morally purposeful process of mobilizing group improvement to most effectively adapt to complexity and change.

A leader must have a purpose/vision. Typical questions that may inspire vision:

- Why are you in school?

- Why do you want to go to college?

- What values do you most want to stand for?

- What purpose do you want your life to have?

- What do you want to do to help people when you grow up, finish college or join an organization or group?

A leader brings others into a shared vision and motivates them to act for the betterment of the business, institution, community, organization, etc.

5.3 INSPIRATIONAL LEADERSHIP

Inspirational leaders create an inspiring culture within their organization. They supply a shared vision and inspire people to achieve more than they may ever have dreamed possible. They are able to articulate a shared vision in a way that inspires others to act.

5.3.1 TEN GOALS FOR INSPIRATIONAL LEADERS

Listed are ten goals to help leaders to improve their leaderships and help others who aspire to be future leaders.

1. Provide an inspiring vision and strategic alignment or launch a crusade

As a leader, you must envision the future, passionately believe that you can make a difference, and inspire people to achieve more than they may ever have dreamed possible. You must see a changed world beyond the time horizon, create an ideal and unique image of what it could become, open your followers' eyes and lift their spirits. You must believe that your dreams can become reality and, through your attitude, get people to see exciting opportunities and possibilities for the future. People change and unlock their inner power when they are emotionally engaged and committed.

2. Help people connect their personal goals to business goals

Leadership is essentially about helping people to achieve a better life. An important measure of your own success as a leader is the success of your followers. Talented and empowered employees are the prime ingredient of organizational success and they need to be able to lead themselves. Provide strategic alignment and be a coach to your people to help each of your followers to develop into an effective self-leader. Establish an attitude of relentless growth to enable your organization and people to achieve their goals.

3. Make relentless innovation a religion

Leaders should encourage innovative behavior and emphasize the importance of seizing opportunities. Establishing a culture of innovation requires a broad and sustained effort of problem solving. Questions are critical to innovation, so start with creating a culture of questioning. Exploration of possibilities, discoveries, innovation, and progress start with questions such as "Why?" and "What if?" questions. To help develop leadership skills, people should be encouraged to challenge assumptions and should be rewarded for both individual and collective contributions.

4. Encourage entrepreneurial creativity and experimentation

In order to nurture leadership skills for employees, ironically, corporations and institutions need an entrepreneurial staff that creates a corporate climate that encourages rule-breakers and outside-the-box thinkers. Experimentation by definition is a trial-and-error process, but experimentation is also the key to discovery. Without action, you cannot know whether or not your innovative ideas will actually work.

5. Involve everyone, empower and trust employees

Talented and empowered human capital is the prime ingredient of organizational success. A critical feature of successful teams, especially in knowledge-driven enterprises, is that they are invested with a significant degree of empowerment, or decision-making authority. Corporations and institutions should formulate strict goals, provide resources, and empower employees and students.

6. Coach and train people to greatness

Empowerment alone is not enough. Future leaders must be trained and coached to enhance their learning ability and performance. Coaching is the key to unlocking the potential of your people, your organization, and yourself; it increases your effectiveness as a leader. As a coach, you must help your people grow and achieve more by inspiring them, asking effective questions and providing feedback. People who want to lead in the future should aggressively seek the right combination of instructor-led training and coaching that includes follow-up advice and constructive criticism.

7. Build teams and promote teamwork with leverage diversity

Teamwork is essential for competing in today's global arena. Build a star team, not a team of stars. Diversity of thought, perception, background and experience enhance the creativity and innovation. A team should not just be diverse; it should get the most effective effort out of each player on the team. Everyone should be involved and team members should facilitate cross-pollination of ideas. In order to harness the power of diversity, experts believe in building and empowering cross-functional teams where people from different disciplines and cultures come up with something better together and achieve creative breakthroughs.

8. Motivate, inspire and energize people, recognize achievements

Financial rewards do encourage people to produce results. But the kind of ownership that really generates energy is not financial; it is emotional. Setting strict goals help energize people. As a leader you should be a positive and encouraging person. Leaders should give people a sense of responsibility and make them feel that their actions make a difference. Leaders should communicate with people frequently and praise them often. Furthermore, leaders should practice whatever they are teaching and/or preaching.

9. Encourage risk taking

Leaders and future leading should take risks and not play it safe. Making mistakes is essential to innovation and organizational growth, as long as systems are developed to learn from failures and to avoid making the same mistake twice. The more people fail, the more they succeed.

People learn from taking action, from making mistakes, and from receiving constructive critical feedback. Failures should be treated as learning opportunities. Leaders and future leaders should develop a tolerance for mistakes and give people freedom to fail, learn from failures and start again more intelligently.

10. Make business fun

As business today is about passion and creating new things, fun has become a big element in the business strategy of many highly successful businesses. Make fun an important part of your corporate cultural to enable relentless innovation and create an inspiring corporate culture. "What really driving the new economy—and confounding the grand pooh-bahs of the old one—is that individuals are having a huge impact. And an awful lot of fun," writes Edward O. Welles in The Fun Factor. People should be happy at work and have fun. Corporate, governmental and academic environments should continue to develop creative programs that encourage just-for-fun programs. "Find some humor in your failures. Don't take yourself so seriously. Loosen up, and everybody around you will loosen up. Have Fun. Show enthusiasm ---always," advised Sam Walton.

5.4 ENTREPRENEURIAL LEADERSHIP

In the new era, of rapid changes and knowledge-based enterprises, managerial work becomes increasingly a leadership task. In the increasingly turbulent and competitive environment, firms face today, a new type of "entrepreneurial" leader distinct from other behavioral forms of managerial leadership is required. Entrepreneurial leadership is based on the poise that the leader is self-employed.

Entrepreneurial leadership is the primary force behind successful change. Entrepreneurial leaders discover emerging business opportunities and empower employers to act on the vision. They execute through inspiration and develop implementation capacity networks through a complex web of aligned relationships.

An entrepreneurial leader has the following specific attributes:

1. Takes initiative
2. Takes responsibility
3. Demonstrates entrepreneurial
4. Takes risks

Lessons learned from failed entrepreneurial leaders

1. Fear of Change
2. Lack of entrepreneurial spirit
3. Leadership style on the part of management is either too directive or too hands-off
4. Managers do not lead and don't manage change

5. They just administrate and micromanage
6. They have weak development programs

Nine Signs of a Losing Organization:

Fuzzy Vision: Corporate vision and mission don't inspire people; lack of strategic alignment; people don't know where the organization is going and what it is trying to achieve in the future.

Lack of Leadership Skills: fear of change; leaders lack entrepreneurial spirit; leadership style on the part of top management is either too directive or too hands-off; managers do not lead, they just administrate and micromanage; weak leadership development program.

Discouraging Culture: no shared values; lack of trust; blame culture; focus on problems, not opportunities; people don't have fun at work; diversity is not celebrated; failures are not tolerated; people lose confidence in their leaders and systems.

High Bureaucracy: bureaucratic organizational structures with too many layers; high boundaries between management layers; slow decision making; too close monitoring of things and subordinates; too many tools and documents discouraging creative thinking; bureaucracy is tolerated.

Lack of Initiative: poor motivation and encouragement; people do not feel their contributions make a difference; management fails to engage the organization effectively; people work defensively and not creatively, they do their job and nothing.

Poor Vertical Communication: people have no clue of the big picture and do not feel their contributions are important; too much uncertainty; people don't know what top-managers are thinking and planning.

Poor Cross-functional Collaboration: functional mindset; lack of cross-functional goals and cross-functional collaboration spirit; functional, no enterprise-wide business process management; no cross-functional management committees; lack of or powerless cross-functional teams.

Poor Teamwork: no organizational commitment to team culture; lack of shared and worthwhile goals; weak team leaders; team members who don't want to play as part of a team are tolerated; team are too large; lack of shared teams.

Poor Idea and Knowledge Management: cross-pollination of ideas is not facilitated; no creativity, idea and knowledge management strategies and evaluation systems; "know-it-all" attitude; "not invented here" syndrome.

5.5 HOW TO DEVELOP LEADERSHIP SKILLS IN STUDENTS

Through their academic course work, residential life experiences, seminar discussions, lectures, conferences, and involvement in academy and co-curricular activities, students experience the challenge of leading others, creating change and having a sense of belonging to a community.

To be successful in today's market, graduates must proficient in essential leadership skills and concepts such as communication skills, service learning, and advocacy. In college, students need opportunities to explore belief systems, values, and the process of ethical decision making. Programs should be in place so that all students may have the opportunity to develop their leadership awareness skills and abilities through a variety of different components. These programs will introduce students to communication, networking, decision making, conflict resolution and critical thinking skills. The skill sets obtain will constitute sustain continued growth through exciting career fairs, networking socials, classroom activities and interactive workshops.

To lead is to invite, inspire, mobilize, and guide ourselves and others to make positive differences in our homes, schools, communities and the world. As an example for students, colleges and universities need to utilize the resources available, create new opportunities to enhance their skills and values, and make decisions based on established community ethical standards.

Students should be challenged to think critically about leadership during peer-to-peer facilitated lectures, class discussions, hands-on exercises, and group work. Topics such as understanding self, social justice/group dynamics, communication, and conflict resolution/negotiation will help build a foundation for leadership skills.

Many colleges and universities have leadership development programs that provide opportunities for students to develop valuable leadership skills and qualities that will assist them in preparing for the challenges of collegiate and career leadership.

Things Colleges and Universities can do to Nurture Leadership Growth in Students:

1. Developed a leadership course can provide opportunities for students to expand their knowledge and experience of leadership through activities, service, guest lecturers, and roundtable discussions

2. Establish a Leadership Library on campus.

3. Set up a consultation where professional staff members are available to assist student organizations with goal setting, program planning, special programming, and provide tailored interactive workshops to suit an organization's needs.

4. Provide freshmen and sophomore students free leadership training through multi-night adventure sessions focusing on individual, team, and organizational leadership skills.

5. Start a Campus Leaders' Speakers Series that provide students the opportunity to attend lectures on various topics of importance to college students. These topics can include making the transition to college, relationship development, hazing and alcohol awareness, AIDS awareness, drug use, date rape, leadership, sex, and much more!!

6. Encourage student organizations to participate in local, state, and national conferences to gain additional training in specific organizational areas. Participation in these events by Recognized Student Organizations reflects the group's commitment to growth and success in organizational management. Conferences also provide a networking opportunity for student leaders to gain access to future employment and other career opportunities.

5.6 IMPORTANT QUALITIES THAT DEFINE LEADERS

If we are to develop leaders, then we must identify the important qualities that define a leader. Figure 5.2 illustrates the additional important qualities of a leader.

emotional stability	conscientiousness	tough mindedness
self assurance	compulsiveness	enthusiasm/energy
intuitiveness	maturity	team orientation
empathy	charisma	communication
courage	responsibility	security
self discipline	vision/envision future	integrity
positive attitude	magnanimity	humility
listening	creativity	fairness
assertiveness	sense of humor	initiative
optimistic	embraces change/open	risk taker
tenacious	honest	forward looking
character	competent	inspiring
intelligent	catalytic	dedicated/committed
passion	discernment	generosity
focus	ability to teach	problem solving
relationships		

FIGURE 5.2 Important Characteristics of Leaders

5.7 PREPARING STUDENTS TO BE SUCCESSFUL LEADERS

Leadership involves influencing other people willingly to get things done to a standard and quality of value. As an element in social interaction, leadership is a complex activity involving; a process of influential interaction between a leader and his or her followers over a range of possibilities.

5.7.1 LEADING BY EXAMPLE—RUBRICS FOR MODELING LEADERSHIP

School leaders must lead by example in order to prepare students to be leaders later on in their lives. Every school leader should regularly ask the question: What impact do I have on my school's success through my knowledge, skills, and dispositions—not simply through the programs I've helped initiate? Too often, school leaders share best practices with colleagues in terms of programs and approaches to leading, but never get around to reflecting on and discussing the personal ingredients for their success, or their strengths or weaknesses—which more often than not are the very things that enabled a best practice to be successfully adopted.

We ask students to learn for the sake of learning and self-improvement. We assess students in knowledge and the use of skills—and help them understand their strengths and weaknesses so that they can work to improve them. Isn't it only fair that school leaders model that behavior in their professional lives?

For more than three decades, the National Association of Secondary School (NASSP) has been assessing and studying the skills of school leaders. As a result of this experience, a job analysis of the principal-ship, observation, and research, NASSP has identified 10 skills that encompass the bulk of what school leadership entails. Figure 5.3 provides an overview of these skills, which have been divided into four themes: educational leadership, resolving complex problems, communication, and developing self and others.

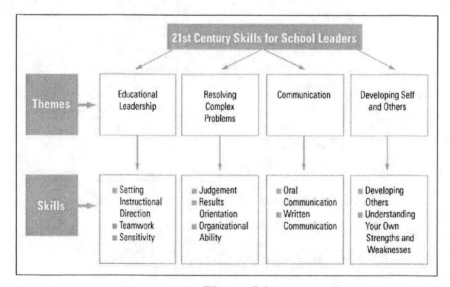

Figure 5.3

As an Individual: Every professional assumes final responsibility for his or her own professional development. Although some reliance on others for providing growth experiences is necessary, each person will benefit from reflection on how skills, knowledge, and attitudes in his or her own performance contribute to success or failure of self and the school. Often, we look inward to attribute our success and outward to explain failures. Through honest reflection and constructive criticism, individuals can develop the practice of specific behaviors that will help them to develop habits that contribute to effective performance.

To guide a Mentor/Protégé Relationship: Many successful leaders credit an effective coach or mentor as one important contributor to building the capacity that led to their success. Effective leaders accept coaching for their own development and then develop the capacity to coach and develop others. Developing skills as a focus for coaching has a strong foundation in any activity that requires performance of complex tasks.

With aspiring Leader Cohorts or in a Principal Preparation Course: In asking thousands of school leaders the question, "How did you get to be as good as you are?" NASSP staff members seldom hear a response that indicates that preparation programs and activities have done more than develop a knowledge base. By including the development of essential skills for effective performance, leadership preparation encompasses application, evaluation, and synthesis of knowledge in the context of practice in simulations or on the job.

To help build Individualized Developmental Activities for an Internship: "What do we want to accomplish during this internship? You have so much to learn and I have so much to teach you." This is often the way that internships work. A more effective model of an internship is one in which the intern has opportunities to apply and practice what has been learned in a real-life context. This requires the incorporation of skill development into the experience.

Figure 5.4 will help leaders to assess his or her knowledge, skills, and dispositions for leading change by examining and practicing the ten leadership skills. Only by doing so can a leader be prepared to take the "what" and the "how" of school change and put them into effective practice so that all students learn and grow.

The deliverables of a successful assessment and development model for leaders include:

1. Understand the skill dimensions that contribute to effective school leadership

2. Understand the behaviors that contribute to a high level of performance in each of the skill dimensions

3. Understand the skills required to accurately reflect on their own behavior

4. Understand how to collect feedback and other data about their own behavior, analyze it, and take action to improve based on the analysis

5. Understand how to use the information from their skills diagnosis to construct a professional development plan with goals for development, strategies for finding excellent models, opportunities to practice, methods to obtain constructive feedback, and systems to evaluate progress and revise the plan accordingly.

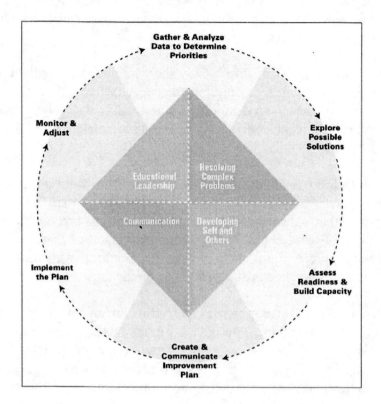

Figure 5.4

Using Table 5.1 and each of the 10 skills of Figure 5.2, leaders complete the four activities of Figure 5.3: reflect on their performances; seek feedback from colleagues; complete a customized chart, based on the date of Table 5.1. With the help of NASSP, leaders can be walked through the steps of the process circle; and identify behaviors from practitioner interviews.

A leadership structure for schools, colleges and universities:

- Administrative support
- Definition (let's decide what it is?)
- Key values, behavioral descriptions of leadership
- Broad support (Teachers, Preachers, Coaches, Parents, Kids, Professors, Chairpersons, Deans, Presidents, Mentors, Counselors, Staff, etc.)
- Integration into academics and extracurricular activities
- Having people specific assigned to overseeing leadership programs
- Lots of opportunities to practice leading
- Assessment/fine-tuning
- Ongoing work on school's ethical climate

176

Table 5.1

Process Circle Step	How Do *You* Put the Skill Into Action?
Gather & Analyze Data	**Ask:** How is my on-the-job performance in this skill area? ■ Reflect on my performance of the behavioral indicators for the skill—the frequency with which I engage in each behavior as opposed to my ability to perform the behavior. ■ Solicit face-to-face feedback from a variety of sources—such as a mentor, a coach, a supervisor, supervisees, and colleagues—that focuses on the skill indicators. ■ Seek anonymous feedback from the 360-degree tool available from NASSP (www.principals.org). ■ Seek data from a formal assessment process (e.g., Selecting and Developing 21st Century Leaders and Leadership Skills Assessments from NASSP). ■ Review my performance on the indicators. Discuss results with mentor or colleague.
Possible Solutions & Strategies	Assignments that stretch and provide practice in this skill: [customized for each skill] Workshops, seminars, and courses: Mentor, coaches, and supervisors: Readings: Off-the-job development opportunities: NASSP resources:
Assess Readiness & Build Capacity	■ Review the possible solutions in light of school data that has implications for my professional development needs: achievement; instructional staff members' qualifications, experience, background, and so on; student, staff member, and school community demographics; attendance; dropout rate; graduation rate and so on. **Ask:** What development can I engage in that will have the greatest impact on my personal/ professional capacity and the needs of the school? Consider how specific personal development activities will affect others with whom you work.
Create & Communicate Plan	■ Develop a personal learning plan (PLP) that delineates how you will practice this skill, your development activities, and goals. ■ Be an example of a head learner by sharing your PLP with others and encouraging every adult in the school to have a learning plan that is based on their developmental needs in the context of the needs of the school and the students.
Implement Plan	■ Practice the indicators to build capacity in the skill: implement the strategies selected from possible solutions.
Monitor & Adjust	■ Take continuous measures of your progress and the impact of your progress on the needs of your school as you practice. ■ Refer to the data sources that formed the basis of your development plan (PLP). ■ Seek feedback from colleagues, peers, mentors, supervisors—and remember the PLP is public. ■ Reflect ■ Keep a journal ■ Return to Gather & Analyze Data to establish new priorities either within the same skill or to begin work on another skill.

5.7.2 LEADERSHIP LEARNING THROUGH EDUCATION

The mission of a school, college or university should say something about leadership. Institutions should be shaped by the pursuit of truth and goodness, providing outstanding preparation for higher learning and life. Institutions should prepare students to learn, to lead and to serve as they discover the promise in themselves and the ever changing global world.

Tables 5.2 through 5.5 are a developmental matrix for evaluating students' skills in leadership. There are four levels of performance and six attributes which are assessed. Tables 5.2 and 5.3 are rubrics of the matrix. Table 5.4 contains the scoring range of the student by the evaluator. The scoring range is 0 to 23. Table 5.5 is used for self-reflection or a follow-up support for student leaders at all levels.

TABLE 5.2

STUDENT LEADERSHIP DEVELOPMENT MATRIX

Name of Student: _____   Class: _____   Year: _____

Evaluation done by: Self / Parent / Instructor / Peer

	SKILLS		
	Interpersonal skills	*Organizational skills*	*Problem-solving skills*
LEVEL 4 *Exemplary*	• Establishes good rapport with anyone. • Persuades and influence others. Garner team spirit and motivate others to work together. Score: 4	• Leads others in planning and successfully implementing a given task independently. Score: 3	• Leads others in solving a problem successfully and independently. • Displays creativity and innovation in solving a problem. Score: 4
LEVEL 3 *Accomplished*	• Relates well with all his peers and teachers. • Articulates thoughts and feelings freely and clearly to others. • Work well in any group. Score: 3	• Displays the ability to work out a plan and implement it given with no or minimal instructions. Score: 2	• Analyses a problem. • Brainstorms for alternatives. • Assesses alternatives. • Selects the most appropriate solutions • Displays independence. Score: 3
LEVEL 2 *Developing*	• Relates well with most of his peers. • Expresses thoughts and feelings freely to others. • Work well only with close friends. Score: 2	• Shows some evidences of planning for the task. • Depends on teacher's close supervision in completing a given task. Score: 1	• Demonstrates comprehension of the problem. • Has limited alternatives. • Requires some degree of teacher intervention. Score: 2
LEVEL 1 *Beginning*	• Only gets along with a few close friends. • Experiences some difficulty in expressing thoughts and feelings. • Prefers to work alone. Score: 1		• States a problem and takes the first solution that comes to mind. Score: 1

TABLE 5.3

	ATTRIBUTES		
	Integrity	*Confidence*	*Commitment*
LEVEL 4 *Exemplary*	• Positively influences others to display values of reliability, trustworthiness and responsibility. • Champions (*telling others*) the character values of reliability, trustworthiness and responsibility. Score: 4	• Articulates well and is at ease in public speaking. • Is comfortable in leading others. • Displays self-belief in one's abilities in performing the roles and responsibilities assigned. Score: 4	• Displays initiatives to perform beyond the roles and responsibilities. • Is able to motivate others to complete a task when faced with challenges/difficulties. Score: 4
LEVEL 3 *Accomplished*	• Consistently displays honor in words and deeds. • Has moral courage to take responsibility for his/her actions. • Is not easily swayed by negative peer pressure Score: 3	• Speaks/presents/shares with poise in front of others. • Volunteers for roles and responsibilities. Score: 3	• Performs roles and responsibilities with pride. • Is able to motivate himself/herself when faced with challenges/difficulties. Score: 3
LEVEL 2 *Developing*	• Demonstrates honesty and uprightness in dealings with others most of the time. • Forthcoming in admitting mistakes. Score: 2	• Volunteers to speak/present/share in front of others. • Is willing to assume roles and responsibilities. Score: 2	• Carries the roles and responsibilities as required. • Needs a lot of encouragement to continue with a task when faced with challenges/difficulties. Score: 2
LEVEL 1 *Beginning*	• Knows right from wrong. • Admits mistakes when questioned. • Is easily swayed by negative peer pressure Score: 1	• Speaks/presents/shares in front of others with some encouragement. • Is hesitant to assume roles and responsibilities. Score: 1	• Needs to be reminded to carry out roles and responsibilities. • Gives up easily when faced with challenges/difficulties. Score: 1

TABLE 5.4

STUDENT LEADERSHIP DEVELOPMENT MATRIX

Name of Student: _____   **Class:** _____   **Year:** _____

Evaluation done by: Self / Parent / Instructor / Peer

Please fill in the table below:

	Skills			Attributes			Total Score	Level (Please refer to table below)
	Interpersonal skills	Organization al skills	Problem-solving skills	Integrity	Confidence	Commitment		
SCORE (Semester 1)								
SCORE (Semester 2)								

SCORE RANGE	LEVEL 4 Exemplary	LEVEL 3 Accomplished	LEVEL 2 Developing	LEVEL 1 Beginning
	Has ability to lead, motivate and inspire others given a task. Demonstrates high level of competence in interpersonal skills, organisational skills and problem-solving skills. Displays high level of confidence, integrity and commitment in the roles and responsibilities.	Has ability to manage others given a task. Demonstrates competence in interpersonal skills, organisational skills and problem-solving skills. Displays confidence, integrity and commitment in the roles and responsibilities.	Has ability to manage a given task. Is developing competence in interpersonal skills, organisational skills and problem-solving skills. Is developing the attributes of confidence, integrity and commitment in the roles and responsibilities.	Has ability to carry out roles and responsibilities that meet expectations. Have little evidences of competence in interpersonal skills, organisational skills and problem-solving skills. Have little evidences of the display in the attributes of confidence, integrity and commitment in the roles and responsibilities.
	SCORE : 18-23	SCORE : 12-17	SCORE : 6-11	SCORE : 0-5

TABLE 5.5

STUDENT LEADERSHIP DEVELOPMENT MATRIX
(SELF REFLECTION)

Name of Student: _____   Class: _____   Year: _____

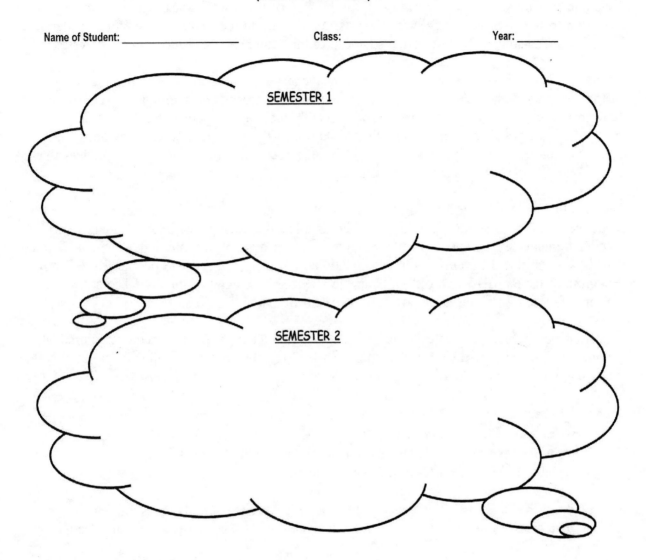

SEMESTER 1

SEMESTER 2

5.8 EMBRACING CULTURE OF DIVRSITY

Sadly, the private sector (Corporate America) has done even worse when it comes to the recruitment, retention, and promotion of people of color. Reports show that women and persons of color continue to be severely underrepresented on corporate boards and in corporate leadership.

According to a review of the Fortune 500[®] companies by the Alliance for Board Diversity ("ABD"), in 2010, white men held 74.5% of the board seats and white women held 12.7% of the seats; in contrast, minority men represented only 9.9% of the directors; and minority women just 3.0%. In 2010, ABD counted 32 Fortune 500[®] companies without a single woman or person of color on the board. That's a lot of boards ignoring a lot of qualified talent.

The director totals for this group of companies include 7.6% African-Americans (compared to 12.6% of U.S. population), 3.0% Hispanics (compared to 16.3% of U.S. population), 2.1% Asian Pacific Islander (compared to 4.8% of U.S. population), and women held fewer than 16% of the board seats (while comprising more than half the U.S. adult population). Clearly, these are disappointing statistics. These statistics fly in the face of multiple studies that show that diverse boards perform better than non-diverse boards. As a result, in recent years, investors, academics, consultants, and some corporate insiders have asked for companies to become more diverse.

Diversity also enhances a company's responsiveness to an increasingly diverse world of customers and stakeholders. In 2012, Forbes published the results of a comprehensive survey of more than 300 senior executives from geographically diverse companies that had revenues of at least $500 million and went up to more than $20 billion. Their findings were noteworthy: 85% of executives agreed that a diverse and inclusive workforce brings the different perspectives that a company needs to power its innovation strategy.

The benefit of diversity in bringing new perspectives into a group's discussion is bolstered by academic research. One study found that "there is a lot of evidence that people's identity groups — ethnic, racial, sexual, age — matter when it comes to diversity in thinking." The study states that these cognitive differences help organizational performance because people from different backgrounds have different "tools" or "varying ways of looking at problems." The study argues the sum of these tools is far more powerful in organizations with diversity.

Unfortunately, publicly-traded companies in the private sector have performed even worse when it comes to diversity in their top management. In 2012, Fortune 500® companies exhibit the following, which is a lack of diversity in leadership:

- Six Black CEOs or 1.2% of all Fortune 500® CEOs
- Six Latino CEOs or 1.2% of all Fortune 500® CEOs
- Seven Asian-American CEOs or 1.4% of all Fortune 500® CEOs
- Twenty-one women CEOs or 4.2% of all Fortune 500® CEOs

So, in light of the benefits that diversity and inclusion appear to have, the question remains as to why, so many entities fail to have representative diversity on their boards or in senior leadership positions.

5.8.1 HOW DOES STEREOTYPING AFFECT THE WORKPLACE ENVIRONMENT?

Stereotyping can cause people in a workplace to treat individuals or groups a certain way based on preconceived notions about that person or group. Diversity factors, including ethnicity, race, culture, religion, gender and age, can all contribute to the propensity of stereotyping in your organization. Promoting a non-discriminatory workplace with openness and acceptance of individual differences helps in preventing common negative effects.

Abuse and Mistreatment

If you stereotype yourself or passively allow others to engage in stereotyping, your workplace is potentially ripe for abuse or mistreatment. Employees with preconceived notions about people sometimes test the waters with basic comments or actions. If you don't step in to address these initial behaviors, the employees may sense that the culture promotes or accepts open displays of discrimination or mistreatment based on personal qualities. This belief only escalates the problem.

Low Morale

A general problem with stereotyping is that it can cause low morale for the individual or groups impacted or potentially make the entire workplace toxic. Employees who face constant comments, criticisms or other negative results from stereotyping can lose motivation and interest in performing their jobs. Low morale can indirectly affect workers and departments not directly involved with stereotyping behaviors. Over time, production is likely lower if your culture has toxic morale.

Bad Working Relationships

If teamwork and collaboration are necessary ingredients to your company's success, stereotyping is a major problem. Employees who act based on stereotypes rather than putting faith in the abilities and effort of coworkers impede group progress. In a work team, stereotyping can prevent an employee from asking for support or offering it to a particular employee. A man may not ask a woman in his team for help, for instance, if he believes that she isn't capable of understanding the task and concepts because she's female.

Legal Tension

Allowing or accepting stereotypes and resulting behaviors can also create legal tension within your organization. There is the potential that someone affected by the discriminatory behaviors will sue you. If you have a Human Resources (HR) Department, your failure to implement and enforce fair policies and practices is a burden for HR staff as well. Successful lawsuits could financially ruin a small business, thus putting everyone in the company out of work.

Racism and the Public Media

Racism, theorized to be a learned trait passed on from generation to generation. How is it that a society claiming to be "modern", and void of barbarism, can unite so easily against its fellow humankind based singularly on the pigment of the outer layers of its flesh? Today's society spreads the disease of racial diversity like maggots multiplying on a vetted corpse, while barking the political fantasies of racial indifference every day. Racism in our modern society may not be as open as lynching a black man in the town square, but the hate continues today in sometimes small, subtle ways. One of the theories describing the adaptive progression of race-hate lies within everything we see and hear in society.

The somewhat self-oriented, rating driven media has a way of contributing to the downward spiral decay of society as well. On almost every channel there is a news program directed at informing the public. Some may see it more as a twisted form of entertainment, similar to slowing down at an accident to watch the crimson blood flow freely like a raging delta from the severed neck of the poor victim in the passenger seat of a mangled sports car. Can we recall a moment when a black man, or woman was depicted as "successful" or awarded for good citizenship? The black community had always been portrayed as hostile in the media, but just as "sex sells", so does violence. The Rodney King incident is a good example of the acceptance of racism in the media. The defense put on by the four white Los Angeles police officers accused of beating Rodney King in 1991 says it all. They claimed that they were fearful, and felt they may have been attacked, a legitimate excuse in the white American society. Their "fear" is a direct result of a deep-rooted media bias that anything black must be a bad thing. This media stereotype of "bad guys" wearing black, or that anything that is black is evil, has been festering for decades like a gangrenous wound on the right hand of society. The color association with evil or negative characters is exemplified in Western films as the "bad guy" always wore the black outfit.

Another example of media bias, illustrated in the 1994 Susan Smith case of South Carolina, deepened the stereotyping media obsession. Smith was a woman who made significant headlines when she claimed that a black male had kidnapped her two young children. Smith herself had killed them, but the grotesque use of the media frenzy when finger pointing at the black culture had, for a time, distracted from the real situation. This same runaway media train can also be guilty in the case of Charles Stuart in Boston. Charles had killed his wife, also blaming it on a black man. The media and its frivolous use of stereotypes have taken the racial stamp a step further in Hollywood. The portrayal of young black males involved in gangs and other acts of violence, has become a multi-million dollar industry. American society today has now accepted these stereotypes within the film industry. Films such as *Boyz in the Hood* and *Menace II Society* have become multi-million dollar success stories, while portraying young black males as uneducated "gangsters" with little or no future. This portrayal, over time, has birthed a false belief in white society that all black males are just as uneducated and violent. What the media refuses to acknowledge is that the vast majority of blacks hold successful careers, do attend school, and are not involved in gangs or other criminal activities. The success of the various races is rarely portrayed in the public media as the norm. Thus, society has only what they see and hear to rely on for information and social etiquette. With this type of heavy sided social acceptance, someone can easily wonder how society has progressed beyond slavery at all.

Racial segregation is not always as "in your face" either. Job applications are the best examples of one type of subconscious grouping. When asked to check the box, indicating race, this acknowledges the differences we see in ourselves. This acceptance of diversity seems harmless at first. However, looking at the vast vacuum of suggestions that flow into our subconscious by telling ourselves that it is "ok to check the box" can be a dam on the verge of catastrophic collapse if pushed in the right direction. Bursting with the force of thousands of tons of water flowing through society like a viral disease unannounced, the carriers unaware. Opening just a small door to acceptance is always the first step. In psychology, it is learned that all someone needs is a simple suggestion to coax an individual into thinking that your idea is his or her own belief. In Las Vegas, Nevada, Gerry McCambridge makes his living as "The Mentalist". His show uses simple tricks to manipulate individuals, and the audience as a collective, into providing predetermined answers to his questions. Although his tricks are performed for entertainment, the show provides some insight into how easily a group of people can be manipulated into thinking they have their own "unique" ideas. When, in fact, the ideas and thoughts of the individual were never their own ideas in the first place.

Society as a whole needs to be more aware of the simple suggestions presented in the vast array of information thrown at each person every day. Whether the media runs away with itself, a show in Las Vegas takes control of our free will, or a simple check within a box causes us to separate ourselves from the general population, we should all take a second look at what is necessary to classify an individual, and really think before we act on first impressions. Although the days of lynching are now gone, racism is just as alive today as it was one hundred years ago.

5.8.2 AVOIDING STEREOTYPES IN THE WORKPLACE

The truth is that we all stereotype certain groups of people. Many of us have grown up with biases in our homes, on television, at water coolers and when we hang out with our friends and family.

Unfortunately these stereotypes, which we find occasionally humorous — jokes about blondes and lawyers etc. — and think are generally harmless are, in fact, the opposite.

In the workplace, stereotypes are quite harmful and limiting not only to those we stereotype but also to ourselves. Unfortunately, labels apply to everyone and chances are you may personally fall under several.

Stereotyping does not only affect the productivity and profits in an organization but it also hurts the self-esteem of the subject.

Types of Stereotypes

Stereotypes encompass every race, religion, gender and sexual preference. They even cover hair color: red haired women are fiery and blonds are dumb. Matter of fact, there are even regional stereotypes, the Westside of Vancouver is better educated, more affluent, intelligent and the Eastside of Vancouver is the opposite. Then there are the stereotypes of Asians who are perceived as hard and effective workers, but are not outgoing. South Asians could be native born, but often are viewed as foreigners. None of these stereotypes are positive or productive in the workplace.

How Do You Define a Stereotype?

One definition is a bias, inflexible belief about a particular person or group. Another definition, provided by Stedman Graham in his book *Diversity Leaders not Labels*, suggests a stereotype might be an exaggerated image of a person or groups, allowing for little or no social variation or individual differences, usually passed along by peers, family members or the media.

Where Do Stereotypes Comes From?

Essentially we are all guilty of forming stereotypes about others. They come to us from the media, from our family members, from our peers, and from our personal experiences. All humans tend to label others because it makes us feel safe and superior; and it is often easier than to look at people too deeply.

It is easy to be judgmental about those who are different from us. But if we do, we run the risk of forming conclusions that are erroneous and mutually detrimental.

How Do Stereotypes Hurt Us?

In the corporate world, there is a high price to be paid for stereotyping:

- Litigation
- Lost employees
- Poor employee morale
- Lost sales and customers
- Difficulty hiring top-level employees
- Difficulty retraining employees
- Diminished productivity/profits

However, we also suffer personal consequences when we judge people based on biases, labels, and stereotypes. We miss out on valuable experiences, insights, and amazing relationships. We also miss out on connecting with others on a genuine level.

Breaking Down Stereotypes

Breaking down, recognizing, and eliminating stereotypes begins with dialogue. Conversation reduces bias because we learn more about each other and reach an understanding. Conversation also reduces preconceptions by educating us on misinformation and it limits the spread of bias.

Steps to Take to Assess and Eliminate Stereotypes

- Respect and appreciate others' differences. Imagine if people looked and acted the same. It would be boring!

- Consider what you have in common with other people; there may be a lot more than you think.

- Avoid making assumptions or creating labels.

- Develop empathy for the others. Try to walk in their shoes.

- Educate yourself about different cultures and groups.

These days it is unacceptable to have stereotypical views of others in the workplace because it can be very costly, not to mention the lack of productivity and profits. It is important to recognize and remember that we all have stereotypes; it is part of the human experience. However, the first step is to be honest and recognize our preconceived notions about others and why we have formed them, and then take an active approach to educate ourselves.

5.8.3 WHAT IS DIVERSITY?

"Diversity" as used here refers to human attributes that are different from your own and from those of groups to which you belong.

When you look at the people in the following image, what diversity do you see?

FIGURE 5.5

You probably said you noticed an African American, an Asian American, an Arab, a younger woman, an older man, etc. What you observed is what we call "visible" diversity. Visible diversity is generally those things we cannot change and are external, such as age, race, ethnicity, gender, and physical attributes.

However, diversity goes beyond this to what we call "invisible" diversity. Invisible diversity includes those attributes that are not readily seen, such as work experience, marital status, educational background, parental status, income, religious beliefs and affiliations, geographic location, or socioeconomic status.

For example, you probably assume the Indian you see was born and raised either in the United States or India. However, he could have been born and raised in Jamaica. Indians arrived in Jamaica in the 1800s and remain a part of the fabric of that island nation today.

It is the combination of diversity attributes, both visible and invisible, that define an individual's "personal" diversity. No one individual's personal diversity is exactly like another's. So, when we recognize, value, and embrace diversity, we are recognizing, valuing, and embracing the uniqueness of each individual.

While each individual is unique, he or she generally has many attributes that are similar to those of others. In life, you will find that people whom you believe are "just like you" are more different than you think, and people you perceive as "different" have a surprising amount in common with you.

Take time to reflect on one person you consider to be "just like you" and see if you can identify ways in which the person is different from you. Also, reflect on one person you consider to be "different" and see if you can identify ways in which the person is like you.

5.8.4 IMPORTANCE OF DIVERSITY IN HIGHER EDUCATION

America's colleges and universities differ in many ways. Some are public, others are independent; some are large urban universities, some are two-year community colleges, others small rural campuses. Some offer graduate and professional programs, others focus primarily on undergraduate education. Each of our more than 3,000 colleges and universities has its own specific and distinct mission. This collective diversity among institutions is one of the great strengths of America's higher education system, and has helped make it the best in the world. Preserving that diversity is essential if we hope to serve the needs of our democratic society.

Similarly, many colleges and universities share a common belief, born of experience, that diversity in their student bodies, faculties, and staff is important for them to fulfill their primary mission: providing a quality education. The public is entitled to know why these institutions believe so strongly that racial and ethnic diversity should be one factor among the many considered in admissions and hiring.

The reasons include:

- Diversity enriches the educational experience. We learn from those whose experiences, beliefs, and perspectives are different from our own, and these lessons can be taught best in a richly diverse intellectual and social environment.

- It promotes personal growth--and a healthy society. Diversity challenges stereotyped preconceptions; it encourages critical thinking; and it helps students learn to communicate effectively with people of varied backgrounds.

- It strengthens communities and the workplace. Education within a diverse setting prepares students to become good citizens in an increasingly complex, pluralistic society; it fosters mutual respect and teamwork; and it helps build communities whose members are judged by the quality of their character and their contributions.

- It enhances America's economic competitiveness. Sustaining the nation's prosperity in the 21st century will require us to make effective use of the talents and abilities of all our citizens, in work settings that bring together individuals from diverse backgrounds and cultures.

American colleges and universities traditionally have enjoyed significant latitude in fulfilling their missions. Americans have understood that there is no single model of a good college, and that no single standard can predict with certainty the lifetime contribution of a teacher or a student. Yet, the freedom to determine who shall teach and be taught has been restricted in a number of places, and come under attack in others. As a result, some schools have experienced precipitous declines in the enrollment of African-American and Hispanic students, reversing decades of progress in the effort to assure that all groups in American society have an equal opportunity for access to higher education.

Achieving diversity on college campuses does not require quotas. Nor does diversity warrant admission of unqualified applicants. However, the diversity we seek, and the future of the nation, does require that colleges and universities continue to be able to reach out and make a conscious effort to build healthy and diverse learning environments appropriate for their missions. The success of higher education and the strength of our democracy depend on it.

5.8.5 DIVERSITY IN THE CORPORATE WORLD

Corporations are undoubtedly one of the most important societal devices that human beings have ever invented. Although the legal concept of corporations has been said to have originated in the Roman era, it was in medieval Europe that the corporation was initiated for various social functions and started to flourish in a variety of domains: religion, learning, politics, philanthropy, trade, and crafts.

Access to the corporate form was limited at this time to the elite, but this decentralized institutional innovation prepared "doorstep conditions" for Europe, allowing it to get one step ahead of other regions and to make an earlier transit to the modern democratic state and corporate economy.

A minimalist conceptualization of corporations can be verbalized as follows: Corporations are voluntary, permanent associations of natural persons engaged in some purposeful associative activities, having unique identity, and embodied in rule-based, self-governing organizations.

A corporation is a permanent entity that can do what individuals with limited biological longevity cannot do. The corporate ability to own property, backed up by the institution of share ownership and share transferability, makes the permanence of business corporations secure.

Actions, physical and cognitive, are also relevant, as corporations can organize associative activities among its members and can cognize and store what a mere collection of individuals cannot. The first prominent types of corporations that emerged in the early medieval period, such as universities and the Roman Catholic Church, were those founded for the encouragement and support of religion and learning. The primary functions of these types of corporations were to understand or interpret the world, accumulate, theorize, and bestow knowledge for future uses and advancement, and sustain culture as common knowledge.

The primary purpose of modern business corporations is to make money, not to learn. But even for them, the reasons why incorporation is vital for religious and learning activities are not entirely irrelevant. As knowledge use and creation (that is, innovation) become more important for the competitiveness of business corporations, this point cannot be overlooked.

Orthodox economic theory of contracts is premised on the idea that cognition can take place only within the mind of individuals, which lies at the heart of micro economics that theoretically supported the shareholder-oriented view of corporations in past decades. However, the recent development of experimental economics, cognitive neuroscience, and related areas increasingly provides evidence and theories that human cognition also takes place in more interactive ways at the group level. The way in which business corporations are organized as systems of associational cognition deserves no less attention than the financial aspects of the corporation.

The orthodox contract theory of the firm considers the human aspects of the business corporation only in terms of authority relationships between the management and the workers. This treats workers merely as "hands." But in his classical treatise, Concept of the Corporation, Peter Drucker posited the idea of "knowledge workers" who can supply brains, not merely hands.

In a business corporation, cognitive activities, such as information collections, processing, uses, and storage are systematically distributed and interrelated between the management and the workers, as well as among the workers, while the investors supply cognitive tools to them. Such cognitive relations inside the corporate organization can be referred to as associational cognition.

If the potential importance of associational cognition is recognized, the questions that follow are: How are cognitions to be distributed and related among the members? How are they related to the system of tools of cognition, such as computers, the Internet, robotics, machines, digital files, and so on? Are the workers simply the bodily extension of the manager's brain? Focusing on this aspect of corporate architecture appears to be particularly important in the era of information technology.

The question of what represents "purposeful activities" for a contemporary business corporation constitutes the crux of the matter we are concerned with: "What do corporations do?" Does it operate "exclusively for profit" as the shareholder-oriented view dictates or for something broader, as the stakeholder-oriented view claims. The proper answer theoretically depends on ways in which a system of associational cognition is architected in corporate organizations.

The shareholder-oriented model is one viable model under certain conditions, but there can also be another model that does not fall into the simplistic classifications of "management-oriented" (traditional American), "labor-oriented" (traditional German), or "state-oriented" (traditional French and Japanese). This model involves rather novel three-way relationships between management, workers, and investors, whose presence may grow with the rising importance of human cognitive assets in business.

It is telling that pre-business corporations, such as the Roman Catholic Church and municipalities, were not the immediate creations of the modern national state. They were voluntarily created, even though some of them needed the explicit or implicit approval of the rulers. As members of voluntary organizations, corporate participants must basically have consented to obey its own rather than any external authority.

This has implications for the inquiry into the nature of business corporations. We may inquire what kind of general rules for governance can be agreeable to and consented to by the constituent members of the corporation. Then we may ask whether those endogenous rules can be consistent with general rules prevailing in society. Without the first property, people would not participate in corporations voluntarily, while without the second property, corporations would not be sustainable in society. They are interrelated.

Social interactions are all games, regardless of whether payoffs are exclusively self-regarding, material-oriented, hedonistic, or otherwise. Those games recursively played in society can be called societal games, although there are different kinds of domains of play. Viewing the societal order as stable patterns of game playing has been expounded by many authors. Differentiating the discrete domains of societal games that embed corporate organizations—commons, economic, social, and polity—by discerning mutually distinct game forms and examining the interrelationship between those games and the organization games played internally within business corporations by their members, including workers.

One great advantage of the application of game theory is its ability to analyze mutual relationships between embedding society rules and corporate self-governing rules as stable outcomes of play, that is, as equilibrium phenomena, of the societal and organization games as linked.

"Equilibrium" refers to the stable and mutually reinforcing aspects of the societal order and its impacts on the structure of business corporations. However, nothing in the societal order is static in a strict sense. Business corporations adapt their associative activities in response to evolving market and society environments, while evolving corporate behavior impacts on the latter. The recent contributions of epistemic game theory suggest that in order for a stable societal order to evolve, something more may be needed, say, common backgrounds in information and inference, as well as various social cognitive categories, such as social symbols carrying some meanings, public propositions, such as laws and regulations acting as focal points for cognition, culture as common priors, and so on. In order to understand the basic nature of institutional evolution, the ironclad methodological individualism needs to be laid to rest.

Japan's "Lost Decade" triggered by the 1992 burst of the financial bubble is a meaningful reference to the societal cognitive crisis than just the economic consequences of macro-policy and banking failures: That is, the state in which traditional rules could not be taken for granted any more. No consensus has yet emerged as regards what the new rules could be. Behind the crisis, the Japanese corporate landscape underwent a tremendous change, and it can no longer be characterized by a single "Japanese model" stereotype. This diversifying phenomenon is not necessary an isolated event limited to Japan, but there is a suggestion of similar phenomena evolving globally, albeit each one in a path-dependent, unique manner.

Evolving corporate diversity is not so much due to national characteristics but a ubiquitous phenomenon across economies exhibiting to differing degrees. It can thus be considered a product of global economic integration.

In order to derive the potential gains from the global process of a "convergence to diversities," the global financial markets need to co-evolve as an infrastructure that will accommodate this evolutionary path, rather than exercise sovereign control over nonfinancial business corporations. The 2008 credit crisis revealed that relationships between financial intermediaries and nonfinancial business corporations are still uneasy. The painful process of a corporate recovery is to become a process of a search for a mutual fit between the two.

By making diversity a competitive advantage, corporations can:

- Make their companies a better place to work
- Better understand their customers' needs
- Provide outstanding service
- Deliver more value to their stockholders

Measurements of success with diversity can be accessed through the following areas:

- Team member diversity and inclusion;
- Marketplace outcomes; and
- Diversity and inclusion advocacy and reputation-building activities

5.8.6 EMPHASIS ON NEW DIRECTION FOR CORPORATE DIVERSITY PROGRAM

The goal of most corporate diversity programs is simple: to increase the percentages of certain minorities in the overall employee pool to mirror the country as a whole. It's a misguided approach, even when it comes with programs designed to help retain minorities that have been hired. It's misguided because it comes with an assumption that the potential employee must change to fit into the current workplace culture. This attitude implies that the employee lacks something that he or she needs in order to succeed and thrive in that culture. This attitude answers the wrong implicit question. Instead of asking, *how can we train diverse employees in order to succeed and thrive in our organizational culture?*, the company should be asking, *how do we need to change to make our workplace one that actually embraces diversity in approach, in culture, and in opportunity?* This is a fundamental problem that US companies have faced for years. Many international competitors have practiced diversity mores strategically than US companies who approached it with a tactical initiative.

FIGURE 5.6

The shift in attitude is important for reasons larger than diversity itself. What's at stake is the survival of the corporation. Company after company is struggling to reinvent itself and survive today, post-2008, sensing that there is a new reality, a new "normal," without really being sure what that means. The old industrial, slow-moving, hierarchical, top-down approaches to strategy, budgeting, product development, and customer service desperately need an update. In reality, business cycles and marketplace shifts are happening so fast today that most large companies can't keep up.

Businesses need to vastly increase their ability to sense new opportunities, develop creative solutions, and move on them with much greater speed. The only way to accomplish these changes is through a revamped workplace culture that embraces diversity so that sensing, creativity, and speed are all vastly improved.

The following six values represent the new type of employee to ensure that companies survive and thrive by embracing innovation through diversity.

1) **Create a Cultural and Generational Mosaic** *(Keep Your Immigrant Perspective)*: support an environment that embraces the power of multicultural talent and diversity in its people and that desires strong generational balance in its workforce.

2) **Embrace Risk as the New Normal** *(Employ Your Circular Vision)*: lead change and proactively take calculated risks based on how the market is changing.

3) **Continuously See and Seize Opportunities** *(Live with the Entrepreneurial Spirit)*: seek to continuously propel new types of innovations, embracing the entrepreneurial spirit.

4) **Make Room for the Individual** (*Unleash Your Passion*): inspire employees to be their own brand; allow them to perform with passion and contribute in areas that utilize their most natural strengths and capabilities.

5) **Do Well by Doing Good** *(Work With Generous Purpose)*: desire to be successful while always positively transforming lives and leaving a legacy for others to follow.

6) **Create a Family** *(Embrace Your Cultural Promise)*: build enduring relationships, engage and seek continuous improvement feedback from vendors, clients and consumers to become better across the entire supply chain.

It's time for America's corporations to reset their workplaces and allow for change in the ways employees think, act and innovate. Employees want to be more entrepreneurial. They desire a workplace that is more meaningful, purposeful, and responsive to changing realities. Today's new workplace requires a new enlightened form of leadership that seeks to make the business successful in order to make humanity significant. Embracing diversity is essential, not just because it's the right thing to do, but also because it will orient companies toward the future and toward success.

5.8.7 DIVERSITY MANAGEMENT

Diversity management is the key to growth in today's fiercely competitive global marketplace. No longer can America's corporations hide behind their lack of cultural intelligence. Organizations that seek global market relevancy must embrace diversity – in how they think, act and innovate. Diversity can no longer just be about making the numbers, but rather how an organization treats its people authentically down to the roots of its business model. In today's new workplace, diversity management is a time-sensitive business imperative.

Diversity is much more than just a multicultural issue. Diversity is about embracing many different types of people, who stand for different things and represent different cultures, generations, ideas, and thinking. For example, on the internet online communities are continuing to grow and represent different voices and points of view. As Ron Glover says, "Innovation is about looking at complex problems and bringing new views to the table. Diversity must drive the formation of new business models. Leaders must think about the changing landscape: the economy is changing, how business is being done is changing, so the question is how diversity can be utilized as a strategic enabler in today's changing landscape."

Diversity is a critical leadership success factor at IBM. Diversity has allowed IBM to be innovative and successful for 100 years and to work across lines of differences in 172 countries, amongst 427,000 employees. As a result of this virtual diversity, innovation continues to thrive in the online world. Diversity is a core belief of IBM in how they succeed in business. IBM was able to expand globally, because they developed a workforce that understands the local market. Their clients are as diverse as their employees and there are now five generations in the workplace. IBM believes in building communities inside of the company to embrace differences that drive innovation globally. These same attitudes, ownership and principals that IBM used can be applied to the workplace especially during a time when America needs innovation to reinvent itself to remain relevant in the global marketplace.

Diversity clearly needs a refresh. The misinterpretations of what diversity means and what it truly represents have limited its ability to have the real impact and influence it warrants in America's corporations. Many organizations are still in the early stages of integrating the basic functional and leadership requirements of diversity In fact, the executives who get it today will tell you how concerned they are for their business, because their people, products, and services do not connect naturally with the new faces of America. Most companies have been forced to react not only to the changing face of America, but the mindsets of the global marketplace. Consequently, executives have started to confront the inevitable: a new business model that fully integrates diversity as a business growth enabler.

Four areas that should be addressed for a diversity management model to be successful:

- Ethics
- Citizenship
- Environmental
- Diversity (talent sustainability)

To better understand the future of diversity management and its role as a business growth enabler, think back to when Information Technology (IT) was viewed as just a cost center. IT was not associated with driving business growth 20 years ago, but rather as a required cost of doing business. Just like diversity today, many people then thought IT got in the way of business. Today, IT is considered a profit center by many and a high priority for organizations as a business growth enabler. In fact, many Chief Information Officers (CIOs) are next in line for the Chief Executive Officer (CEO) role. As a result, to be an influential CIO; you must be a business strategist with a Master of Business Administration (MBA) and not just a computer science degree.

Chief Diversity Officers (CDOs) will experience many of the same functional role and responsibility shifts as have CIOs. They will not only be required to assume their practitioner responsibilities, but they must also learn to play a more integral strategic role in the design of new business models. Globally diverse leaders are maximizing the effectiveness of their teams. IBM has recognized the importance of building teams across the company from different countries. It's not just about leadership, but capability. Diversity is fundamentally focused on talent. Those differences create real opportunities for those who learn to master them and a disaster for those who do not.

Diversity management will begin to develop rapidly, out from under the traditional human resources and talent acquisition roles, to assume more dotted-line responsibilities that will touch corporate strategy, corporate social responsibility, organizational design & effectiveness, corporate marketing and even sales. Therefore, the requirements to be an effective CDO will mean that they must include operating more holistically in a general management and operational capacity to ensure that diversity becomes an embedded mindset with common threads that touch all functional areas (internally) and the supply chain (externally). Every employer and employee must be accountable for advancing diversity.

5.8.8 DIVERSITY MATRIX

Table 5.6 is a diversity matrix that can be used to assess the diversity of a field of study within a college or university. There are ten elemental rubrics that are used in the model.

TABLE 5.6

College:
Department:
Program:

ELEMENTS	PROGRAM INFORMATION	COURSES	FIELD EXPERIENCES	MEASURES OF ASSESSMENT	AGGREGATED DATA	INTERPRETATION REPORT & IMPACT FOR PROGRAM CHANGE
		- List classes that address diversity-related goals and outcomes.	- Identify field experiences that are available in your program. If none, leave blank	- Identify how elements are assessed (artifact, rubric, etc.)	- Identify data available	- Identify program changes made based on data
1. Candidate proficiencies						

related to diversity are articulated by the unit.					
2. Candidates understand diversity.					
3. Candidates develop & teach lessons that incorporate diversity.					
4. Candidates connect instruction & services to students' experiences & cultures					
5. Candidates demonstrate sensitivity to cultural & gender differences					
6. Candidates incorporate multiple perspectives in their instruction **(could be only student teaching)**					
7. Candidates develop classroom/ school climates that value					

diversity **(could be only student teaching)**					
8. Candidates understand teaching & learning styles & can adapt instruction.					
9. Candidates demonstrate dispositions valuing fairness & learning by all (one assessment is the initial disposition inventory; at the advanced level, this does not need to be course based).					
10. Assessments provide data on candidate ability to help students from diverse populations learn **(could be only student teaching).**					

Example 5.1 is a sample of the use of Table 5.6.

Example 5.1 Interpret the rubric of a diversity matrix for a school counseling program.

College: College of Sciences
Department: Psychology
Program: School Counseling

ELEMENTS	PROGRAM INFORMATION	COURSES	FIELD EXPERIENCES	MEASURES OF ASSESSMENT	AGGREGATED DATA	INTERPRETATION REPORT & IMPACT FOR PROGRAM CHANGE
		- List classes that address diversity-related goals and outcomes.	- Identify field experiences that are available in your program. If none, leave blank	- Identify how elements are assessed (artifact, rubric, etc.)	- Identify data available	- Identify program changes made based on data
1. Candidate proficiencies related to diversity are articulated by the unit.	Multicultural competencies are addressed in the school counseling conceptual framework, mission statement, coursework, and internships.	PSY 574 (Multicultural Counseling) PSY 552 (Human Development) PSY 559 (Advanced Educational Psychology) PSY 561 (Group Counseling) PSY 567 (Counseling Strategies for Children and Adolescents) PSY 568 (Counseling Strategies for Adults) PSY 569 (Administering School Counseling Programs) PSY 571 (Counseling for Relationships and Families) PSY 573 (Career Development) PSY 584 (Behavior Disorders and Psychopathology) PSY 555 (Design and Analysis for Applied Research)	PSY 593A&B (Practicum). Both practical classes address multicultural/ diversity issues. PSY 682A&B (Internship). Candidates are required to have a multicultural internship experience and they must log the number of hours spent with ethnically diverse students.	Multicultural Awareness, Knowledge, Skills Survey Counselor Edition-Revised (pre and post-test are given during PSY 574) Internship assessment (based on WAC and CACREP Standards) Evaluation of Candidate's Multicultural Competencies	Three years of aggregated data are presented in our report Three years of aggregated data are presented in our report All candidates received scores at the "good" level or higher	The data show consistent progress in the program. No changes were recommended from the first assessment. Candidates have demonstrated near the top of this scale for each of the three years. However, narrative responses indicated that some candidates could benefit from additional field experiences prior to internship. We have integrated additional diversity experiences into PSY 569 and PSY 574 to satisfy this.

199

		PSY 589 (Professional and ethical issues) PSY 593A&B (Practicum) PSY 682A&B (Internship)				
3. Candidates develop & teach lessons that incorporate diversity.	During PSY 569, candidates engage in 10-20 hours of teaching experience. These are designed to occur at multicultural schools. During PSY 682, candidates are required to participate in classroom lessons in diverse schools.	PSY 569 (Administering School Counseling Programs) PSY 682 (Internship)	PSY 682 (Internship)	WAC and CACREP Standards Evaluation of Candidate's Multicultural Competencies	Three years of data. All candidates received scores at the "good" level or higher.	Scores for the candidates admitted in 2008 will be available in fall of 2009. The data for the past four years indicates that candidates are highly regarded in their multicultural competencies (with a score of "4" being "good" and "5" being "excellent."). There is a slightly disturbing trend downward. However, this may be partly explained by increased exposure to ethnically diverse sites in internship; i.e., scores may have been artificially high in 2004 because the evaluators were rating their interns in mostly white settings whereas all interns in 2007 had to work in areas that were primarily ethnically diverse. Despite the possible reasons for the downward trend, we are taking active strides to remedy a possible deficit. Beginning fall 2009, we will have an African American faculty member joining our program. Her primary research focus has been on sexual and ethnic diversity issues. We are also going to launch a multicultural research center and have applied for two multicultural

						based grants. The latter will employ five candidates in the program this summer and expose them to additional diversity settings.
5. Candidates demonstrate sensitivity to cultural & gender differences	Gender and sexuality differences are discussed at length in PSY 574 and PSY 552. We also have a transgendered faculty member in our program.	PSY 574 (Multicultural Counseling) PSY 552 (Human Development) PSY 559 (Advanced Educational Psychology) PSY 561 (Group Counseling)	PSY 593A&B&C (Practicum). Candidates frequently work with clients presenting with GLBT issues during their three practical. PSY 682A&B (Internship). Gender and cultural differences are discussed regularly in weekly supervision.	Multicultural Awareness, Knowledge, Skills Survey Counselor Edition-Revised (pre and posttest are given during PSY 574) The quantitative assessments for practicum address how well candidate counselors meet the needs of their clients. The qualitative sections provide faculty assess competence with diversity. Evaluation of Candidate's Multicultural Competencies	All candidates received scores at the "good" level or higher. When candidates received individual assessment regarding gender or cultural bias, they were given one additional quarter to demonstrate competence in this area. This only happened with one candidate. All candidates received scores at the "good" level or higher.	During 2008, we engaged in a program assessment of gender bias, while our candidates are open and accepting, they also had subtle biases. The results were presented at the American Counseling Association's 2009 conference. Because of what we found, in 2010, we are forming the center for Gender and Ethnicity Mediation (GEM). This group will involve candidates as we engage in research and intervention protocols at the national level.

5.9 COMPETENCY MODEL FOR DIVERSITY AND INCLUSION PRACTITIONERS

Ten years ago, the word "inclusion" was rarely used, and only by a few organizations. Now, the phrase "diversity and inclusion" has its own acronym—D&I. Focus has progressed from valuing differences, which was largely achieved through awareness training and multi-cultural celebrations, to strategic global business growth. Emphasis today is on cornering new markets, building effective and efficient global teams, and managing a brand reputation. Clearly, the 21st century D&I practitioner, embracing this more public, decidedly strategic role, requires a challenging new set of competencies.

There are five primary trends driving changes in the D&I practitioner's role and that define the need for new thinking regarding competencies.

These are:

- Globalization
- Demographic shifts
- Technology
- Legal environment
- Socio-political climate

5.9.1 BACKGROUND FOR THE D&I COMPETENENCY MODEL

The model includes 1) categories of like competencies, 2) the competencies themselves, and 3) behaviorally-based definitions for each competency. The seven categories and their related competencies are:

1. Change Management

- Organizational Development
- Corporate Communication
- Critical Interventions

2. Diversity, Inclusion, and Global Perspective

- Cultural Competence
- Negotiation and Facilitation
- Continuous Learning
- Complex Group Dynamics
- Judgment
- Subject Matter Expertise

3. Business Acumen

- External Market Knowledge
- Holistic Business Knowledge
- Diversity and Inclusion ROI (Return on Investment)

4. Strategic External Relations

- Corporate Social Responsibility / Government / Regulatory
- Strategic Alliances
- Diverse Markets / Supplier Diversity
- Brand / Reputation Management

5. Integrity

• Ethics
• Resilience
• Influence
• Empathy
• Communication

6. Visionary & Strategic Leadership

• Diversity & Inclusion Future State
• Pragmatism
• Political Savoir-Faire (At Head Quarters (HQ) and Local Levels)

7. Human Resources (HR) Disciplines

• Total Rewards / Talent Management / Organizational Development / Work and Life Balance / Training
• Compliance

FIGURE 5.7

To be used effectively, these competencies should be integrated into a company's business metrics. Organizations would do best to customize simple, clear measures that are part of an organization's overall metrics for each of the global diversity competencies, or even for each category. In order to satisfy the metrics, companies should ask questions like: How can this person use this competency to strengthen the business? Or, what does this person need to achieve to further our organizational goals? By attaching simple, business-based metrics to each competency, or even to each competency category, organizations lay the foundation for D&I practitioners to achieve success, thereby best supporting organizational goals.

5.9.2 D&I PRACTITIONER COMPETENCIES

1. Change Management

Organizational Development

• Understands and facilitates the change process through completion
• Gains leadership involvement and line ownership

Corporate Communication:

• Communicates the full spectrum of inclusion
• Utilizes multiple communication vehicles such as web sites, brochures, talking points, and more
• Maintains a balanced global perspective that offers flexibility and variations for use at the local level
• Keeps what is best for the business at the forefront
• Elaborates on benefits of D&I
• Acknowledges and addresses possible unfavorable impact
• Tracks and communicates strategy progress and setbacks
• Acknowledges and addresses challenges / obstacles / opportunities

Critical Interventions

• Offers useful and timely interventions in cases where progress is impeded due to a diversity Related issue

2. Diversity, Inclusion, and Global Perspective

Cultural Competence

• Understands multiple cultural frameworks, values, and norms
• Demonstrates an ability to flex style when faced with myriad dimensions of culture in order to be effective across cultural contexts
• Understands the dynamics of cross-cultural and inclusion related conflicts, tensions, misunderstandings or opportunities
• Understands the history, context, geography, religions, and languages of the regions in which the organization does business
• Is fluent in more than one, and ideally several, languages

Negotiation and Facilitation

• Negotiates and facilitates through cultural differences, conflicts, tensions, or misunderstandings

Continuous Learning

• Recognizes and addresses one's filters, privileges, biases, and cultural preferences
• Commits to continuous learning / improvement in diversity, inclusion, and cultural competence
• Seeks and utilizes feedback from diverse sources

Complex Group Dynamics

• Understands and effectively manages complex group dynamics and ambiguity

Judgment

• Is able to discern when to inquire, advocate, drive, or resolve more decisively

Subject Matter Expertise

• Knows and applies best practices in diversity and inclusion practices, strategies, systems, policies, etc.
• Understands subtle and complex diversity and inclusion issues as they relate specifically to marginalized groups (while these vary by region, they often include women, people with disabilities, older people, and racial, ethnic or religious minorities)
• Establishes and manages D&I councils effectively
• Collaborates with other functional teams
• Is a role model for inclusive and culturally competent behavior

3. Business Acumen

External Market Knowledge

• Understands and is current on global and local trends / changes and how they inform and influence D&I
• Gathers and uses competitive intelligence
• Understands diverse customer / client needs
• Understands and is current with global socio-political environments
• Understands context and lessons learned

Holistic Business Knowledge

• Understands the impact of the financial, economic, and market drivers on bottom line results
• Understands core business strategies

- Possesses solid financial acumen
- Uses information from multiple disciplines and sources to offer integrated ideas and solutions on issues important to the organization

Diversity and Inclusion ROI (Return on Investment)

- Determines and communicates how D&I contributes to core business strategy and results
- Creates insights on how D&I contributes both to people and HR strategies as well as business results
- Designs and develops D&I metrics that exhibit the ROI impact

4. Strategic External Relations

Corporate Social Responsibility / Government/Regulatory

- Well-informed about external pressure points (e.g., society, work councils, environment, regulatory, government, customers, and related trends)

- Effectively anticipates and manages stakeholders (e.g., advocacy, community, non-government organizations)

- Recognizes and addresses human rights issues through policy and practice

- Influences media and marketplace via communication and community outreach to competitively position the organization

Strategic Alliances

- Identifies, partners, and leverages relationships with key external organizations / leaders to enhance business results

Diverse Markets / Supplier Diversity

- Identifies, partners, and leverages relationships with key external diverse suppliers, organizations, and customers to:
  - Enhance the supply chain
  - Increase market share, revenues, and loyalty

Brand / Reputation Management

- Positively influences media and marketplace
- Forges strategic partnerships with internal constituencies through community outreach
- Supports communities in which the organization operates

5. Integrity

Ethics

- Acts ethically and with integrity
- Behaves in a way that leads others to trust him/her
- Speaks with candor and tact
- Acts as a voice for perspectives, levels, and cultures that are not otherwise represented

Resilience

- Pursues goals with drive and energy; seldom gives up before finishing, especially in the face of resistance
- Maintains positive and constructive outlook

Influence

- Negotiates and persuades effectively at all levels of the organization
- Navigates corporate landscape and has an impact up, down, and sideways
- Listens and adapts approach to fit audience
- Manages and mediates conflict effectively

Empathy

- Understands the point of view and emotions of others, in the context of their cultures, including both minority and majority groups
- Acknowledges, in a stated or unstated fashion, other's perspectives
- Understands how to motivate and work with both minority and majority groups

Communication

- Knows where resources are, and how to access them
- Communicates effectively
- Engages audience

6. Visionary & Strategic Leadership

Diversity & Inclusion Future State

- Collaborates appropriately with others to envision and convey an inspiring, compelling, and relevant D&I future state

- Actively seeks new ideas, experiences, and thought leaders.

- Is a catalyst for change. Translates / makes connections between new ideas and applications
- Frames new directions in understandable, innovative, and inspiring terms

Pragmatism

- Differentiates between strategy and tactics
- Drives alignment with clients, partners, and stakeholders
- Is pragmatic regarding working within business realities
- Proactively creates foundation for influence at all levels of the organization

Political Savoir-Faire

- Facilitates and manages complex and sensitive matters
- Knows to whom and where to go to get things done (including working with the Board, CEO, and top leaders)

- Collaborates with other functional areas to maximize outcomes for all (especially HR, Organizational development, Leadership development)
- Possesses the ability to influence and execute beyond positional power.
- Is seen, at all levels, as a trusted source for advice and counsel

7. HR Competencies

Total Rewards/Talent Management/Organizational Development/Work and Life Balance/Training

- Understands the basic tenets and workings of compensation and benefits programs, policies, and best practices
- Provides program options that ensure equitable treatment and mitigate disparities
- Possesses knowledge of programs, policies and best practices that ensure equity and achievement of organizational D&I objectives in a variety of HR areas, including but not limited to recruiting and staffing, OD, work and life balance, succession planning, training / development, and performance management

Compliance

- Understands applicable laws, regulations, and government requirements and their impact on the business
- Ensures compliance through effective programs, policies, and practices

Employee Relations

- Works with others appropriate to the situation to resolve individual and group conflict, including the development and delivery of successful interventions
- Sustains and improves the work environment in the face of change and environmental changes

5.9.3   THE NEED FOR A NEW SET OF COMPETENCIES

The role of diversity and inclusion in business is changing due to rapid technological advancements, globalization, immigration, increased demand for skills and education, and an aging workforce in a large part of the world. From being compliance-driven and tactical at its inception, diversity has grown into a business-driven, strategic function.

No longer a fledgling discipline, the D&I function is now a recognized and accepted component of organizational structure in many large corporations. An HR Magazine article reports, "More organizations are dedicating senior level executives to drive their diversity initiatives for bottom-line effect."

Yet, many lament the lack of cohesion and clarity regarding what, exactly, a D&I practitioner does. "Though many businesses know that they want someone in charge of diversity efforts, they're not necessarily sure what they want her [or him] to actually do," asserts Vadian Liberman in an article in *The Conference Board Review*. He points out that it is this very vagueness that causes companies to place lesser value on their D&I directors. After all, it is difficult to respect someone when his/her achievements and expectations are unclear. "Without a clear job profile, many companies become disillusioned with those they hire to manage diversity," and, Liberman stresses, companies frequently confuse those in diversity leader roles with the initiative itself. Thus, the whole discipline is affected when a D&I leader fails in the role.

5.9.4   FIVE KEY TRENDS FOR D&I PROFESSIONAL'S ROLE

Five key trends are driving changes in the diversity and inclusion professional's role, thus defining a need for new thinking regarding competencies. These are globalization, demographic shifts, technology socio-political climate and legal environment / regulation.

5.9.4.1   GLOBALIZATION

An August 2007 survey by the Human Resources Planning Society reports accelerating globalization as the most significant trend having an impact on human resources today. As employees and managers are asked to work with team members, business partners, and customers from around the world, a global perspective and cultural competencies have become imperatives, and D&I leaders are often responsible for driving these skills. Similarly, immigration has changed the face of many workforces around the world. This, too, calls for increased cultural competence, as well as making the success of D&I strategies more urgent than ever.

5.9.4.2 DEMOGRAPHIC SHIFTS

In developing parts of the world, soaring economic growth rates coupled with limited numbers of skilled workers have caused high levels of turnover. In other parts of the world (such as the European Union (EU), Canada, and the United States) the labor pool is aging, causing demands for increased flexibility and redefining employee needs and expectations. These concurrent trends require organizations to rethink traditional methods of recruiting and retaining workers, and require D&I leaders to be at the forefront of workforce strategies that exhibit cultural competence, flexibility, and business acumen.

5.9.4.3 TECHNOLOGY

Technology has increased accessibility to information and transparency on the part of organizations. It has also made global communication simpler and faster than ever. At the same time, some worry that technology could de-personalize industry, if not used judiciously. Rapid advances in technology translate into freer availability of information. This provides rich opportunities for diversity and inclusion functions to provide employees and managers with access to communication, education, and resources. It also increases employee expectations regarding flexibility, the openness of the culture, and availability of information.

5.9.4.4 SOCIO-POLITICAL CLIMATE

In the midst of rapid globalization, strong religious, political, and nationalist divides are emerging in communities around the world. Managing these sensitive conflicts and building a culture of inclusion within an organization despite these types of divides is, to say the least, a major challenge for D&I practitioners everywhere.

5.9.4.5 LEGAL ENVIRONMENT / REGULATION

Increased regulation and media attention have added new dimensions to organizations' compliance requirements. More than ever, companies need to be just as concerned about the damage legal problems will do to their reputation, brand image, community relationships, and stock price as they are about legal fees and financial awards. The 2007 Human Resource Competency Study points to the U.S. Sarbanes-Oxley Act (a law that, in short, regulates financial reporting and accounting controls at all levels of organizations), privacy laws in the European Union, and other regulatory pressures as a reason for "CEOs relying more on HR to manage culture." Organizations in the EU are faced with the challenge of keeping up with rapidly changing anti-discrimination directives, local laws, and regulations in their own and neighboring countries such as the equal opportunity regulations recently enacted.

5.9.5 GLOBAL DIVERSITY AND INCLUSION COMPETENCY MODEL

Competencies are defined as knowledge, skills, abilities, behaviors, and attributes to fulfill a certain role. People who are successful most frequently exhibit these competencies. A competency model that will be applicable to D&I practitioners world-wide is presented is shown in Figure 5.8. The competencies are behavioral and measurable.

FIGURE 5.8

5.9.5.1 CHANGE MANAGEMENT

D&I is, in its essence, a culture change and growth strategy. Given the rapidly shifting business realities, D&I strategies are routinely challenged to nimbly change course to reach business objectives. Therefore, change management is a critical success factor for every D&I practitioner. The D&I practitioner must be able to shepherd the organizational change process through facilitation, clear communications, and appropriate, effective interventions when things go off-course. Figure 5.9 shows the competency and definition of change management.

Change Management

Competency	Definition
Organization Development	Understands and facilitates the change process through completion Gains leadership involvement and line ownership

Corporate Communication	Communicates the full spectrum of inclusion:
	  Utilizes multiple communication vehicles such as web sites, brochures, talking points, and more
	  Maintains a balanced global perspective that offers flexibility and variations for use at the local level
	  Keeps what is best for the business at the forefront
	  Elaborates on benefits of D&I
	  Acknowledges and addresses possible unfavorable impact
	  Tracks and communicates strategy progress and setbacks
	  Acknowledges and addresses challenges / obstacles / opportunities

Critical Interventions	Offers useful and timely interventions in cases where progress is impeded due to a diversity-related issue

FIGURE 5.9

5.9.5.2 DIVERSITY, INCLUSION, AND GLOBAL PERSPECTIVE

Globalism has perhaps done more to increase organizations' need for the D&I practitioner's expertise than any other single trend. New markets require advanced insights and skills in order to navigate effectively across unfamiliar and varied cultural terrains. More than ever, companies are seeking the expertise of D&I practitioners to instill knowledge and skills to enter new markets, build relationships, and develop credibility across cultural contexts. This is not a stand-alone competency, but influences every other competency in this model. D&I practitioners must, in effect, be cultural interpreters, global marketers and, when needed, mediators. They must recognize and understand cultural norms as they impact modes of marketing, working, and communicating. They must understand subtle dynamics of cultural tensions or conflicts, and be able to negotiate and facilitate others through these challenges.

D&I practitioners are role models. They must be sure that their behaviors demonstrate inclusion and cultural competence, and that their own teams represent a broad range of diversity.

Of course, human beings are a complex species, and no one person will ever have complete mastery of all of the myriad dimensions of diversity, inclusion, and cultural competence. This is why a commitment to continuous learning is critical. Continuous learning requires intellectual energy and curiosity, as well as humility and courage. In order to be open to learning, we must be humble enough to admit that we do not have all of the answers; we must be courageous enough to experience the discomfort that comes with applying new skills.

An essential part of expertise in diversity is the ability to manage complex group dynamics. We also must be aware of when it is appropriate to inquire, when we need to advocate, or when an issue requires more decisive, or even unilateral, resolution.

Finally, D&I practitioners must be conversant on best practices and emerging trends within the industry, and able to customize and apply these to their own organizations in a way that enhances business outcomes. Figure 5.10 shows the competency and definition of diversity, inclusion and global perspective.

Diversity, Inclusion, and Global Perspective

Competency	Definition
Cultural Competence	Understands multiple cultural frameworks, values, and norms
	Demonstrates an ability to flex style when faced with myriad dimensions of culture in order to be effective across cultural contexts
	Understands the dynamics of cross-cultural and inclusion-related conflicts, tensions, misunderstandings, or opportunities
	Understands the history, context, geography, religions, and languages of the regions in which the organization does business
	Is fluent in more than one, and ideally several, languages
Negotiation and Facilitation	Negotiates and facilitates through cultural differences, conflicts, tensions, or misunderstandings
Continuous Learning	Recognizes and addresses one's filters, privileges, biases, and cultural preferences
	Commits to continuous learning / improvement in diversity, inclusion, and cultural competence
	Seeks and utilizes feedback from diverse sources
Complex Group Dynamics	Understands and effectively manages group dynamics and ambiguity
Judgment	Is able to discern when to inquire, advocate, drive, or resolve more decisively
Subject Matter Expertise	Knows and applies best practices in diversity and inclusion practices, strategies, systems, policies, etc.
	Understands subtle and complex diversity and inclusion issues as they relate specifically to marginalized groups (while these vary by region, they often include women, people with disabilities, older people, and racial, ethnic or religious minorities)
	Establishes and manages D&I councils effectively
	Collaborates with other functional teams
	Is a role model for inclusive and culturally competent behavior

FIGURE 5.10

5.9.5.3 BUSINESS ACUMEN

Business acumen has three areas of focus: external market, holistic business, and D&I ROI.

An effective D&I practitioner is required to be a full business partner. As such, practitioners must be conversant with global and local trends in their industries. They must gather and use competitive intelligence in the same manner as any other business person. Critically, they must also understand diverse customers, be current in global sociopolitical environments in which the organization does business, and be mindful of the business context and lessons learned.

The D&I practitioner should also be fully conversant with the impact of financial drivers on bottom line results and understand her/his organization's core business strategies. This knowledge, coupled with solid financial acumen, positions the D&I practitioner to lead the organization as a key strategic player.

Making the business case for diversity falls under business acumen as well. Through a thorough understanding of the market and the business, the practitioner is better positioned to create insights on how D&I will contribute to business results, as well as to People and HR strategies. By clearly expressing the bottom line implications of D&I, the practitioner underscores the merits of D&I work as part of the organization's business strategy. Figure 5.11 shows the competency and definition of business acumen.

Business Acumen

Competency	Definition
External Market Knowledge	Understands and is current on global and local trends/ changes and how they inform and influence D&I
	Gathers and uses competitive intelligence
	Understands diverse customer/client needs
	Understands and is current with global socio-political environments
	Understands context and lessons learned
Holistic Business Knowledge*	Understands the impact of the financial, economic, and market drivers on bottom line results*
	Understands core business strategies
	Possesses solid financial acumen
	Uses information from multiple disciplines and sources to offer integrated ideas and solutions on issues important to the organization
Diversity and Inclusion ROI	Determines and communicates how D&I contributes to core business strategy and results
	Creates insights on how D&I contributes both to people and HR strategies as well as business results.
	Designs and develops D&I metrics that exhibit the ROI impact.

* Adapted from The Campbell Soup Company's Compass Model

FIGURE 5.11

5.9.5.4 STRATEGIC EXTERNAL RELATIONS

Increasingly, the D&I practitioner is responsible for contributing to external relationships. From tapping emerging markets to managing positive media and community relations, D&I practitioners are no longer solely focused on internal employee issues. Today's D&I practitioner is involved in organizations' philanthropic efforts, responsible for supplier diversity, contributes her/his expertise to marketing campaigns, and is a key player in the creation and enhancement of organizations' brands and reputations. Figure 5.12 shows the competency and definition of strategic external relations.

The competencies falling under the rubric of strategic external relations address these expectations in four key areas:

- corporate social responsibility (along with government relations and regulatory requirements);
- strategic alliances with external community organizations;
- managing supplier diversity to enhance the supply chain and increase market share, revenue, and loyalty;
- brand/reputation management through media and community relationships.

Strategic External Relations

Competency	Definition
Corporate Social Responsibility / Government / Regulatory*	Well-informed about external pressure points (e.g., society, work councils, environment, regulatory, government, customers, and related trends)
	Effectively anticipates and manages stakeholders (e.g., advocacy, community, non-government organizations)
	Recognizes and addresses human rights issues through policy and practice
	Influences media and marketplace via communication and community outreach to competitively position the organization
Strategic Alliances	Identifies, partners, and leverages relationships with key external organizations / leaders to enhance business results
Diverse Markets / Supplier Diversity	Identifies, partners, and leverages relationships with key external diverse suppliers, organizations, and customers to: Enhance the supply chain / Increase market share, revenues, and loyalty
Brand / Reputation Management	Positively influences media and marketplace
	Forges strategic partnerships with internal constituencies through community outreach
	Supports communities in which the organization operates

* Adapted from The Conference Board Diversity Executive

FIGURE 5.12

5.9.5.5 INTEGRITY

If you ask any CEO of a company with a successful D&I strategy, she/he will agree that it takes a special kind of person to succeed as a D&I practitioner. The D&I practitioner must be ethical, resilient, influential, empathic, and a skilled communicator. These are the characteristics, council members suggest, that have enabled them to have the strength and fortitude to succeed in an exceptionally complex field. They have used these skills to gain credibility and stature, build relationships, and garner support during times when diversity and inclusion were misunderstood or undervalued. Figure 5.13 shows the competency and definition of integrity rubric.

Integrity

Competency	Definition
Ethics	Acts ethically and with integrity
	Behaves in a way that leads others to trust him/her*
	Speaks with candor and tact
	Acts as a voice for perspectives, levels, and cultures that are not otherwise represented
Resilience	Pursues goals with drive and energy; seldom gives up before finishing, especially in the face of resistance
	Maintains positive and constructive outlook**
Influence	Negotiates and persuades effectively at all levels of the organization
	Navigates corporate landscape and has an impact up, down, and sideways
	Listens and adapts approach to fit audience
	Manages and mediates conflict effectively
Empathy	Understands the point of view and emotions of others, in the context of their cultures, including both minority and majority groups
	Acknowledges, in a stated or unstated fashion, other's perspectives***
Communication	Understands how to motivate and work with both minority and majority groups
	Knows where resources are, and how to access them
	Communicates effectively
	Engages audience

* Adapted from the Merrill Lynch Leadership Model
** IBID
*** Schwartz, W.,(2002) "From passivity to competence: A conceptualization of knowledge, skill, tolerance, and empathy". *Psychiatry 65(4)* pp. 338-345.

FIGURE 5.13

5.9.5.6 VISIONARY & STRATEGIC LEADERSHIP

Successful D&I practitioners are not only strategic leaders, but also visionaries. They envision D&I success for the organization, and convey it in a manner that rouses the enthusiasm of others. They are imaginative and innovative, and yet not altogether dreamers. Practitioners understand the business realities of the organization, and ground their visions of the future state in pragmatic strategies. A skilled organizational politician, the D&I practitioner has the power to get things done through relationships and influence. Figure 5.14 shows the competency and definition of visionary & strategic leadership rubric.

Visionary & Strategic Leadership

Competency	Definition
Diversity & Inclusion Future State	Collaborates appropriately with others to envision and convey an inspiring, compelling, and relevant D&I future state
	Actively seeks new ideas, experiences, and thought leaders
	Is a catalyst for change. Translates / makes connections between new ideas and applications
	Frames new directions in understandable, innovative, and inspiring terms
Pragmatism	Differentiates between strategy and tactics
	Drives alignment with clients, partners, and stakeholders
	Is pragmatic regarding working within business realities
	Proactively creates foundation for influence at all levels of the organization
Political Savoir-Faire	Facilitates and manages complex and sensitive matters*
	Knows to whom and where to go to get things done (including working with the Board, CEO, and top leaders)
	Collaborates with other functional areas to maximize outcomes for all (especially HR, Organization development, Leadership development)
	Possesses the ability to influence and execute beyond positional power
	Is seen, at all levels, as a trusted source for advice and counsel

* Adapted from The Campbell Soup Company's Compass Model

FIGURE 5.14

5.9.5.7 HR COMPETENCIES

Understanding the various HR disciplines and their interrelationship with D&I, the D&I practitioner acts as an expert resource to HR colleagues. Not only does she or he offer insights into legal compliance issues, but she or he identifies opportunities for total rewards, talent management, Organizational Development (OD), work and life balance, training, and employee relations to align their work with the D&I strategy, each furthering the other's objectives. Figure 5.14 shows the competency and definition of HR competencies.

HR Competencies

Competency	Definition
Total Rewards/ Talent Management/ Organizational Development/Work and Life Balance/Training	Understands the basic tenets and workings of compensation and benefits programs, policies, and best practices
	Provides program options that ensure equitable treatment and mitigate disparities
	Possesses knowledge of programs, policies and best practices that ensure equity and achievement of organizational D&I objectives in a variety of HR areas, including but not limited to recruiting and staffing, OD, work and life balance, succession planning, training/ development, and performance management
Compliance	Understands applicable laws, regulations, and government requirements and their impact on the business
	Ensures compliance through effective programs, policies, and practices
Employee Relations	Works with others appropriate to the situation to resolve individual and group conflict, including the development and delivery of successful interventions
	Sustains and improves the work environment in the face of change and environmental challenges

FIGURE 5.14

CHAPTER 6
The Technical Laboratory

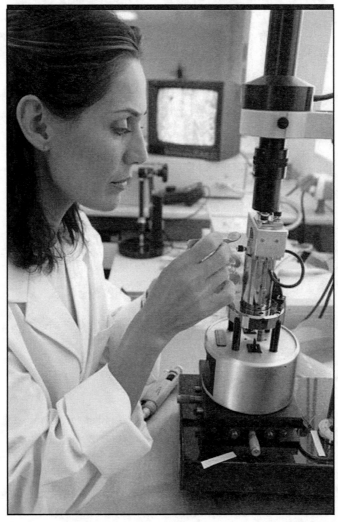

CHAPTER 6
THE TECHNICAL LABORATORY

3.1 LAB SAFETY TRAINING

A laboratory is a location set aside for experimentation, observation and testing. The type of experimentation taking place defines the purpose of laboratory and the safety training needed. The goal of laboratory safety training is to give everyone working in the laboratory a basic knowledge of the safety issues they may encounter, and how to work around these issues to reduce the chance of accidents. With proper laboratory safety training a workplace can reduce accidents, improve efficiency and decrease costs.

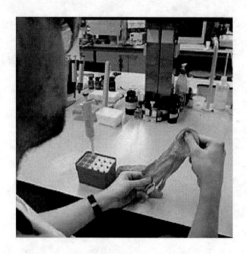

FIGURE 3.1 SCIENTISTS WEAR PROTECTIVE EQUIPMENT IN LABORATORIES

3.1.1 LABORATORY HAZARD ASSESSMENT

In order to create a proactive training program, responsible personnel must first assess the hazards associated with their workplace. This can be done with the help of an industrial hygienist, safety officer or other safety professional who is available to work with laboratory personnel on safety issues. Topics for consideration will include, but are not limited to, the type of research being conducted, the materials being used (such as chemical, biological or radiological materials), security issues, personnel and equipment.

3.1.2 TRAINING MATRIX

Once a safety assessment has been conducted, a training program can be created. Any training program must take into consideration the audience to which the training materials are being presented. Some training programs require all personnel to take the same basic classes. Others create a training matrix that cross references job titles or skills with specific training components.

For example, a laboratory manager of a small analytical testing laboratory works in all areas of the laboratory. Because of this, the safety officer has decided the lab manager must take courses in chemical management, laboratory safety and radiation safety. A laboratory technician who is supervised by the lab manager is described as a person who works in very specific areas of the laboratory. The technician needs to take only the chemical management and laboratory safety courses because he does not work in or around radiological materials

The same training matrix principle can be applied to personnel based on specific job tasks, the experiments they are doing, or their educational background and/or previous work experience.

3.1.3 EMERGENCY PREPAREDNESS

Once a training program is outlined, specific training classes must be created or purchased and presented to laboratory personnel. It is important to include specific information that applies to unique equipment, materials or experiments performed in the laboratory. But laboratory safety must also include basic information. A proactive goal of safety training is to prepare personnel to handle emergencies before they occur. Emergency preparedness should include information on how and when to contact emergency response crews, what to do in case of environmental emergencies such as severe weather or earthquakes and what to do in case of the release of hazardous materials.

3.1.4 UNIVERSAL ISSUES

Other information to include in laboratory safety training are the scientific issues that apply to all laboratories. Topics such as food and drink in a laboratory, workplace security, preventing contamination, disposal of hazardous materials and proper chemical storage and segregation are all important laboratory safety training issues. These topics, and others associated with a laboratory, can be approached in one comprehensive course or in separate training classes that deal with specific safety issues.

3.1.5 LABORATORY SAFETY CULTURE

The ultimate goal of any laboratory is to create a safety culture where everyone is working safely and possess a shared goal of maintaining a safe working environment. Training is an important part of safety culture. Laboratory safety training gives all laboratory personnel safety knowledge so each can contribute to a safe working environment.

3.2 LAB SAFETY REQUIREMENTS

Paying close attention to safety is crucial while working in a lab setting. Open flame is often necessary for experiments, and chemicals used may be toxic or corrosive. Know the rules of lab safety before setting foot in the laboratory.

FIGURE 3.2 SAFETY IS CRUCIAL WHILE WORKING IN A LAB SETTING

3.2.1 FOOD AND DRINK

Do not bring food or drink into the lab; they could be contaminated by chemicals you are using. Plus, the chance of spilling something onto computer equipment is greater with food and drinks nearby.

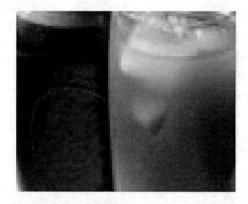

**FIGURE 3.3 THERE'A A GREATER CHANCE OF SPILLAGE
OR CONTAMINATION WHEN DRINKS ARE IN A LAB.**

3.2.2 SAFETY EQUIPMENT

Know where safety equipment is located in the lab before you start working. This equipment may include a fire extinguisher, eyewash station, safety shower and fire alarm.

FIGURE 3.4 ALWAYS KNOW THE LOCATION OF SAFETY EQUIPMENT

3.2.3 SHOES

Wearing open-toed shoes or sandals is not advisable while working in a lab environment due to the possibility of corrosive liquids spilling or broken glass. Wear sturdy, close-toed shoes that are slip resistant to avoid injury.

3.2.4 CHEMICALS

Use caution when working with any chemicals. Read all chemical bottles twice before using because some labels can be confused with others. Wear gloves, goggles and never taste any chemicals in the lab. If chemicals get into eyes, immediately wash eyes in the eyewash station.

3.2.5 BURNS

Always wear gloves when dealing with an open flame. Minor burns should be plunged into cold water immediately.

3.3 LAB SAFETY RULES

THIRTEEN SAFETY RULES FOR LABORATORY WORK

1: No eating or drinking in the lab. This means no gum, cough drops, applying chap-stick, chewing hair ends, holding a pencil in your mouth, nail-biting, etc.

2: Handle everything as if it's pathogenic. Use good microbiological practice. Soil and water samples that students try to culture in class or for a science project should be handled with standard microbiological practice under adult supervision. Autoclave sterilize for 0.5 hr or flood with freshly prepared 10% bleach for 0.5 hr and rinse before disposing in the regular trash.

3: Keep flame and flammable solutions far apart. Set up your classroom so that if a flame IS to be used, it is located far from the exit, so most students are closer to the exit. Have any open alcohol beakers far from the flame --- for instance on another workbench --- so some of the alcohol evaporates while the tool is brought to the flame.

4: Keep electrical equipment far from water. Keep areas around electrical equipment dry (aquaria excluded, of course!).

5: Clean spills from the outside IN. Apply paper towels over the spill, then, carefully starting from the outside, wipe in.

6: Use proper safety protection --- fume hood, goggles, gloves. NOTE that latex allergies can develop!

7: Always clean glassware before you use it to be sure that residues are cleaned away. Add at least some water first, before adding any liquid or solid solutes.

8: Be careful weighing out chemicals and reagents. Do NOT return excess materials to the stock container.

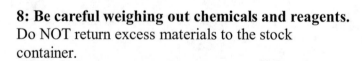

9: Check all water-baths with a thermometer before putting your hand into the water.

10: All sharps (needles, razors, pins, toothpicks) should be discarded in a sturdy container. A coffee can with plastic lid works well. Cut a small slit in the lid and make a bright clear label for the can.

11: Science and writing go hand-in-hand; keep a proper laboratory notebook or write Standard Operating Procedures.

12: Be Prepared: Wash your hands before AND after lab work.

13: Learn how the professionals learn about safety.

3.4 FIRST AID SAFETY RULES

A lab is a room that allows students to experiment and conduct scientific research. Typically this is done in a science laboratory. Most of the time a teacher or a professor is facilitating the lab so that a more professional and experienced person can be present.

3.4.1 RISK FACTORS

In some labs risk factors are extremely higher than others. Science labs have many hazards such as poisons, chemicals, flammable explosives, and infectious agents. Also, people who are in the lab may sometimes encounter higher temperatures and moving equipment.

3.4.2 RULES

The rules in the lab are important to help users stay safe. Normally the safety rules are posted throughout the facility. Safety attire is also provided for the room to prevent any accidental spills are splashes in your eyes.

3.4.3 OSHA AND CHP GUIDELINES

Occupational Safety and Health Administration (OSHA) developed the "Safety Standard." Each lab must contain information about the Chemical Hygiene Plan (CHP); the plan helps users locate chemical hazards in their work area and how to deal with them when necessary. CHP must be reviewed every year to make sure that the plan is continuously meeting standards. Schools and Businesses employ people in this area so that they can asset CHP. Inspections in labs are routine. The purpose of these inspections is to make sure that hazards are being asset correctly and also to make sure that all chemicals and flammable products are being stored in proper containers and compartments. Facilitators are constantly being trained to reduce and eliminate accidents in the laboratory.

3.4.4 HOT PLATES

When using a hot plate, make sure that your hair and articles of clothing aren't dangling. Hot plates stay extremely hot for a long time, so it's important to use tongs are heat protected gloves to pick-up the beaker. Never touch any chemicals with your fingers! Remember to report any and all accidents as soon as possible to the laboratory facilitator.

3.4.5 SAFETY RULES

The user should always conduct themselves in a responsible manner while they are in the lab. All questions and concerns should be asked before starting the lab. All users must be accompanied by an expert when doing a lab assignment. Never touch any lab equipment unless you know their capabilities or if you have been instructed to do so. Always work in a well-ventilated area. Be alert of your surroundings! Dispose of all chemicals and hazardous by-products completely. Never touch your face, eyes, mouth, nose, or any other body part while dealing with chemicals. If a chemical does get in your eye, rinse your eye out for 20 minutes. Most importantly wear the proper attire: lab coat, goggles, gloves, and closed toe shoes.

3.5 DEVELOPMENT OF GOOD LAB SKILLS

To become very skillful in a technical lab you me:

- Be patient and pay close attention to detail. Methodically performing the steps of an experiment may sometimes be frustrating. Many times the experiment does not turn out as planned; this means it may have to be redone, costing much precious time and energy.

- Be a good planner, have confidence in your plan, and prepare well to accomplish the main objective of the assigned lab. Often, your instructors will be willing to go only part of the way in explaining theory and methodology, not because they do not want to help, but because the greatest benefit come from figuring it out for yourself.

- Be accurate and objective in data collection. Simply recording data expected, or wished for, from the experiment and not mastering the skills of accurately and objectively interpreting meters, gauges, or other measurement devices will eventually be detected on a report or on a lab practical examination.

- Communicate clearly and effectively. Only when the reader can understand what you are trying to convey is your work of any benefit.

Whether you are in a general laboratory, such as physics, or in a technology-specific laboratory, many or most of the labs will be spelled out in some detail. Equipment will be specified and documented. Data sheets will be used and theoretical concepts must be understood. Even with such support information, experimentation will take you into the unknown because there is great variability in technique, methodology, environmental conditions, and even in the inherent characteristics of the equipment, such as friction. Identifying the reasons for variability is one of the great lessons you will learn in experimentation—no two experiments are the same.

In some cases only the experimental "statement of the problem" to be explored is described. For instance: "The student will design an amplifier to convert a 5 milli-volt (mV) signal to 10V signal," or "The student will determine the bulk modulus and compressibility of a concrete sample." You must make decisions on appropriate equipment, review equipment manuals for instrument accuracy and precision, and perhaps read research reports on experiments similar to what you are attempting. Your skill, creativity, and perseverance will really be challenged. But these school laboratories will prepare you for the real world of industry, where failures occur frequently.

Often, you will work with others on group projects, just as you will be solving problems with others in industry. Always keep in mind, however, that you alone are responsible for the final results. It is ultimately up to you to verify data, assure correct equipment setup, and draw conclusions from the results of your laboratory.

3.6 REDUCING ERRORS IN THE LABORATORY

During the experiment you will encounter variability. All of your measurements are subject to variability, and you should learn to recognize the major causes. You must eliminate the errors and record those impossible to eliminate. Later, when you write your report, you will be able to explain the causes of errors that occurred during the experiments. To better understand errors it is best to classify them in three general categories: gross, systematic, and random.

3.6.1 GROSS ERRORS

Gross errors are errors that completely invalidate data. Gross errors are just blunders or mistakes. Personal errors (careless of the observers) are the sources of gross errors. Of course, these errors should be eliminated in the laboratory and not be discussed in the report. Gross errors include misuse of equipment, not following the procedure or the proper sequence of the procedure, or recording data incorrectly. The characteristics of Gross errors are its magnitude is significantly very large or different in comparison to the measured values. The effect is inhomogeneous observables.

Examples of Gross errors:

1. A tape reading of 38.23 m may be recorded as 38.32 m in the field book
2. The thermometer may be misread
3. Measurement may be made between the wrong pegs

In practice there are variety of ways that can be employed to reduced gross errors:

1. Taking multiple reading and checking for reasonable consistency
2. Careful checking of both pointing and recording
3. Using simple and quick technique for verification
4. Applying logic and common sense
5. Checking and verifying the performance of equipment, particularly those with automatic readout
6. Repeating the experiment with perhaps slightly different technique
7. Increasing redundancy of the observation used in a model

3.6.2 SYSTEMATIC ERRORS

Systematic Errors– Errors due to the design and execution of the experiment. They can be identified through a careful analysis of the experiment and associated experiments, and measures can be taken to correct them. Systematic errors occur with the same magnitude and sign every time the experiment is performed, and affect the accuracy of the results, but not the precision. If an experiment has small systematic errors, it is **accurate**. The **accuracy** of a measurement is how close the measurement is to the true value of the quantity being measured. The accuracy of measurements is often reduced by systematic errors, which are difficult to detect even for experienced research workers.

Systematic errors exhibit an orderly character. Systematic errors may be caused by the environment, the measuring instrument, or the experimenter. Systematic errors may also be identified and eliminated during the laboratory and often will not show up in a report.

Systematic errors are reproducible inaccuracies that are consistently in the same direction. Systematic errors are often due to a problem which persists throughout the entire experiment.

Figure 3.5 is an example of what could be considered either a gross or systematic error. In Figure 3.5 an indicator not zero-set usually causes a systematic error (a consistent error), however, in some cases it will cause random errors (e.g., ohmmeter errors).

FIGURE 3.5 AN OFF-SET INDICATOR

Not zeroing the meter is a gross error because it represents misuse of equipment. Zero offset may also cause a systematic error, but in the case of an ohmmeter the error may not be systematic. You cannot assume that zero offset is always a systematic error.

Examples of systematic errors are equipment out of calibration, failure of mechanical devices, such as steel measuring tape that lengthens with temperature change (ambient temperature should often be monitored during experimentation), gauges affected by barometric pressure, carbon resistors that tend to increase in resistances they are used over and over again in the laboratory, and oscilloscope sensitivity adjustments that are not locked into the calibrate (cal) mode. Parts A and B of Figure 3.6 are examples of systematic error. Failure to level a height gauge could result in a systematic error known as cosine error. In B, the error can be readily seen. Can you see why it is referred to as cosine error?

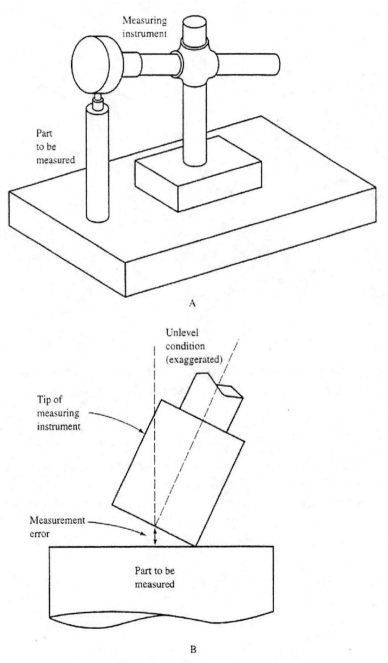

FIGURE 3.7 THE COSINE ERROR

Some instruments display a systematic error known as hysteresis. Hysteresis is a Greek word meaning lag. A more complete definition for **hysteresis** is the inability of a moving or deformed object to follow the same displacement curve in both increasing and decreasing directions as shown in Figure 3.7. Some laboratory or instrument user's manuals will ask the technician or technologist to always approach the final setting from one direction only—e.g., clockwise or counterclockwise.

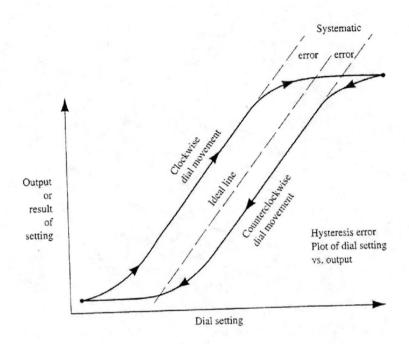

FIGURE 3.7 HYSTERESIS CURVE ATTRIBUTED TO MECHANICAL "LAG" IN AN INSTRUMENT

Observation errors are often systematic. **Observation errors** are errors caused by an observer misreading the scale of an instrument. The most common type of observation error is parallax. Parallax is an error resulting from the indicating needle on an analog scale being some distance from the scale as shown in part A) and Part B) of Figure 3.8. A technician or technologist who consistently reads the instruments from the side will have a systematic error in the data collected.

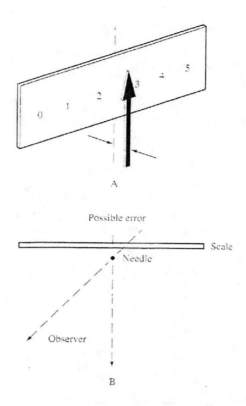

**FIGURE 3.8 THE DISTANCE BETWEEN THE NEEDLE AND THE
SCALE IN (A) MAY OFTEN CAUSE PARALLAX ERROR (B)**

Systematic errors are also sometimes called bias or special cause errors. These types of errors are always in one direction. For example, a machine with a systematic error dispensing a liquid may always dispense a volume that's below the desired amount. Rather than being due to normal, expected variation, as are random errors, systematic errors are generally due to a problem of some sort. The problems causing systematic errors can range from faulty equipment to a poorly trained employee.

Systematic errors have properties which are quite different from random errors. They tend to have a sudden onset, since they're often due to a machine or process failure. So a process which is working one day and not the next may be exhibiting systematic errors. As well, systematic errors often, although not always, tend to be on a larger scale than random errors. Finally, they'll always occur as either high or low, rather than as a mixture of the two, and the magnitude of the error will usually be consistent.

Systematic errors in experimental observations usually come from the measuring instruments.

They may occur because:

- there is something wrong with the instrument or its data handling system, or
- because the instrument is wrongly used by the experimenter.

Two types of systematic error can occur with instruments having a linear response:

1. **Offset** or **zero setting error** in which the instrument does not read zero when the quantity to be measured is zero.
2. **Multiplier** or **scale factor error** in which the instrument consistently reads changes in the quantity to be measured greater or less than the actual changes.

Systematic errors are shown in Fig. 3.9. Systematic errors also occur with non-linear instruments when the calibration of the instrument is not known correctly. In Figure 3.6, the full line shows the systematic errors in a linear instrument; the broken line shows the response of an ideal instrument without error.

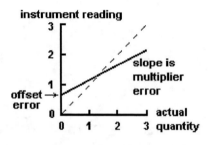

FIGURE 3.9

Examples of systematic errors caused by the wrong use of instruments are:

- errors in measurements of temperature due to poor thermal contact between the thermometer and the substance whose temperature is to be found,
- errors in measurements of solar radiation because trees or buildings shade the radiometer.

Another frequent error is adjusting the data to fit the desired or theoretical results. This may not be deliberate on the part of the experimenter, but may simply result from taking readings several times before a particular data point. Because there is variability in all experiments, you can eventually obtain a reading close to the one you want or expect. Inspectors in industry are often guilty of "editing the data" so product quality will look good. Editing the data or biasing the data is also considered systematic in that all data will be closer to the ideal than they would if the experimenter recorded every measurement—not just good measurements. Beware of such conscious or unconscious activity. It will lead to unpredictable results.

3.6.3 RANDOM ERRORS

Random Errors – Errors due to indeterminate causes throughout the experiment, such as unpredictable mechanical and electrical fluctuations affecting the operation of the instrument or experimental apparatus or even human errors arising from psychological and physiological limitations. These errors are determined by repeating the measurements. They occur with a different sign and magnitude each time an experiment is executed. If an experiment has small random errors, it is **precise**. The precision of a measurement is how close a number of measurements of the same quantity agree with each other. The precision is limited by the random errors.

Random errors are due to chance causes, often affecting the measurement at different times and in varying directions. Friction is a good example of a random error. Friction may always be in one direction (for instance, in an inclined plane experiment), but the magnitude of the error will usually vary, or never be constant.

Random errors in science are the usual, everyday variations that are expected and anticipated in certain processes. They're often associated with measurements and transfers. For example, if someone is filling a calibrated beaker up to a mark with water, they won't always add precisely the same amount. Sometimes they'll add slightly more, sometimes slightly less. Such errors can be reduced by using machinery to perform tasks instead of humans, but they can never be completely eliminated.

Random errors are statistical fluctuations (in either direction) in the measured data due to the precision limitations of the measurement device. Random errors usually result from the experimenter's inability to take the same measurement in exactly the same way to get exact the same number.

Random errors have several common characteristics. In a well-run process, they're typically quite small and may often be small enough to be inconsequential to that particular process. As well, as the name suggests, they're truly random. This means that the error will sometimes be on the high side, sometimes on the low side and there will be an approximately equal number of misses in each direction over a reasonable time frame. The direction of the miss, high or low, will also be random and unpredictable and the magnitude of the error may vary slightly from time to time.

Random errors in experimental measurements are caused by unknown and unpredictable changes in the experiment. These changes may occur in the measuring instruments or in the environmental conditions.

Examples of causes of random errors are:

- electronic noise in the circuit of an electrical instrument,
- irregular changes in the heat loss rate from a solar collector due to changes in the wind.

Random errors often have a Gaussian normal distribution. In such cases statistical methods may be used to analyze the data.

Environmental errors are a type of systematic error, however many environmental errors are random, too. Drafts or air currents often disturb the measurement system. Unknown temperature fluctuations cause the components of sensitive measurement equipment to expand and contract in an unpredictable fashion. Relative humidity (the amount of moisture in the air) may reduce static electricity forces, but increase small friction—"striction"—forces. Vibration is also considered an environmental error. Sometimes vibration is purposely introduced at a pivot point to elimination striction. Random errors can never be eliminated, but the impact of such errors can be reduced by the use of statistics. Averaging the data is a simple way to reduce the effects of random errors.

Systematic and random errors refer to problems associated with making measurements. ***Mistakes*** made in the calculations or in reading the instrument ***are not considered in error analysis***. It is assumed that the experimenters are careful and competent!

EXAMPLE 3.1: HOW TO MINIMIZE EXPERIMENTAL ERROR

Type of Error	Example	How to minimize it
Random errors	You measure the mass of a ring three times using the same balance and get slightly different values: 17.46 g, 17.42 g, 17.44 g	Take more data. **Random errors** can be evaluated through statistical analysis and can be reduced by averaging over a large number of observations.
Systematic errors	The cloth tape measure that you use to measure the length of an object had been stretched out from years of use. (As a result, all of your length measurements were too small.) The electronic scale you use reads 0.05 g too high for all your mass measurements (because it is improperly tared throughout your experiment).	**Systematic errors** are difficult to detect and cannot be analyzed statistically, because all of the data is off in the same direction (either too high or too low). Spotting and correcting for systematic error takes a lot of care. • How would you compensate for the incorrect results of using the stretched out tape measure? • How would you correct the measurements from improperly tared scale?

EXAMPLE 3.2

Five pieces from an assembly line have had one quality characteristic, designed to be 5.33 mm, measured by a micrometer as follows: 5.34 mm, 5.30 mm, 5.34 mm, 5.33 mm, and 5.31 mm. Assuming the variability to be due to chance or random variation, find the true average or mean ($\bar{X}$) of the manufacturing process and determine if the process is centered.

SOLUTION

The average, mean, or $\bar{X}$ is calculated by

$$\bar{X} = \frac{5.34 + 5.30 + 5.34 + 5.36 + 5.31}{5} = 5.33 \; mm$$

The process is centered and the operator may continue to produce parts, not stopping to adjust the process.

As shown in Figure 3.10, the family of errors is large, and pinpointing a particular error is often difficult. Throughout your career you will be dealing with variability. To recognize and attempt to categorize the causes of errors will allow you to separate the natural variability of a manufacturing process or research experimentation from variability caused by errors, gross or systematic, that can be controlled to improve the quality of the product.

The following definitions will aid you in developing a suitable vocabulary for explaining instrumentation practices in the laboratory.

ACCURACY: A quantitative estimate of the error or uncertainty in a measurement or calculation. The greater the accuracy, the smaller the value of the error.

CORRECTION: A quantity, equal to but opposite in sign from the error value, added to the measured value to obtain the accepted true value. Calibration often results in a correction factor for an instrument.

ERROR: The deviation of a calculated or observed value or observed value from the true or ideal value. Usually expressed as percentage of deviation (percent error).

PRECISION: The ability of an instrument to repeat the same measurement after a certain length of time and often after varying the instrument before resetting and performing the next measurement. Also, the instrument's ability to repeat a measurement and obtain the same result with a different operator.

RESOLUTION: A measure of how well a device can respond to small changes and indicate that change on the scale. Also referred to as sensitivity.

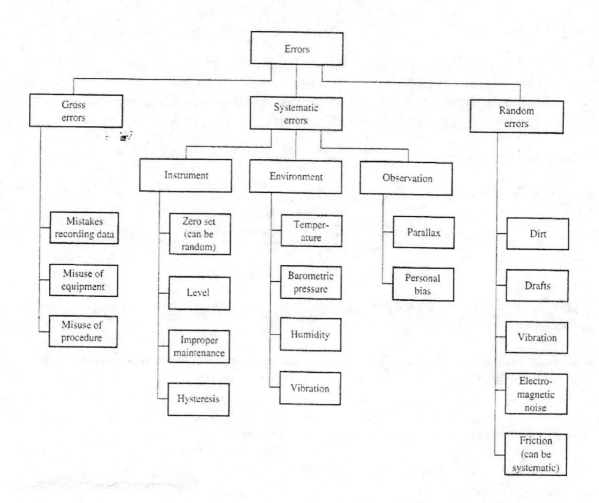

FIGURE 3.10 THE FAMILY OF ERRORS

Percent error (called relative error in some textbooks) is the combined error of the experiment. It may be determined by comparing the value of a parameter determined by experiment to the theoretical value (accepted true value) of the parameter under study.

Put into equation form:

$$percent\ (\%)\ error = \frac{|experimental\ value - accepted\ true\ value|}{accepted\ true\ value} \times 100$$

For the measured value in Example 3.1, the percent errors from the $\bar{X}$ are calculated as shown in Table 3.1.

TABLE 3.1 PERCENT ERROR CALCULATIONS FOR EXAMPLE 3.1

Measurement	% Error Calculation[*]	% Error
5.34	|5.34 – 5.33|/5.33 = 0.0019	0.19
5.30	|5.30 – 5.33|/5.33 = 0.0056	0.56
5.34	Repeat Calculation	0.56
5.36	|5.36 – 5.33|/5.33 = 0.0056	0.19
5.31	|5.31 – 5.33|/5.33 = 0.0038	0.38

[*]Note: The use of the absolute value sign and the difference of the numerator is always is always positive. All values are dimensionless; 5.33 is the theoretical or expected outcome—the accepted true value—of the experiment.

3.7 DATA COLLECTION AND CALCULATING RESULTS

Accurate reading of instrument scales is a challenge. First, the technician or technologist must determine what the scale division means. In Figure 3.11, the smallest instrument scale graduations are read as A, 1.0; B, 0.2; and C, 0.1. These scale readings may then be multiplied by the scale multiplier.

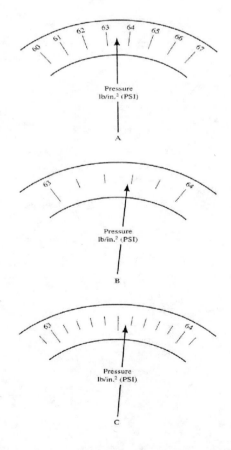

FIGURE 3.11 THREE METER SCALES: READINGS ARE (A) 63.5, (B) 63.6, (C) 63.55

239

It is important to understand how closely you can interpret a scale. The most common practice is to *consider the scale resolution to be no better than one-half of the smallest division*. The scales in Figure 3.11 can be interpreted to 0.5, 0.1, and 0.05 units, respectively. Never read (or interpret) an instrument scale to less than one-half of the smallest division. This number is known as the **doubtful digit**.

Most instrument manufacturers graduate an instrument's scale to approximate the accuracy of the instrument. **Accuracy** is defined as how true the value measured is. Only through traceability can accuracy be determined, and because the manufacturer of the instrument may not guarantee accuracy to the smallest graduation, a plus and minus ($\pm$) value is stated in the documentation or owner's manual.

Precision also contributes to collecting "good" laboratory data. Precision is defined as the ability of an instrument to repeat a measurement (repeatability). Of course, the technician or technologist using the instrument affects the precision of the reading, especially when using an analog (as opposed to a digital) scale. Precision and accuracy are often confused. Figure 3.12 helps separate the concepts of precision and accuracy.

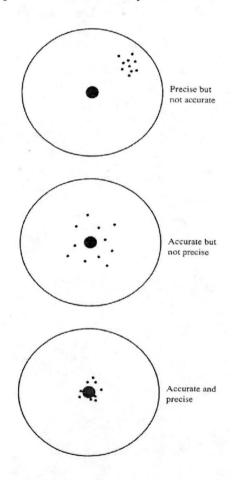

FIGURE 3.12 THE CONCEPTS OF PRECISION AND ACCURACY

Precision and accuracy may be reported as (1) percent of full scale, (2) ± some portion of the last digit, or (3) a combination of 1 and 2, as shown in Parts A) and B) of Figure 3.13. A stated accuracy of ± 5 percent of full scale means that any reading taken with the scale in Part A of Figure 3.12 may be in error as much as 0.5 (full scale of 10 multiplied by 0.05).

FIGURE 3.13

EXAMPLE 3.3

The analog scale in Part A) of Figure 3.13 is the indicator for a voltmeter with a stated accuracy of ± 5 percent. The reading is 13 V on the 100 V scale (full scale). Write the value of the reading and include the possible range of the measurement due to its accuracy.

SOLUTION

Simply take 5 percent of the 100 V full scale,

$$0.05 \times 100 = 5 \text{ V}$$

and write the reading as 13 ± 5 V; the true voltage can be anywhere from 8 to 18 V.

EXAMPLE 3.4

The technician or technologist in Example 3.3 switches the voltmeter scale multiplier switch down to the 50 V scale (50 V is now full scale). Determine the new position of the pointer and calculate the range of the true value of 13 read on this scale.

SOLUTION

The meter's pointer is now on the 13th scale division. Multiply 0.05 times 50, and write the true voltage 13 ± 2.5 V. The true voltage "window" has been halved by moving to a lower, more sensitive scale.

EXAMPLE 3.5

For the digital display in Part B) of Figure 3.13, what is the confidence range of the reading?

SOLUTION

The actual value of the reading could be anywhere between 873.3 and 873.5.

Most digital meters use a combination of accuracies. A typical accuracy may be read as "Accuracy is specified as $\pm$ ([percent of reading] + [number of units in least significant digit])."

All data you collect in the laboratory are known as **primary data**. Technicians and technologists make use of secondary data: that is data that have been taken by someone else, and possibly weeks, months, or years ago. You may be directing operators to collect **secondary data**. More importantly, you will have to interpret these data later. Therefore, you need to specify the number of significant figures in which the data will be recorded, or chaos will result.

As an example consider Part A) of Figure 3.11. The measurement is read as 63.5 PSI and the doubtful digit is 0.5. The 0.5 in the reading is underlined because it is estimated and considered to be a doubtful digit. If operators, as they were recording data, attempted to read the scale closer they would be beyond the accuracy of the instrument. Also, different operators may record the data to a different number of significant figures. You would have to direct the operators to record data to only three significant figures. If a pressure gauge with smaller scale graduations is used, as in Parts B) and C) of Figure 3.11, a more precise measurement can be made.

EXAMPLE 3.6

Read and record the pressure in Figure 3.14 and underline the doubtful digit. To how many significant figures would you instruct operators to record data using this scale?

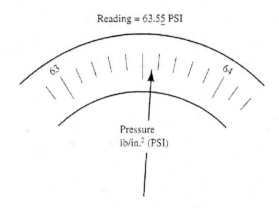

FIGURE 3.14 A PRESSURE GAUGE WITH "UNITY" SCALE DIVISIONS

SOLUTION

The reading, with the doubtful digit underlined is 63.5<u>5</u> PSI. Operators using this pressure gauge should record data to four significant figures of accuracy.

We have used the term *significant figures* up until this point without definition. The number of significant figures in a data point is defined as "a number equal to the number of digits the datum contains, with zeros merely holding a decimal place not counted." Use the following rules for counting the number of significant figures in a quantity (the significant figures illustrating the rule are underlined):

1. All digits other than zero are counted as significant figures (example: <u>64.5</u>).

2. All zeros between significant figures are also significant (example: 15<u>0</u>.<u>02</u>)

3. For non-decimal numbers greater than one, all zeros placed after the significant figures are *not significant* (example: 500 000 or 5×10^5 [only the 5 is significant]).

4. If a decimal point is shown after a non-decimal number larger than one, the zeros are then considered significant (example: 500 <u>000</u>.).

5. Zeros placed after a decimal point that are not necessary to set the decimal point are significant (example: 500.<u>00</u>).

243

6. For numbers smaller than one, all zeros placed before the significant figures are *not significant* (example 0.002 05 or 2.05×10^{-3} [only the three nonzero numbers (205) are significant; the other zeros establish the decimal point of fix the magnitude of the number]).

EXAMPLE 3.7

Determine the number of significant figures in the following quantities. Underline the significant figures.

1. 5100
2. 2053
3. 2034000.
4. 2034000.00
5. 0.0000321
6. 0.00003201

SOLUTION

1. 5100   has two significant figures
2. 2053   has four significant figures
3. 2034000.   has seven significant figures (because of the appearance of the decimal point)
4. 2034000.00   has nine significant figures
5. 0.0000321   has three significant figures
6. 0.00003201   has four significant figures

Once you have collected data and can appreciate the accuracy of the data taken you will begin to appreciate how to treat the result of multiplying and dividing such data.

With the advent of handheld calculators, students often report calculations eight or ten significant figures. In other words, they record all or most of the numbers appearing on their particular calculator's display. Such a practice is misleading—no quantity can be more exact or accurate than the numbers used to generate that quantity.

EXAMPLE 3.8

In the schematic diagram of Figure 3.15 the resistor has been measured in the laboratory as 24 Ω and the current is measured with a sensitive galvanometer as 3.6582 A The two numbers must be multiplied to determine the voltage ($E = I \times R$, Ohm's Law). Solve for the voltage.

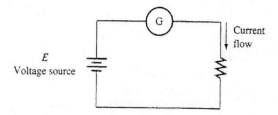

Current flow

E
Voltage source

FIGURE 3.15 THE SENSITIVE GALVONOMETER IS CONNECTED IN SERIES WITH THE RESISTOR TO MEASURE CURRENT TO AN ACCURACY OF 100 μA

SOLUTION

$E = I \times R$
$\quad = 3.6582 \times 24 = 87.7968$ V

But the 4 in 24 is doubtful. This means the true value of the resistor, according to what doubtful digits means could be between 23.6 and 24.4 Ω. Performing the multiplication again using two extremes,

$23.6 \times 3.6582 = 86.3$

$24.4 \times 3.6582 = 89.26$

These calculations show that the true voltage is in a *range of almost 3 V.*

Clearly, the two results in Example 3.8 vary so much that to report the data to more than the number of significant figures of the 24 Ω is inappropriate. Such reporting implies a precision of measurement greater than exists. To avoid reporting results that are misleading, use the following rule:

When multiplying or dividing quantities, record the result to the number of significant figures of the measurement with the *least* number of significant figures.

In Example 3.8, the resistor's value had two significant figures, and the next step is to round the result off to two significant figures:

$24 \times 3.6582 = 87.7968$

We can see that the result should not contain more than two significant figures, and the next step is to round the result off to two significant figures:

$24 \times 3.6582 = 88$

EXAMPLE 3.9

Round off the following calculations:

a) $\underline{5}000 \times 3.25$

b) $2010 \times 6.7\underline{7}$

c) $1.025/0.040\underline{2}$

SOLUTION

a) $\underline{5}000 \times 3.25 = 16250$, but is recorded as $\underline{2}0000$

b) $2010 \times 6.7\underline{7} = 13607.7$, but is recorded as $13\underline{6}00$

c) $1.025/0.040\underline{2} = 25.497512$, but is recorded as $25.\underline{5}$

The multiplication and division rules do not apply for counting numbers. For example, when you average data you divide by the number of data points. The number of data points is not considered a datum, so it can ignored in terms of significant figures.

When rounding a number to the doubtful digit use the following rules:

1. If the number to the right of the doubtful digit is greater than 5, increase the number by one:

$1\underline{2}.63$ rounds up to 13

$363.\underline{5}7$ rounds up to 363.6

$4999\underline{9}9$ rounds up to 500000

2. If the number to the right of the doubtful digit is less than 5, do not change the number:

7.5247 rounds down to 7.52

0.00365493 rounds down to 0.0036549

If you change rule number 1 to include 5 (numbers *greater than or equal* to 5 round up) they are all you need to handle data sets of less than 100. Later, you may collect data by computer for a manufacturing operation; manufacturing processes often yield large amount of data. The following rule is used only when analyzing large amount of data and ensure an equal distribution of "rounding ups" and rounding downs."

  3. If the number to the right of the doubtful digit is a 5, leave the number unchanged if it is even and round up if it is odd (i.e., always leave the doubtful digit an even number).

The rule for adding and subtracting numbers, when consideration of the number of significant figures is required , is quite different from the rule for multiplication and division. This is due to the nature of addition and subtraction. The decimal point must be aligned when adding and subtracting numbers (multiplication and division operations do not require decimal point alignment). Addition and subtraction operations, then require a decimal place approach:

When adding and subtracting quantities, record the result to the number of significant figures of the number with the *least* number of digits beyond the decimal point. For non-decimal numbers greater than one, record the result to the last accurate number's place value (zeros placed after the last significant figure are not significant).

EXAMPLE 3.10

For the following calculations demonstrate the addition and subtraction rule.

Perform the arithmetic for the following number:

a) 3.25 + 2.63 + 4.25   (each number has three significant figures)

b) 12523.544 - 200

c) 12523.544 – 200.

SOLUTION

a) 10.13 (all four figures are significant)

b) 12323.544, but is recorded as 12300

c) 12323.544, but is recorded as 12324

Significant-figure approach, accuracy, and precision are complex and often interrelated phenomena. You will acquire further information regarding the many rules for handling data during your college education and in training programs on the job. Quality product and predictable manufacturing cannot be attained without accurate and reliable data collection methods.

3.8 REPORTING

The ability to report technical information in a clear and concise manner is one of the most important practical skills that a technically trained person can develop. This is true because, the result and conclusions drawn from experimental methods are of little value unless they can be communicated to others.

Writing lab reports that describe experimental methods, results, discussions, and conclusions that can be drawn from those results is an excellent way to gain the practice and experience needed to become an effective technical writer. It is only by writing and being corrected that one can learn to write. A beginner will find it helpful to follow a certain format for his or her reports. This will help ensure that the report is complete and well organized.

3.8.1 WRITTEN REPORTING

3.8.1.1 WRITING A LAB REPORT [STYLE 1]

Written lab reports should consist of the following parts:

Title Page

This should be the first (cover) page of the report. When writing the title page of a lab report, the following should be included:

1. The title of the experiment.
2. The students name in full.
3. The instructor or person for whom the lab report is being compiled.
4. The date on which the experiment was performed or the date the lab report was written.

Introduction Page

Under this heading should be an overview of what the experiment was about. A sound definition of what was learned about the process being carried out during the experiment should be included.

Materials and Methods

This section should contain a description, in the students own words, of the experimental procedure that was followed in the performance of the experiment. The materials and methods section should be complete enough so that another student with the same background, but unfamiliar with the experiment, could perform the same experiment without additional instructions. Procedures and equipment used should be written in a sentence form. Do not list!

Results

The result section should contain raw data. Raw data consist of actual measured values recorded during the experiment. Use tables to present this information. All tables should have descriptive titles, and they should show the units of data entries clearly. The data section should also contain any graphs that are required. This is an effective method for communicating experimental results. The following steps should be taken into consideration while plotting a graph:

1. Do not use tiny dots, use symbols like X or O.
2. Do not draw a series of straight line segments between experimental data points plotted on a graph. The purpose of many of the experiments is to verify theoretical relationships between variables.
3. All graphs should have descriptive titles. These titles should tell what the graph is intended to show. Each axis of a graph should be labeled with the variable and unit it represents. Always use graph paper and always label graph coordinate lines so that it is easy to see how many units each division represents.

Discussions and Conclusions

This is the interpretation-and-conclusion of your report. This section should include the following:

1. How the conduct of the experiment met the objectives.
2. What took place during the process.
3. All questions should be answered within this section in a very logical and clear manner. The questions should be put into statement form.

4. The conclusions should be relevant to the experiment that was performed and should be based on facts learned as a result of the experiment.
5. You should also include any recommendations that you feel would improve the experimental procedure. If you have any further investigations that might be suggested by the data, you should also include them here.

Lab Report Example

Title Page:

Transpiration

Prepared for: Dr. Chuks Ogbonnaya

By: Deborah A. Smith

February 27, 1990

Introduction Page:

Introduction

Transpiration is the evaporation of water particles from plant surfaces, especially from the surface openings, or stomates, on leaves. Stomatal transpiration accounts for most of the water loss by a plant, but some direct evaporation also takes place through the surfaces of the epidermal cells of the leaves.

The amount of water given off depends somewhat upon how much water the roots of the plant have absorbed. It also depends upon such environmental conditions as sunlight, humidity, winds and temperature. A plant should not be transplanted in full sunshine because it may lose too much water and wilt before the damaged roots can supply enough water.

Transpiration occurs as the sun warms the water inside the blade. The warming changes much of the water into water vapor. This gas can then escape through the stomata. Transpiration helps cool the inside of the leaf because the escaping vapor has absorbed heat.

Materials and Methods Page:

Materials and Methods

The 1000 milliliter flask fitted with a three hole rubber stopper, separatory funnel and a measuring pipet. First, fill Erlenmeyer flask with 250 milliliters of distilled water. Put the glass tube with a right angle bend into one hole of the three hole stopper. Place stopper in flask making sure no air bubbles are trapped.

Take a plant shoot and cut in the sink under running water. Remove the shoot from water and place the stem through the hole in the stopper and allow one inch of the stem to go into the water in the flask. Place a separate funnel in third hole and fill with water to the upper mark. Coat all joints will sealant and record the position of the meniscus at two minute intervals for 30 minutes.

Move the apparatus to the fume hood and measure every two minutes for 30 minutes.

Place a plastic bag over the leafy part of the shoot and fasten with a rubber band. Measure this for an additional ten minutes.

Results Page:

Results and Discussion

This experiment was conducted to show how different effects such as wind or temperature affect transpiration. The results of transpiration under normal room conditions on the plant showed the fastest rate of transpiration. This faster rate showed that the temperature had the greatest effect on the pea plant leaves. This also was indicated by the control group.

The next effect on transpiration come from the wind factor present in the fume. The rate of water loss and demand was 0.45 centimeters. This proved that plants do lose water when outside conditions change such as in the presence of windy conditions.

When our plant was placed in the bag and the carbon dioxide and water vapor level was cut the plant had no movement of transpiration going on. It was at this time that our plant had taken in enough water to meet the plants current water level needs. Therefore, the stomata was closed. The plant had no water loss to the atmosphere and so water was not taken into the plant.

Table 1: Room Conditions 25 degrees Celsius

Time	Measurement	Amount of Change
12:13 pm	1.5 cm	-----
12:15 pm	1.75 cm	0.25 cm
12:17 pm	2.0 cm	0.25 cm
12:19 pm	2.25 cm	0.25 cm
12:21 pm	2.25 cm	-----
12:23 pm	2.45 cm	0.20 cm
12:25 pm	2.50 cm	0.05 cm
12:27 pm	2.50 cm	-----
12:29 pm	2.60 cm	0.10 cm
12:31 pm	2.65 cm	0.05 cm
12:33 pm	2.65 cm	-----
12:35 pm	2.65 cm	-----
12:37 pm	2.65 cm	-----
12:39 pm	2.7 cm	0.35 cm
12:41 pm	2.7 cm	-----

* Total Transpiration - 1.5 cm

Table 2: Under Hood 20 degrees Celsius

Time	Measurement	Amount of Change
12:45 pm	1.9 cm	-----
12:47 pm	1.9 cm	-----
12:49 pm	1.9 cm	-----
12:51 pm	1.9 cm	-----
12:53 pm	2.0 cm	0.1 cm
12:55 pm	2.1 cm	0.1 cm
12:57 pm	2.1 cm	-----
12:59 pm	2.1 cm	-----
1:01 pm	2.2 cm	0.1 cm
1:03 pm	2.2 cm	-----
1:05 pm	2.3 cm	0.1 cm
1:07 pm	2.3 cm	-----
1:09 pm	2.3 cm	-----
1:11 pm	2.35 cm	0.05 cm
1:13 pm	2.35 cm	-----

*Total Transpiration - 0.45 cm

Table 3: Plant at Room Temperature 25 Degrees Celsius
(Variable Plastic Bag Placed Over Plant)

Time	Measurement	Amount of Change
1:12 pm	2.5 cm	-----
1:14 pm	2.5 cm	-----
1:16 pm	2.5 cm	-----
1:18 pm	2.5 cm	-----
1:20 pm	2.5 cm	-----

*No Transpiration Change

Table 4: Control Peas (At Room Temperature 25 degrees Celsius)

Time	Measurement	Amount of Change
12:13 pm	1.5 cm	-----
12:15 pm	1.75 cm	0.25 cm
12:17 pm	2.0 cm	0.25 cm
12:19 pm	2.25 cm	0.25 cm
12:21 pm	2.25 cm	-----
12:23 pm	2.45 cm	0.20 cm
12:25 pm	2.50 cm	0.05 cm
12:27 pm	2.50 cm	-----
12:29 pm	2.60 cm	0.10 cm
12:31 pm	2.65 cm	0.05 cm
12:33 pm	2.65 cm	-----
12:35 pm	2.65 cm	-----
12:37 pm	2.65 cm	-----
12:39 pm	2.7 cm	0.05 cm
12:41 pm	2.7 cm	-----

*Transpiration Amount - 1.2 cm

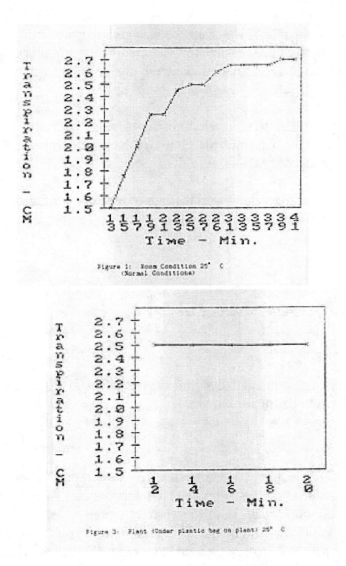

Figure 1: Room Condition 25° C
(Normal Conditions)

Figure 3: Plant (Under plastic bag on plant) 25° C

Conclusion Page:

Conclusion

A shoot was placed in the hole in the rubber stopper and inserted into colored water in the flask. As the plant takes up water, air moves into the pipette. Under set conditions the measurements were made on the volume and the rate at which water was transpired by following the movement of the interface between the water and air in the pipette.

Once the shoot was removed the rate of water uptake was greatly increased to 1.5 centimeters. This was a new rate of water uptake. The fact that the equilibrium rate of the plant freed from its roots was higher shows that the roots were unable to take up water as rapidly as the shoot was capable of transpiring it.

The rate of water uptake rose steadily during the first experiment and continued to rise at a slower rate in the fume. Once the plant was placed under the plastic bag equilibrium had been reached and therefore, the plant was full and turgid.

Since the roots on the plant no longer depressed the rate of movement of water into the plant, transpiration reached a new, constant equilibrium rate which was higher than that of the intact plant.

3.8.1.2 WRITING A LAB REPORT [STYLE 2]

Title Page

The title page provides the name of the lab experiment, the names of the lab partners, the date, and any other information your instructor requires.

Abstract

The abstract is the report in miniature. It summarizes the *whole* report in one, concise paragraph of about 100-200 words. As distinguished from the introduction, the abstract tells the reader what *will* be done and lays the groundwork Also, the abstract summarizes *the report itself*, not the actual experiment. Hence, you cannot write the abstract until after you've completed the report. Before writing the abstract, it is often helpful to summarize each section of the report (introduction, methods and materials, procedure, results, discussion, and conclusion) in one sentence. Then try to arrange this information into a short paragraph. Remember, the abstract should be a precise and specific summary.

Introduction

Whereas the abstract summarizes the whole report, the introduction presents the subject of the report and acquaints the reader with the experiment. Typically, the introduction states the problem to be solved or the experiment to be performed and explains its purpose and significance. It also provides whatever background theory, previous research, or formulas the reader needs to understand and perform the experiment (or solve the problem). Usually, the instructor does not want you to repeat such information verbatim from the lab manual; you can simply make the appropriate references to the manual.

Methods and Materials (or Equipment)

This section can consist of a list. Be complete, accurate, and precise.

Experimental Procedure

This section is a full descriptive narrative. Be complete, accurate, and precise, listing all steps in the correct order. State what you really did and what actually happened, not what was supposed to happen or what the textbook said.

Results

Again, give your actual results, not what should have happened. Although results are usually presented quantitatively, you should always introduce each block of information verbally and provide clear and accurate verbal labels.

Discussion

In this section, you must explain, analyze, and interpret your results, being especially careful to explain any errors or problems. This is probably the single most important part of the report, since it is here that you demonstrate that you understand and can interpret what you have done.

Conclusion

Draw conclusions from the results and discussion that answer the question, "So what?" Then go on to explain your conclusions. In this section, you may also criticize the lab experiment and make recommendations for improvement. Such criticisms and recommendations, however, should focus on the lab as a learning experience; mere complaints about faulty equipment or amount of time spent are not appropriate.

Note: The results, discussion, and conclusion sections can be combined in various ways. Use whatever combination is most appropriate for your situation.

References

Some reports require references at the end. Use the correct forms for the particular field you are working in. Always consult your instructor about reference forms, and check a style manual for the field.

Appendices

Appendices may include raw data, calculations, graphs, and other quantitative materials that were part of the experiment, but not reported in any of the above sections. Refer to each appendix at the appropriate point (or points) in your report. For example, at the end of your results section, you might have the note, *See Appendix A: Raw Data Chart.*

3.8.1.3 PREPARING AND SUBMITTING THE WRITTEN REPORT

It is a good idea to learn keyboarding and word processing early in your career as a technical student. Once you can write on the computer and retain your reports on data files so changes can be readily made, you will never wish to report in any other way. Neatness will be improved and you will be much more productive. Spelling and grammar are also important to good report writing. Most word processing software has a very useful spell-check and grammar-check feature.

Finally, complete your reports on time. Timeliness is difficult for many; they continually want to polish the report and never submit it on time. But deadlines in the workplace are crucial; your instructor expects you to develop good work habits and will demand prompt submission of reports. Penalties will be imposed on those who do not comply.

Use the following report checklist in editing your written reports:

- The report is attractive. (Neatness does count and papers with ragged edges, torn from a notebook, should never be submitted.) The cover page is well laid out, including such items as your name, the date, the title of the laboratory, other team members' names, and the course section identifier.

- The abstract or objective lets the reader know immediately what the report entails.

- The body provides all essential information, such as the list of equipment with equipment diagrams; a clear, concise procedure supported by theoretical considerations; a good data presentation well supported by attractive and appropriate graphs; and example calculations with literal equations that are representative and in order of use.

- A conclusion that reveals the results obtained, errors encountered, and recommendations for improvement.

- A report that is concise. Conciseness, ironically, takes extra to achieve, but is always desired in technical reports.

- A well-proofed report, free from typographical errors (typos), misspelled words, and poor grammar. This last check will become easier after you have successfully completed several communication courses required for all graduates. Be concise and avoid excess verbiage—when proofing, take out all that does not directly apply to the problem under investigation.

3.8.1.4 TEN MOST COMMON WRITING ERRORS IN LABORATORY REPORTS

1. Incompleteness

Be sure to express all thoughts and concepts completely, and to draw out the conclusions explicitly. When you finish drafting your report, try to read your writing with an objective eye, being especially sensitive to information you may have not provided that a reader will need to understand the report. Each equation, for example, should be part of a sentence, the terms should be defined, and the equations should be numbered sequentially in the right margin, as in the following example:

The process yields

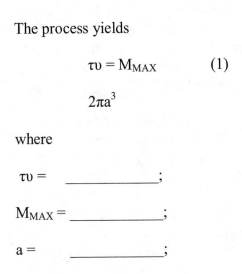

$$\frac{\tau\upsilon = M_{MAX}}{2\pi a^3} \qquad (1)$$

where

$\tau\upsilon = $ _____ ;

$M_{MAX} = $ _____ ;

$a = $ _____ ;

2. Lack of Order, Unclear Logic, Missing Transitions

Again, avoiding these errors means keeping your reader constantly in mind and making sure that you've included all information that your reader needs to understand the logical progression of your argument. It is also important, for order, that you put the right information in the proper part of the report and that you make use of the transitions to guide your reader. For example, suppose a student wrote the following paragraph for his or her Summary section :

"The purpose of this laboratory was to obtain a plot of C_D versus Re for a spherical model in a fluid flow. Three experiments were performed with the hope of modeling an Re range of 0 to 10^6. The change in C_D v. Re for the Re range around 10^4 was found using a spherical model in a wind tunnel. This experiment yielded constant values for C_D over this range and, therefore, agreed with the theory. An experiment with a spherical model in a free stream was performed to model the dependence of C_D on Re for Re approximately equal to 10^6."

Unless you're sure that your reader knows what C_D and Re mean, spell out the terms first, with the abbreviations following in parentheses. For example, write "Coefficient of Drag (C_D) vs. Reynolds Number (Re).." for the first reference. Then use the abbreviations every time thereafter.

The simple use of transitions would make the progression of this summary easier to follow. For instance, the writer says above, "Three experiments were performed. . . ." It would help the readers if the writer provided transitions that specify which experiment was being discussed: "In the first experiment, knowledge of the change in C_D for the Re range of 0 to 10. . ."; "In the second experiment, C_D vs. Re for the Re range around 10^4. . ."; and "The third experiment used a spherical model in a free stream. . ."

3. Inconsistency

Remember to keep your language consistent throughout, particularly verb tense and voice. Don't change verb tenses unnecessarily. When you describe an experiment that took place in the past, use past tense verbs. You may put conclusions and generalizations in the present tense Also, don't switch voice from first (I/we) to second (you) to third (he/she) person. For example, suppose a student wrote the following paragraph for his or her Procedure:

"You should measure the dimensions of the specimen, and the strain and load are balanced to zero. The cross-head speed was set at 0.2 in/min for the steel specimen, and then increased the load on the specimen quasistatically. You will stop the load applicator after the yield point is reached. Finally, the extensometer is dismounted."

.

The student lacked consistency in verb tense and voice. Note how the tense jumps from present to past and even to future, and the voice jumps from an impersonal passive voice to "you." The verbs should remain in the past tense, and the voice should be impersonal, as in the following example:

"The dimensions of the specimen were measured, and the strain and load were balanced to zero. The cross-head speed was set at 0.2 in/min for the steel specimen, and then the load on the specimen was increased quasistatically. The load applicator was stopped after the yield point was reached. Finally, the extensometer was dis-mounted."

4. Wordiness/Redundancy

Be specific and direct in your language. Don't fill up space with a lot of verbiage that you think sounds impressive. Here's an example of the beginning of a summary that is overblown and ultimately meaningless:

"Temperature gradients increased are known to increase external influences becoming more pronounced. Such situations are known as transient problems. Typically transient problems arise when boundary conditions of a system are perturbed. When influences such as a pressure gradient around an object are present, the object will experience a faster change to thermal equilibrium than would be expected if it were in a still air environment."

Because this lab was designed to determine heat transfer coefficients in forced convection, it would be better to state this directly and simply:

"The purposes of this experiment were to determine the heat transfer coefficients for different geometric shapes and velocities and to determine the unknowns in the relationships among the Nusselt, Reynolds, and Prandtl Numbers in forced convection. This was done by heating two copper spheres, one large and one small, each embedded with the thermocouple. The spheres were then placed in front of an air duct that had variable velocities. Temperature with respect to time (while cooling), sphere diameter, air temperature, and pressure differences in the air duct were recorded. Temperatures were recorded at two different velocities for the large sphere and at three different velocities for the small sphere."

5. Vague Pronoun Use

Specificity and concreteness are always called for, and rather than using a pronoun, it is better simply to restate the noun to which the pronoun refers. Note the vague use of "this" below:

"The smaller sphere is heated to approximately 300 degrees F and placed in an air duct with the air velocity at the maximum setting. Temperature readings of the sphere are recorded every thirty seconds for fifteen minutes. This is then repeated for air velocities at the middle and lowest settings."

The problem with "This" in the last sentence is that it is unclear how much preceding "This" is encompassed by it. The following revision states it clearly:

"The small sphere is heated to approximately 300 degrees F and placed in an air duct with the air velocity at the maximum setting. Temperature readings of the sphere are recorded every thirty seconds for fifteen minutes. The other sphere is also heated to 300 degrees F and placed in the air duct for air velocities at the middle and lowest settings."

6. Choppiness

Choppiness usually results from expressing each thought in a separate simple declarative sentence. Remedies include using adjectives and clauses to combine several thoughts in a single more complicated sentence, and avoiding non-descriptive terms like „various" and „some" if more thorough descriptions are also provided. For instance, suppose that one student wrote for his or her "Summary" section:

"In this laboratory three experiments were performed dealing with dynamic systems. There were various models used to describe the systems. These models were RC and RLC circuits, high pass filters, and thermal systems."

Here, the first sentence provides a good general overview of what the lab was about. The second and third sentences, though, provide basically the same information; sentence 2 tells us that 'various models" were used, and sentence 3 tells us what those models were. The student could have communicated the same information more economically by combining sentences and switching the models' names from functioning as direct object (as they do in sentence 3) to subject (as they do in the re-written version below). This switch would give us the following re-write:

"In this laboratory three experiments were performed dealing with dynamic systems. RC and RLC circuits, high pass filters, and thermal systems were the models used to describe these systems."

7. Improper Style in "Procedure" Section

Reports, in general, should be written in the third person, past tense, using an impersonal style. The "Procedure" section in your lab manuals will be written in an imperative since it is telling you, the student, <u>what to do</u>.

When you write your report, you are telling us, your audience, <u>what was done</u>, so an imperative mood is not appropriate. **This means that it is inappropriate to copy your lab manual's Procedure section and use it as the Procedure section in your lab report. The instructions must be rewritten in paragraph form, to reflect how you actually did the experiment.**

For example, a recent mechanical engineering report included the following "Procedure" section:

1. Connect the high pass filter and the rest of the system.
2. Apply a 1-volt rms sin wave as the input signal.
3. Vary the frequency from 10 Hz to 10,000 Hz.
4. Record the rms output voltage and phase difference
   between the input-output signals, observing the input and signals on the oscilloscope.
5. Acquire data at a minimum of 10 frequency values.

These are the in the lab manual. Because the student's report should tell <u>what was done</u> in the experiment, the directions need to be rewritten so that they are in the past tense and in an impersonal style. Past tense is self-explanatory; impersonal style means that pronoun subjects suck as "*I*" and "*we*" are inappropriate. Also, using a numbered list is inappropriate; the procedure should be written out in paragraph form.

The high pass filter was connected to the rest of the sys-tem, and a 1-bolt rms sin wave was applied as the Input. The frequency was varied from 10 Hz to 10,000 Hz. Next, the rms output voltage and the phase difference be-tween the input-output signals were recorded...

The first sentence <u>should not be written</u> as follows:

I/We connected the high pass filter and the rest of the sys-tem.

The above example converts the original instruction to past tense, but it uses *I/we* as the subject, which is generally inappropriate.

8. Agreement Problems

Problems with agreement in lab reports generally fall into two categories: subject-verb agreement and noun-pronoun agreement. Students usually make errors for one of two reasons: either they are uncertain about whether the subject or noun is singular or plural or because they fail to catch a hastily written error when they proofread carelessly or neglect to proofread altogether.

To avoid this kind of error, make sure that you know what the subject of your sentence is and whether that subject is singular or plural. Then choose the appropriate singular or plural verb or pronoun.

For example, suppose a student wrote: "A plot of the results were obtained." Because the subject of this sentence is *plot*, a singular noun, the sentence should read: "A plot of the results *was* obtained." This is a problem of subject-verb agreement.

9. First- and Second-Person Pronouns

Because lab reports should be written in an impersonal style, all personal pronouns (*I, you, we*) should be omitted. This will often mean using passive constructions in order to focus on the action that was done rather than on the person who did the action.

For example, suppose one student wrote: "As you can see by the following data, high pass filters are used when..." The pronoun should be removed altogether. "As can be seen from the following data, high pass filters are used when..."

I and *me* should be kept out of lab reports as well. Suppose one student's Conclusion section contained the following sentence: "The computer-based data acquisition system helped me to better understand the effects of alias frequencies." The pronoun can be re-moved by switching the verb from active to passive: "The computer-based data acquisition system was helpful in understanding the effects of alias frequencies." Better yet, you can make the equipment the actor in the sentence, thus eliminating the need for a personal pronoun:

"The computer-based data acquisition system thoroughly demonstrated the effects of alias frequencies."

10. Procrastination Problems

Errors in spelling, punctuation, and simple grammar are unprofessional and seriously diminish the effectiveness of your report.. Producing a professional-appearing product depends on leaving yourself enough time to review your work. Be sure to use a spell-checker on the final version, and then proofread it as well. **Spell-checking does not take the place of proofreading.** Spell-checkers won't catch usage errors (using *their* for *there*, for example), nor will they catch problems such as disagreement, choppiness, pronoun errors, wordiness, and incompleteness. The only way to ensure that you're handing in a quality report is to proofread carefully—which means reading through your report <u>after</u> you think you've produced a finished version to make sure that it's as polished as you want it to be—and to leave yourself enough time to correct whatever problems you find.

Sentences such as

"Both circuits represented well behavior in the systems."
"Eventhoughthe table gave a value...."

have all appeared in submitted lab reports, and all of the errors in them could be easily spotted if the students who wrote the reports had allowed themselves enough time to proofread. **Don't lose points by making silly errors: proofread.**

3.8.2 ORAL REPORTING

You will have to give presentations to many different audiences during your career as a technologist. Thus, you must know how to prepare and deliver formal oral reports. The more successful you are, the more presentations will be demanded of you. Most importantly, be aware that you must be as relaxed as possible during your presentation. *The best way to be relaxed is to be prepared.*

Begin your presentation by knowing your audience. For example, managers will ask that you present your ideas on how to improve the company's processes. You might act as a trainer on a new process involving complicated equipment. As a supervisor or manager you will be expected to present on such topics as safety, quality, and productivity in the workplace. You do not want to use complex technical terms with skilled workers who do not have your education. (On the other hand, you do want to act as though you have the skills those workers possess or that you are somehow "better than they.") You will wish to use your technical language skills and avoid too much detail when presenting to managers that probably have access to much of the information you will share.

3.8.2.1 BASIS OF A GOOD PRESENTATION

Many oral reports are ineffective not because they lack good content but because they are presented in a way that does not connect with the audience. Here are some of the basics for a good report, followed by a list of enhancements.

Basics of a Good Presentation

A good oral presentation should include the following:

1. Planning, Preparation, Structure. To avoid a rambling, stream-of-consciousness talk that goes nowhere, take the time and effort to plan your presentation, put it into an orderly shape, and learn it well enough that it can be delivered effectively. A good way to understand why preparing adequately is important is to think about what makes a terrible presentation:

- reading the whole thing from a script, or worse, rambling off the top of the head
- mumbling through
- saying "um" a lot
- speaking too fast
- speaking without pauses
- looking down, not making eye contact
- standing in one place, holding the lectern with a death grip
- never gesturing or looking alive
- gesturing as if you're doing tai chi while you talk

If you think about it, you will see that these errors are all caused by a lack of planning, preparation, and structure. Planning your talk, rehearsing it to become familiar with it, practicing your enunciation and volume, organizing until the presentation is clear and logically structured-- these steps will help prevent the terribles from occurring.

2. Communication. To communicate well, be sure that you

- speak loudly and clearly
- pause between ideas and do not speak overly fast (or too slow)
- make eye contact with the audience
- use your time well
- use visual aids
- gesture and move around some

3. Credibility. This is the issue of character (or *ethos* as the Greeks called it). Provide some evidence that you are worth listening to. Those who introduce speakers provide some background that builds credibility, as do biographical notes for books, which list the author's credentials. For an oral report, you have less of an opportunity to establish your credibility, but here are some things that will help:

- dress seriously so that you will be taken seriously
- provide support or authority for claims and information
- make visual aids look professional
- be accurate and exact with quotations, names, dates, and facts

Oral Report Enhancements

Your oral report can be made more vital, interesting, and compelling (as well as more understandable) by using some of the following enhancements:

1. PowerPoint Slides. PowerPoint can be used to present outlines, tables, graphs, pictures, photographs, illustrations, cartoons, music, and video. With a tablet PC, you can connect ideas with arrows or lines, circle a key word or concept, underline an important phrase or sentence. Be sure to read the PowerPoint Tips article.

2. Slides. Take some photographs with a digital camera and create a presentation with PowerPoint or PhotoStory (or a similar product). Titles can be included easily by using a word processor to print them in large headline size and photographing them close up. Hand drawn titles will also work, but look less professional. A slide show provides an opportunity to bring in large-scale outdoor scenes into your presentation. These might be natural scenes (trees, meadow, lake) as a backdrop for some comments or special illustrations (factory, product, people engaged in activity).

3. Video. Show some professional, purchased video clips, tape some interesting segments from TV, or use a video camera and shoot some custom material. Many news magazine shows and educational programs sell DVDs of their programs. Most video stores have specialty sections that carry useful program material from public broadcasting or other sources. If you film your own material, you can include interviews with people, "man on the street" surveys of opinion or reaction, or simply background shots similar to what you might do with slides: a photo of a factory making or packaging some product, or even of consumers eating, walking, reading, etc.

4. Charts. Use some spreadsheet software or graphics software to create some organization charts, tables, or diagrams. Blow these up for putting on posterboard (an enlarging copier can help here, as can a photo service), or photograph these for your slide show or video presentation. Do not create charts that are too small and do not do something that looks amateurish.

5. Graphs. Use a spreadsheet or graphics package to create some graphs. Use a color printer or hand color them after you enlarge them. A computer display would be ideal, since you can project the graphs on a screen.

6. Drawings. Find or create some line art or other kinds of drawings of things, places, people, or ideas. There is a lot of old etching art available to illustrate your talk.

7. Photographs. You can buy a throw-away camera with film for just a few dollars. Get prints, have enlargements made or make color copies to include in a handout. Photographs can be printed very large and hung or mounted individually, pasted on posterboard, collected in a portfolio, or used in a document or handout. You can find many great photos online by searching for "free stock photography." Stock Xchange (www.sxc.hu) is one example.

8. Posters. If you have artistic talent, you can draw a poster. If you cannot draw, you can still paste cut-outs from magazines, use stencils, spray paint, or attach charts and graphs rather than projecting them. Remember, though, that a poorly done poster is probably worse than none at all.

9. Sound. Add music or sounds to your presentation. You can record sound effects like traffic, bird chirps, crashing noises, narration, singing, instrumentals, or factory noise. Attach amplified speakers to an MP3 player for playback. Additionally, while not as effective as a video interview, sound-only interviews can be recorded and portions played at intervals during your presentation.

10. Mock-ups and Models. Build a mock up or a working model of your project, city, device, experiment, technique, process, or object. Remember there is clay, *papier mache*, casting plaster, wood, metal, wires, cardboard, tape, glue, paint, fabric, and more. Toothpicks, hot glue, newspaper, and some paint can make almost anything.

11. Props. Even ordinary items can be used to help people visualize your ideas or attach your concepts to something concrete. If a can of hairspray or a shoe or a CD helps illustrate something, bring it in and show it. Remember that the classroom is usually a rather austere environment separated from most of the physical attributes of the outside world. So when you bring in a piece of this outside world--a board, a plant, a tool, a consumer product--the item will gain special attention and can be used to connect an idea to something visual and familiar. And even if you are really cute, people like to have more to look at than just you while you talk.

12. Experiments and Demonstrations. Design an experiment that will illustrate something. The experiment can be realistic (like a model of a volcano to show how volcanoes erupt) or metaphorical, just to illustrate a concept (like cutting one string after another between two objects, to illustrate the gradual separation of parent and child).

13. Skit. Get a few friends together and write a skit that will illustrate an idea. Show how your idea works in the lives of people, how they respond to it, and so on. A skit can also be used for exposition, just to tell information about something. Three people speaking two sentences each will probably be more interesting than one person speaking six sentences. Skits are great for demonstrating concepts in sociology, psychology, philosophy, anthropology, business, and education. And they can be used very effectively for recreating events in history, law, and literature. While you're at it, grab that video camera and film the skit.

14. Costume. Think of a costume as a one-person, minimalist skit. You can dress up as a particular person (famous or infamous), or in a particular style. Quite effective is the two-in-one costume, where one costume is worn over another and then removed at the appropriate time, during a "before and after" presentation.

15. Web Site Visit. If you are presenting to a small class or have projection capability, you might visit one or more pertinent Web sites to take a survey, demonstrate an application, show some video clips, visit an online museum and so on. The possibilities are endless.

16. The Five Senses. The more senses you engage, the better opportunity you have to make a lasting impression on your audience. Eyes and ears are of course going to be reached, but what about touch (pass around your props), or taste (bring something to eat or drink), or smell (perfume, fruit)? Citrus aromas are supposed to focus attention, so why not shoot a burst of citrus air freshener into the room at the right moment?

17. Handout. Compile an outline, some illustrations, diagrams, cartoon, descriptions, or any other useful information and make copies for everyone in class to look at and keep for future reference. Handouts make presentations tangible and more memorable, and the fact that something is in print lends an aura of solidity to the information. (Yes, the print bias is still strong.)

3.8.2.2 GIVING AN ORAL REPORT

In many ways, planning an oral report is similar to planning a written report.

- Choose a subject that is interesting to you. What do you care about? What would you like to learn more about? Follow your interests, and you'll find your topic.
- Be clear about your purpose. Do you want to persuade your audience? Inform them about a topic? Or just tell an entertaining story?

An oral report also has the same three basic parts as a written report.

- The **introduction** should "hook" your audience. Catch their interest with a question, a dramatic tale or a personal experience that relates to your topic.
- The **body** is the main part of your report, and will use most of your time. Make an outline of the body so that you can share information in an organized way.
- The **conclusion** is the time to summarize and get across your most important point. What do you want the audience to remember?

It's important to really know your subject and be well organized. If you know your material well, you will be confident and able to answer questions. If your report is well organized, the audience will find it informative and easy to follow.

Think about your audience. If you were listening to a report on your subject, what would you want to know? Too much information can seem overwhelming, and too little can be confusing. Organize your outline around your key points, and focus on getting them across.

Remember—enthusiasm is contagious! If you're interested in your subject, the audience will be interested, too.

Rehearse!

Practicing your report is a key to success. At first, some people find it helpful to go through the report alone. You might practice in front of a mirror or in front of your stuffed animals. Then, try out your report in front of a practice audience-friends or family. Ask your practice audience:

- Could you follow my presentation?
- Did I seem knowledgeable about my subject?
- Was I speaking clearly? Could you hear me? Did I speak too fast or too slow?

If you are using visual aids, such as posters or overhead transparencies, practice using them while you rehearse. Also, you might want to time yourself to see how long it actually takes. The time will probably go by faster than you expect.

Report!

- Stand up straight. Hold your upper body straight, but not stiff, and keep your chin up. Try not to distract your audience by shifting around or fidgeting.
- Make eye contact. You will seem more sure of yourself, and the audience will listen better, if you make eye contact during your report.
- Use gestures. Your body language can help you make your points and keep the audience interested. Lean forward at key moments, and use your hands and arms for emphasis.
- Use your voice effectively. Vary your tone and speak clearly. If you're nervous, you might speak too fast. If you find yourself hurrying, take a breath and try to slow it down.

Nerves

Almost everyone is nervous when speaking before a group. Many people say public speaking is their Number 1 fear. Being well prepared is the best way to prevent nerves from getting the better of you. Also, try breathing deeply before you begin your report, and remember to breathe during the report. Being nervous isn't all bad-it can help to keep you on your toes!

One last thing

Have you prepared and practiced your report? Then go get them! Remember: you know your stuff, and your report is interesting and important.

3.8.2.3 BEST PRACTICES FOR GIVING PRESENTATIONS

Follow these guidelines to ensure success in giving an oral report:

1. Select a topic.
2. Research the topic at the library and on the internet.
3. Decide on a thesis and find evidence to back up your thesis statement.
4. Create a written outline on paper.

5. Write notes to yourself on paper or on index cards on the main points of the report.
6. Practice speaking the report to yourself.
7. Practice the oral report in front of a mirror.
8. Practice the oral report in front of a friend or family member.
9. Select the appropriate attire for giving the oral report.
10. Give the oral report with your notes in hand.

While these suggestions may seem initially quite simple, they are rather self-explanatory. It is important to remember that oral reports are just another strain of written reports. The same information must be presented. The only difference is in the way the information is presented. People who appear calm and collected can convey information sometimes better than well-informed people who are anxious in front of a group. Some people write better than they can publicly speak. Consequently, the written report will benefit them more.

Here are some tips on giving an oral report.

1. Do practice in front of people.
2. Do practice in front of a mirror so that you can see what you look like.
3. Do make eye contact with some people "in the audience."
4. Do not spend the entire oral report staring at your notes.
5. Do not recite a written report aloud.
6. Do remove all flashy jewelry or noise-making attire before you speak. You do not want distractions from your presentation..
7. Do speak slowly and coherently..

It is important to remember that your oral report is not your written report. Do not write the report in your notes. Simply write an outline of the report as your notes. If you write too much information in your handheld paperwork, then you may run the risk of simply reading an oral statement instead of presenting an oral report.

3.8.2.4 ORAL REPORT CHECKLIST

Use the following checklist in preparing to present an oral report:

- Find out, or somehow determine, how long the presentation should be, who the audience is, what the facilities are, and what visual aids will be available.

- Prepare a thorough, easy-to-read outline, keeping in mind the time that is available and leaving suitable time for questions. Use earlier information from the *written report*, in preparing the outline.

- Research facts and collect data to support the presentation.

- Prepare the visual aids, especially data presentations.

- Practice the outline, with the visual aids.

- Dress approximately for the day of the presentation and use relaxation methods prior to the actual presentation.

Good oral and written reporting is never easy. It requires thoroughness, good attention to detail, great organizational ability, strong analysis skills, and polished communication skills. These characteristics or qualities seldom occur naturally in any of us, but they can be developed. Good reporting may lead to promotion and perhaps more importantly, a greater contribution in society.

3.9 POPULAR TECHNOLOGICAL TOOLS FOR LEARNING

As education advances in the twenty-first century, an increasing number of teachers are incorporating technology into their classroom and a larger number of teachers wish to do so. Technology in the classroom is defined as "cognitive tools that make higher-level mathematical activities accessible to students". Technology can strengthen student learning by presenting content numerically, graphically, and symbolically without the burden of spending time to create each representation by hand. Instead of focusing on the computations, technology can help foster students' ability to make connections between the three representations quickly thereby leading to deeper. Additionally, incorporating technology into a mathematical lesson increases computational speed after student mastery, allows students to correct themselves, helps students leap over cognitive hurdles, aids students in making connections within mathematics and beyond, and creates a realistic context for mathematics. The latter benefit contributes significantly to student engagement, motivation, and attitude toward mathematics.

Technology should not be the sole venue to present content to students. Technology is one of many tools to help students learn material in a deeper and more meaningful way. Moreover, the way in which technology is used dictates the effectiveness of it. Technology should never compute something that a student can compute for himself or herself or be used as an activity that does not connect to content. Instead, the sole goal of technology should be to enrich students' learning experience.

The use of technological tools in the classroom and laboratory will allow students to apply the mathematics in three different representations: symbolically, graphically, and numerically. Computers and calculators can be used as visual tools to help all students to investigate each of these representations in hopes that they can make connections between them and fully understand the mathematics behind the concepts they are studying. Utilizing software of this nature allows for a change in the type of problems teachers give their students.

FIGURE 3.16 [LAPTOP COMPUTER & GRAPHING CALCULATOR]

Sections 3.9.1 through 3.9.4 are popular technological tools that can be used in a technical environment (classroom & laboratory) to all types of calculations. Each tool can be used for teacher demonstration, but it is preferred that students have their own equipment so that they can freely explore mathematical conjectures.

3.9.1 THE GRAPHICAL CALCULATOR

Graphing calculators have been around since the mid 1980's and have evolved over the years to become indispensable in a technical environment. As of the year 2000, graphing calculators were very popular in high schools and colleges throughout the United States. The wide spread use of the graphing calculator can be attributed to its portability and its education inspired design. The most recent advances in graphing calculators include the ability to integrate dynamic geometry software, spreadsheet calculations and functionality as well as enhanced interface that eliminates the formatting issues seen in earlier versions.

The most basic use of the graphing calculator is as a computational tool. In order for the graphing calculator to be effective, students must be trained to correctly enter symbols and parentheses before they proceed with any computations. When completing computations, students should understand the difference between the precision of the calculator and precision that can be attained in real life. The role of the teacher is to encourage students to question the output of the calculator and verify its validity within the context of the problem. Similarly, when performing complicated tasks students should be constantly reminded of the interpretation of the numbers so that meaning is not lost. For example, the graphing calculator is an excellent tool for performing regression analysis but students must be able to interpret the constants that are output from the graphing calculator in terms of the context.

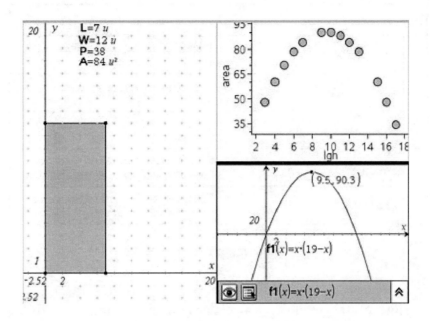

FIGURE 3.17

The graphing calculator can be used as a tool to spur discussion among students about their mathematical ideas; however students can tend to use the calculator as a private device that regularly leads to the breakdown of group interactions. Research has also shown guess and check techniques often overtook any reflective thinking and led to meaningless button pressing activities. Some researchers argued that many of the students simply copied what they saw on the screen of the calculator, without thinking about whether or not this was reasonable for the function under consideration and students often operated under the assumption that technology will always give the correct answer. The graphing calculator may also further extend students misconceptions about mathematical concepts. Understanding the role of the graphing calculator and how students adapt to the technology can aid the teacher in focusing instruction to eliminate these common pitfalls of the graphing calculator.

Role of the Graphing Calculator	Description of Student Actions
Computational Tool	Evaluating numerical expressions, estimating and rounding
Transformational Tool	Changing the nature of the task
Data Collection and Analysis Tool	Gathering data, controlling phenomena, finding patterns
Visualizing Tool	Finding symbolic functions, displaying data, interpreting data, solving equations
Checking Tool	Confirming conjectures, understanding multiple symbolic forms

FIGURE 3.18

The obvious benefits of the graphing calculator are that it increases the speed at which computations are completed and it allows students to visualize complex mathematical ideas in a way that is difficult with paper and pencil. The graphing calculator can also change the role of a teacher in the classroom. Rather than being the leader and person who assigns tasks, by having students explore and develop ideas through the use of the graphing calculator, the teacher becomes a consultant and participant in a discussion of mathematical ideas. With the help of the teacher, students can begin to see "mathematics as a dynamic activity" and the teacher will note an enrichment of students' solution approaches to mathematics. Perhaps most important, students can find the graphing calculator to be useful. Further research has shown that students who used handheld graphing technology have a better understanding of functions, of variables, of solving algebra problems in applied context, and of interpreting graphs than those who did not use the technology.

3.9.2 COMPUTER ALGEBRA SYSTEMS

While computer algebra systems have existed outside the arena of education, they only recently have been introduced into the mathematics classroom. Computer Algebra Systems, which are usually referred to as CAS, were created to both assist mathematicians in completing complicated computations and to streamline the mathematical process. CAS is a powerful computer program that allows the user to perform high level computations very quickly and eliminate the capacity for mistakes. Three of the most common platforms for CAS include Maple, Mathematica, MATLAB, and Mathcad. Additionally, many of the new graphics calculators include some form of a computer algebra system.

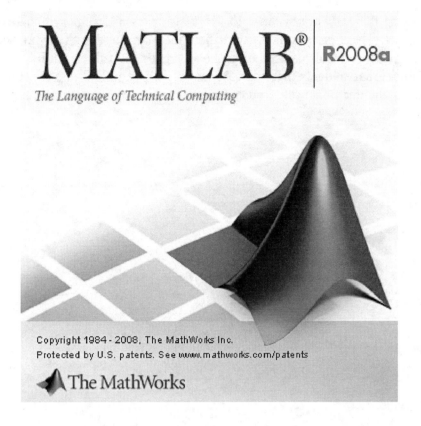

FIGURE 3.19 [MATLAB]

Within education CAS is used to eliminate bulky computations so that students are able to focus on the deeper concepts. A wide range of studies show that the conceptual understandings of CAS students were the same or better than those that did not use CAS. Computer algebra systems can be used to graph, build spreadsheets, and manipulate expressions and equations. These abilities allow students to easily connect between graphical, symbolical, and numerical representations. Through the use of CAS, students learn to value the importance of differentiating between variable, parameter, and function. Computer algebra systems can also be used to help students solve problems using various methods because the calculations are done for the students. This allows them to explore different approaches rather than "the best" or "the quickest.".

While CAS is a beneficial tool to use in the classroom, it does have its drawbacks, the most important of which is assessment. Using computer algebra systems in the classroom may conflict with certain high stakes tests because students may not be allowed to use technology as an aid on the test. If the software is not appropriately used, research suggests that CAS's ability to help students overlook complicated computations may make them dependent on the software. Another issue is that when students find a solution within the CAS system, they tend to rely on just one representation of the solution instead of examining all three representations to verify their answer. There are there drawbacks for both students and teachers when using computer algebra systems. Instructors must have deep content knowledge of the mathematics and the software to properly implement CAS; however, if teachers can overcome this, the software can help deepen their own content knowledge. There is a learning curve for both teachers and students when using the software because the software uses different symbols than are used in regular mathematics. There are people within the education community who assume that CAS will lead to atrophy of by-hand manipulation; however, of the fifteen studies conducted on this topic, fourteen found that students that use CAS in the classroom did just as well as students that did not use CAS on the items that required computational and procedural skills.

Appendices

HOMEWORK FOR CHAPTER 2

1. What are some unfortunate circumstances that can lead to a violation of ethics in the workplace?

2. What are some possible resolutions to maintaining ethics?

3. What are the five principles of a morally good person?

4. List some inner strength realistic goals that can help prevent an employee from violating ethics?

5. List some outer strength realistic goals that can help prevent an employee from violating ethics?

6. What is the definition of ethics?

7. Would a person who avoids stealing from a store only because it has a surveillance camera be considered an ethical person?

8. Who should you consult if you are faced with an ethical dilemma on your job?

9. Describe the two types of sexual harassment that can occur in the workforce?

10. What are the four key categories of attributes that will help you to maintain and nurture your repudiation?

11. Why is it is very difficult to obtain a software patent compared to a software copyright?

12. What is the purpose of a cover letter?

13. What three paragraphs should be included in your cover letter?

14. How far back should "years of experience" go on your resume?

15. What is the recommend font and font size for a hard copy of your cover letter and resume?

16. What is the purpose of the thank-you letter after your interview? How should this letter be sent?

17. What are the items to include on a letter acknowledging a job offer?

18. What does accepting a job offer ethically obligates you to?

19. What is the definition of a resume?

20. What should you do if you rather work for General Electric Company, but Westinghouse Electric Corporation has given you a great offer, and you don't want to turn that down if General Electric Company doesn't want you?

21. What are the two categories of interviewing?

22. How do you prepare for a telephone interview?

23. How do you prepare for a video interview?

24. What are the benefits of hiring co-op students?

25. What are the employers' responsibilities of the co-op student?

HOMEWORK FOR CHAPTER 3

1. What does the freshman-to-sophomore retention rate measures?

2. Define the cohort graduation rate?

3. Student success statistics consist of what?

4. How is student success beneficial to society?

5. Describe the following:

   a) Student Retention
   b) Student Persistent
   c) Educational Attainment
   d) Academic Achievement
   e) Student advancement
   f) Holistic Development

6. Describe the following elements of Holistic Development:

   a) Intellectual Development
   b) Emotional Development
   c) Social Development
   d) Ethical Development
   e) Physical Development
   f) Spiritual Development

7. List the three key student outcomes that scholars deem necessary for students to obtain a successful education.

8. Pick one of the seven potent principles of student success of Section 6.3; write a two to three paragraph summary of how it has impacted your college experience so far.

9. What percentage of academic success in college is due to concentrating on grades?

10. What other things influence a student's academic success in college?

11. What are some of the most common changes you can expect in the first year on campus?

12. Describe the most common stressors that first-year students experience.

13. What recommendations for first-year college students are offered, according to the textbook?

14. List the three most important items to put into an academic planner?

15. Write a weekly plan for all your courses for this month.

16. Discuss the three common barriers to student time management.

17. Describe the common strategies for college recruitment.

18. Name the seven variables used to model retention and progression.

19. *Institutions will fail to "retain" students most of the time.* Pick an American college or university and do research to report the percentage of students who graduated from the "original" school they attended.

20. Describe the four interventions to retaining students.

21. Within the university infrastructure who is responsible for student success.

HOMEWORK FOR CHAPTER 4

1. What is the difference between communicating and communicating effectively?

2. What are the barriers of effective communication?

3. What are the stages of the communication process?

4. At what stage in the communication process that you must know who your audience is?

5. A videoconference is an example of which stage of the communication process?

6. What barriers may influence how your messages(s) are interpreted by the person(s) receiving your message(s)?

7. Which stage in the communication process allows adjustment for future communication?

8. Which stage of the communication stage helps determine the tone and style of your communication.

9. What factors could affect our perspective of communication?

10. What are the causes of prejudices?

11. Why are prejudices harmful?

12. Describe the two ways in which your feelings can influence your communication with another person.

13. How can the environment influence the way you communicate?

14. Name the three elements of face-to-face communication.

15. What is the least impactful element in face-to-face communication?

16. What does non-verbal communication consist of in a face-to-face communication situation?

17. The tone of voice we use is responsible for what percentage of the message we are sending?

18. Explain how body language can be a useful tool.

19. What are the four different communication styles?

20. What are the two different dimensions in communication styles?

21. Describe the two different dimensions in each communication styles.

22. Which communication style involves an uneasiness of expressing feelings about things and the communicator(s) do not like conflict?

23. Which communication style involves talkativeness and the communicator(s) have a hard time sticking to the agenda or to one topic?

24. Under which communication style are the communicators reluctant to share an opposing opinion, even if it's important information, because they are concerned about keeping the peace and being liked?

25. Which communication style may appear insensitive or cold to others?

26. Develop five interview questions for Figure 4.10, Figure 4.12, Figure 4.14 and Figure 4.16. Interview four other people (roommates, classmates, teammates, family members, workmates, etc.). Classify the communication style of each interviewee.

27. Which communication style(s) should you avoid using the phrase " I feel….?"

28. Which communication style(s) is acceptable for using the phrase " I feel….?"

29. According to most experts, what percentage or information is heard by listeners?

30. Why is self-awareness important for good listeners?

31. What is active listening?

32. What are the five key aspects of becoming an active listener?

33. Under what circumstances is written communication the most effective choice of delivery?

34. Under what circumstances is written communication not the most effective choice of delivery?

35.Best subject lines of written letters and emails do what?

36. Why is it important to know your audience for communication?

37. Why should all capital letters be avoided within the organization of the text in written communication?

HOMEWORK FOR CHAPTER 5

1. How is leadership skills developed?

2. What are the outward characteristics or qualities of leaders?

3. What are the inner or personal qualities of leaders?

4. Besides the questions listed in Section 5.2, you can think of another question that can inspire a vision or purpose for a leader?

5. Pick one of the leadership goals of Section 5.3.1; write a two to three paragraph summary of a real life experience of someone achieving that goal. The internet and magazines are good sources. **Please do not plagiarize and be sure to include name and date of the source.**

6. What are the specific attributes of an entrepreneurial leader?

7. List the six lessons learned from failed entrepreneurial leaders?

8. Pick one of the nine signs of a losing organization of Section 5.4; write a two to three paragraph summary of a real life entrepreneur or entrepreneurship that failed because of this. The internet and magazines are good sources. **Please do not plagiarize and be sure to include name and date of the source.**

9. What activities exist in college that will allow students to sustain continued growth of leadership skills?

10. Summarize what colleges and universities can do to nurture leadership growth in students?

11. Why is it so helpful for leaders to share their personal strengths or weaknesses when engaging with students who hope to be future leaders?

12. List at least five elements that should be included in a leadership structure for schools, colleges and universities.

13. Use Tables 5.2 through 5.5 to interview a classmate and assess his or her student leadership status.

14. According to the textbook, what is the definition of diversity?

15. What is the major benefit of bringing diversity and inclusion into the workforce?

16. What diversity factors contribute to the propensity of stereotyping?

17. Why should stereotyping be avoided in the workplace?

18. Where do stereotypes come from?

19. List five ways stereotypes hurt us in the corporate world.

20. Describe the five steps for assessing and eliminating stereotypes.

21. Summarize the four reasons why racial and ethnic diversity are important for higher education.

22. According to the textbook, what is the definition of a corporation?

23. What were the first prominent types of corporations?

24. Distinguish between the shareholder-oriented interpretation of a corporation and the stakeholder-oriented view of a corporation.

25. What had limited the ability of diversity to have a real impact in US corporations?

26. What can corporations do when they make diversity a competitive advantage?

27. Pick one of the six values representing the new type of employee for corporations in Section 5.8.6. Write a two to three paragraph summary of a corporation that survived by embracing innovation through diversity. The internet and magazines are good sources. **Please do not plagiarize and be sure to include name and date of the source.**

28. Diversity is much more than just a multicultural issue. Explain.

29. List the four areas that should be addressed for a diversity management program to be successful.

30. Distinguish among the acronyms: CIO, CDO and CEO.

31. According to the textbook, what is of a competency?

32. List the seven competencies for D&I practitioners.

33. Describe the five primary trends driving changes in the Diversity & Inclusion (D&I) practitioner's role in corporations.

34. Why do most companies place lesser value on their D&I directors?

35. Other than just solely focusing on internal employee issues, what external

responsibilities must D&I practitioner do?

36. What are the personal characteristics that D&I practitioners should possess?

HOMEWORK FOR CHAPTER 6

1. What are the major attributes of a good laboratory student?

2. You are performing an experiment with two others. You are reading the meter scale, Kenjoseph is varying the voltage and Demora is taking data. Who is responsible for recording the data correctly?

3. Classify the following errors as gross (G), systematic (S), or random (R). In some cases more than one classification applies. Hint: Use the internet to research more about each case.

Type of Error	*Classification (G, S, or R)*
a. meter incorrectly zeroed	G, S
b. not following approved procedure	
c. oscilloscope attenuator controls not dented (locked into) in the cal mode	
d. micrometer caliper not zeroed	
e. sloppiness in an instrument's adjustment	
f. drafts	
g. friction	
h. friction in inclined-plane experiment where lubricant and other variables are constant	
i. reading a meter scale from the side (always the same side)	
j. dirt in a balance scale pivot	
k. failure to level a surface plate	

13. What recommendations for first-year college students are offered, according to the textbook?

14. List the three most important items to put into an academic planner?

15. Write a weekly plan for all your courses for this month.

16. Discuss the three common barriers to student time management.

17. Describe the common strategies for college recruitment.

18. Name the seven variables used to model retention and progression.

19. *Institutions will fail to "retain" students most of the time.* Pick an American college or university and do research to report the percentage of students who graduated from the "original" school they attended.

20. Describe the four interventions to retaining students.

21. Within the university infrastructure who is responsible for student success.

HOMEWORK FOR CHAPTER 7

1. Convert the following numbers to scientific notation:

   a) 123
   b) 4,500
   c) 750,000
   d) 1,250,000
   e) 0.25
   f) 0.0056
   g) 0.0000002

2. Convert the following scientific notations to normal (conventional) numbers:

   a) 1.23×10^2
   b) 4.5×10^3
   c) 7.5×10^5
   d) 1.25×10^6
   e) 2.5×10^{-1}
   f) 5.6×10^{-3}
   g) 2×10^{-7}

3. Add the following and express the final answer in scientific notation:

   $$4.5 \times 10^3 + 6.8 \times 10^3$$

4. Add the following and express the final answer in scientific notation:

   $$4.5 \times 10^3 + 3.4 \times 10^4$$

5. Express the following numbers as power of ten:

   a) 100,000
   b) 10,000,000
   c) 0.00001
   d) 0.01

6. Express the following numbers as power of ten:

   a) 1
   b) 100
   c) 0.1
   d) 1000
   e) 0.0001

f) 1,000,000

7. Perform the following operations and express your answer as a power of ten using scientific notation:

a) $300 + 75,000$
b) $5 \times 10^4 + 25 \times 10^3$
c) $0.2 \times 10^{-2} - 4 \times 10^{-3}$
d) $3 \times 10^3 - 250 \times 10^2 + 0.07 \times 10^4$
e) $4000 - 850$

8. Perform the following operations and express your answer as a power of ten using scientific notation:

a) $0.1 \times 10^3 - 0.001 \times 10^5$
b) $100 \times 10^{-1} + 0.12 \times 10^4$
c) $10^3 + 10^4$
d) $18.3 \times 10^6 + 7.7 \times 10^8$
e) $10^1 - 0.003 \times 10^4$

9. Perform the following operations and express your answer as a power of ten using engineering notation:

a) $(10) \times (1000)$
b) $(0.1) \times (100)$
c) $(10^3) \times (10^5)$
d) $(10000) \times (10^{-4})$
e) $(10^{-3}) \times (10^5) \times (10^2)$

10. Perform the following operations and express your answer as a power of ten using engineering notation:

a) $(100000000) \times (0.0000001)$
b) $(0.01) \times (1000)$
c) $(100000) \times (10^{-6})$
d) $(0.0001) \times (0.001)$
e) $(0.1) \times (0.01) \times (0.0001)$

11. Perform the following operations and express your answer in scientific notation:

a) $(20,000) \times (0.0002)$
b) $1100 \times (0.001)$
c) $(0.000076) \times (1,600,000)$
d) $(20 \times 10^{-3}) \times (0.008) \times (3 \times 10^5)$
e) $(0.044) \times (0.006)$

12. Perform the following operations and express your answer in engineering notation:

a) $\dfrac{100}{100,000}$

b) $\dfrac{0.001}{0.00001}$

c) $\dfrac{0.00000001}{10,000}$

d) $\dfrac{1,000,000}{1,000}$

e) $\dfrac{10^{\frac{3}{2}}}{10^{\frac{-1}{2}}}$

13. Perform the following operations and express your answer in engineering notation:

a) $\dfrac{7000}{0.00006}$

b) $\dfrac{0.005}{50,000}$

c) $\dfrac{0.000330}{0.00002}$

d) $\dfrac{72}{648}$

e) $\dfrac{52 \times 10^5}{26 \times 10^3}$

14. Perform the following operations and express your answer in engineering notation:

a) $(1000)^6$

b) $(0.0001)^{1/3}$

c) $(10,000)^9$

d) $(0.00001)^6$

e) $(10)^{1/2}$

15. Perform the following operations and express your answer in scientific notation:

  a) $(100)^3$

  b) $(500,000)^{1/5}$

  c) $(0.001)^2$

  d) $(0.1)^{1/4}$

  e) $(0.0001)^{1/2}$

16. Perform the following operations and express your answer in scientific notation:

  a) $(-0.01)^2$

  b) $\dfrac{(1000) \times (10^{-3})}{100}$

  c) $\dfrac{(0.001)^2 \times (1000)}{10,000}$

  d) $\dfrac{(10^6) \times (10^{-3})}{0.0001}$

  e) $\dfrac{(0.1)^2 \times (100)}{0.01}$

  f) $\dfrac{[(100) \times (0.01)]^{-2}}{(10)^2 \times (0.01)}$

17. Perform the following operations and express your answer in engineering notation:

  a) $(10)^3$

b) $-\dfrac{(10^7)\times(10^{-5})}{0.01}$

c) $\dfrac{(3000)^2\times(.01)}{100,000}$

d) $\dfrac{(5)^2}{(0.05)^{1/2}}$

e) $[0.000025]^{1/2}\times[100]^3\times[0.01]$

f) $\dfrac{\{(0.001)^3\}\times\{0.005\}^{-2}\times\{(25)^2\}}{\{(400)\times(0.006)\}^{-1/2}}$

18. Fill in the blanks of the following conversions:

a) $5\times10^3 = $ _____ $\times10^6$
b) $2\times10^{-6} = $ _____ $\times10^{-3}$
c) $25\times10^3 = $ _____ $\times10^{-3} = $ _____ $\times10^{-6}$
d) $100\times10^0 = $ _____ $\times10^{-3} = $ _____ $\times10^3 = $ _____ $\times10^6$
e) $0.001 = $ _____ $\times10^{-3} = $ _____ $\times10^{-6} = $ _____ $\times10^3 = $ _____ $\times10^{-9} = $ _____ $\times10^6$

19. Express the data in Scientific Notation with one nonzero digit to the left of the decimal.

a. 154.65	**b.** 300.85	**c.** 940.01	**d.** 80 000.2
e. 80000	**f.** 0.0017	**g.** 8.00065	**h.** 4000.
i. 5500	**j.** 5500.	**k.** 1800.0	**l.** 4000.0
m. 0.0204	**n.** 0.2100	**o.** 0.0091400	

20. Express the data in Scientific Notation with one nonzero digit to the left of the decimal.

a. 2700	**b.** 4400	**c.** 490.06	**d.** 8700.0
e. 60000	**f.** 0.0071	**g.** 0.7800	**h.** 7000.
i. 200.58	**j.** 658.93	**k.** 60000.7	**l.** 0.0905
m. 3000.0	**n.** 3.00056	**o.** 0.0027900	

21. Find the equivalent fractions using the indicated denominators.

a) $\dfrac{3}{4} = \dfrac{?}{32}$

b) $\dfrac{2}{3} = \dfrac{?}{15}$

c) $\dfrac{7}{8} = \dfrac{?}{64}$

22. Reduce each fraction to the lowest terms.

a) $\dfrac{8}{12}$

b) $\dfrac{34}{64}$

c) $\dfrac{2}{8}$

23. Change the decimals to fractions in the lowest terms.

a) 0.0125

b) 0.83

c) 0.001

d) 0.872

24. Change the fractions to decimals. If necessary, round to the nearest hundredth.

a) $\dfrac{1}{5}$

b) $\dfrac{1}{10}$

c) $\dfrac{2}{7}$

d) $\dfrac{15}{16}$

25. Write the improper fractions as whole or mixed numbers.

a) $\dfrac{9}{3}$

b) $\dfrac{39}{8}$

c) $\dfrac{27}{6}$

d) $\dfrac{22}{7}$

e) $\dfrac{43}{8}$

26. Add the following fractions and reduce to the lowest terms. Convert improper fractions to whole or mixed numbers.

a) $\dfrac{5}{16} + \dfrac{1}{16}$

b) $\dfrac{3}{8} + \dfrac{1}{8}$

c) $3\dfrac{1}{3} + 1\dfrac{7}{16}$

d) $\dfrac{1}{6} + \dfrac{7}{9} + \dfrac{2}{3}$

e) $4\dfrac{1}{2} + 9$

f) $1\dfrac{5}{8} + 2\dfrac{1}{2}$

27. Subtract the following fractions and reduce to the lowest terms. Convert improper fractions to whole or mixed numbers.

a) $\dfrac{7}{8} - \dfrac{5}{8}$

b) $\dfrac{7}{16} - \dfrac{3}{8}$

c) $\dfrac{3}{8} - \dfrac{7}{32}$

d) $9\dfrac{1}{32} - 3\dfrac{3}{8}$

28. Multiply and reduce answers to lowest terms. Convert improper fractions to whole or mixed numbers.

a) $\dfrac{3}{10} \times \dfrac{4}{15}$

b) $\dfrac{7}{12} \times \dfrac{4}{5}$

c) $\dfrac{1}{2} \times \dfrac{3}{4} \times \dfrac{8}{9}$

d) $\dfrac{3}{8} \times \dfrac{5}{6} \times \dfrac{1}{2}$

e) $\dfrac{1}{5} \times 7\dfrac{5}{8}$

f) $\dfrac{2}{3} \times 3\dfrac{1}{4}$

29. Divide and reduce answers to lowest terms. Convert improper fractions to whole or mixed numbers.

a) $\dfrac{1}{2} \div \dfrac{7}{12}$

b) $\dfrac{1}{5} \div \dfrac{1}{2}$

c) $8 \div \dfrac{1}{4}$

d) $2\dfrac{1}{2} \div 4$

e) $2\dfrac{2}{9} \div 1\dfrac{2}{3}$

30. A fruit-stand owner mixes $10\dfrac{3}{4}$ lb of apples, 20 lb of oranges, and $8\dfrac{1}{2}$ lb of bananas. What is the total weight of the mixed fruit?

31. If $6\dfrac{1}{4}$ ft of wire is needed to make one extension cord, how many extension cords can be made from $68\dfrac{3}{4}$ ft of wire?

32. Marlene needs $3\dfrac{1}{3}$ yd of red velvet to make a dress. How many yards she needs to make two dresses?

33. A baker has $5\dfrac{1}{2}$ cups of sugar on hand to make a batch of cookies requiring $1\dfrac{2}{3}$ cups of sugar. How much sugar is left over?

34. Change the fractions to percent equivalents:

a) $1\dfrac{1}{4}$

b) $3\dfrac{2}{3}$

c) 5.3

d) 5.12

35. Change the percent to their fraction and decimal equivalents: 75%, 38%, and 5%.

36. Change the numbers to their percent equivalents.

a) $\dfrac{7}{1000}$

b) $3\dfrac{1}{2}$

c) 15.1

d) $1\dfrac{1}{3}$

e) 36.25

f) $3\dfrac{1}{2}$

37. Change the percent to both fractional and decimal equivalents.

a) 18.75%

b) $\dfrac{1}{5}\%$

c) 45%

d) 0.05%

e) $66\dfrac{2}{3}\%$

38. $\dfrac{1}{4}\%$ of 875 is what number?

39. 325% of 86 is what number?

40. Estimate a 15% tip on a restaurant bill of $48.00.

41. A taxi fare is $24.00. Find the amount of a 20% tip.

42. 20% of what number is 45?

43. If a type of solder contains 55% tin, how many pounds of tin are needed to make 10 lb. of solder?

44. If a 150-horsepower (hp) engine delivers only 110 hp to the driving wheels of a car, what is the efficiency of the engine?

45. The effective value of current or voltage in an ac circuit is 71.3% of the maximum voltage. If a voltmeter shows a voltage of 110 volts (V) as the effective value in a circuit, what is the maximum voltage?

46. A motorist with an annual income of $18,250 spends each year $3,420 on automobile financing, $652 on gasoline, $625 on insurance, and $150 on maintenance and repair. What percent of the motor's annual income is used for automotive transportation?

47. There are 25 women in a class of 60 students. Find the percent of men in the class.

48. A 78-lb alloy of tin, copper and silver have 50 lb of tin and 12 lb of copper. Find the percent of silver in the alloy.

49. If a dress is marked 25% off the original price, what percent of the original price does the buyer pay?

50. An engine that has a 4% loss of power has an output of 336 hp. What is the input (base) horsepower of the engine?

51. Melissa Silvers was earning $90,000 and received a 10% raise. Find her new annual earning.

52. $\frac{1}{8}$% of 320 is what number?

53. Find the sales tax and the total bill on an order of DVDs costing $121.72 if the tax rate is 8%.

54. Tammy has net salary of $1,000.00 and a gross salary of $1500.00. What percent of the gross salary is the total of the deductions?

55. Cast iron contains 4.25% carbon. How much carbon is contained in a 25-lb bar of cast iron?

56. An engine operating at 91% efficiency transmits 170 hp. What is the engine's maximum capacity (base) in horsepower?

57. The voltage of a motor is 110 Volts. If 9 Volts are lost, what is the rate of voltage lost?

58. Gertrude earns $6,150 in one pay period. Medicare tax is 1.52% of the earnings. How much is deducted for Medicare tax?

59. Dora receives 6% commission on all sales made as an Avon lady. If she sells $100,000 in merchandise during a given period, what is the commission?

60. Beulah is paid a salary of $12,000 monthly as a corporate consultant of a small investment firm plus a 1% of the net earnings of the business. Find the total salary of a month when the net earnings of the business is $10,000,000.

61. The city of Metropolis has 1,285, 792 people living within its city limits. If the population is expected to grow by 25% over the next year, how many new people will be living there? What is the total number of people living in that year?

62. Compute the % error if the calculated voltage in a circuit is 30 and the measured value is 29.5.

63. Solve for x in the following equation: $3x + 6 = 12$.

64. Find the unknown variable z in the following equation: $-6z - 24 = -2z - 36$.

65. What is the value of t in the following equation: $2t = 10$?

66. Solve for the variable u.

$u - 3 = 2u + 3$

67. Find the unknown variable a in the following equation: $\dfrac{-a}{2} - 3 = 7$

68. Find the unknown variable j in the following equation: $\dfrac{-3j}{4} + 2 = -1$

69. What is the value of p in the following equation?

$3p - \dfrac{1}{4} = 2$

70. Solve for the variable s.

$\dfrac{1}{s} = 3$

71. Find the unknown variable c in the following equation.

$$\frac{2-c}{3} + 3 = 6$$

72. Find R in the following equation.

$$\frac{1}{R} = \frac{1}{3} + \frac{1}{4}$$

73. Solve for the variable v.

$$\frac{1}{v} - 1 = 9$$

74. Solve for the variable d in the equation below.

$$-\frac{1}{2d+1} + 2 = -3$$

75. Solve for the variable x in the following equation.

$$4 + \frac{16}{3-x} = 12$$

76. What is the value of g in the equation below?

$$\frac{g-2}{5} = 4$$

77. Solve for w in the following equation: $2w - 6 = \dfrac{-3w+6}{4} - 2$

78. Solve for the variable y in the equation below.

$$\frac{1}{2} = \frac{1}{2y} + \frac{4}{4y}$$

79. Solve for angle θ in degrees. Round off your answer to the nearest hundredth.

$$7 \sin(\theta) = 6$$

80. Solve for angle β in degrees. Round off your answer to the nearest hundredth.

$$10 \cos (\beta) = 5$$

81. Solve for angle α in degrees. Round off your answer to the nearest hundredth.

$$\frac{3}{\tan(\alpha)} = 15$$

82. Solve for angle δ in degrees. Round off your answer to the nearest hundredth.

$$\frac{2}{\cos(\delta)} + 5 = 2$$

83. Solve for angle γ in degrees. Round off your answer to the nearest hundredth.

$$\frac{\sin(\gamma)}{4} - 0.04 = 0.05$$

84. In a right triangle, all three angles add up to 180°. Suppose that a right triangle has angles, χ (Chi), ψ (Psi) and τ (Tau). What is the angle of τ, if χ is 90° and ψ is 30°?

85. In physics, the speed of light (c) is directly proportional to the wavelength (λ) and frequency (*f*) in an equation $c = f \times \lambda$. Compute the value of λ if c is 3×10^8 and *f* is 100,000.

86. In an electrical circuit, the current is inversely proportional to the resistance (R) and directly proportional to the voltage (V) in an equation called Ohm's Law $\left[I = \frac{V}{R} \right]$. Solve for R, if I = 0.001 and V = 20.

87. In a DC electrical circuit, the power (P), voltage (V) and resistance (R) are governed by the following equation: $\left[P = \frac{V^2}{R} \right]$. Compute the value of R if V = 25 and P = 0.15.

88. Using the same equation from Problem 25, solve for V when R = 500 and P = 2.5.

89. In a DC electrical circuit, the power (P), current (I) and resistance (R) are governed by the following equation: $P = I^2 R$. Compute the value of R if I = 0.025 and P = 0.75.

90. Using the same equation from Problem 27, solve for I when R = 10 and P = 30.

91. Power (P), energy (E_n) and time (t) are related by the following equation: $P = \dfrac{E_n}{t}$.

 If P = 15 and E_n = 45, what is the value of t?

92. In electric circuits, charge (C), is directly proportional to current (I) and inversely proportional to time (t). This relationship is shown in the following equation: $I = \dfrac{Q}{t}$. Compute the value of t, when I = 0.0090 and Q = 0.0002.

93. Using the same equation from Problem 30, compute Q, when I = .008 and $t = 3 \times 10^{-3}$.

94. In Electronic Communications, the modulation of index (m) is related to the Modulating Voltage (E_m) and the Carrier Voltage (E_c) by the following equation: $m = \dfrac{E_m}{E_c}$. What is the value of m if E_c = 25 and E_m = 20.

95. Convert the modulation index (m) computed in Problem 32 to a percent.

96. The current gain (β) of a BJT transistor is related to the collector current (I_C) and the base current (I_B) by the following equation $\beta = \dfrac{I_C}{I_B}$. Compute I_B if β = 1000 and I_C = .00845. Write your answer in Scientific Notation.

97. Compute the value of I_C from Problem 34, if β = 100,000 and $I_B = 3 \times 10^{-3}$.

98. The efficiency (η) of a motor is related to the Input Power (P_{in}) going into the motor and the Output Power (P_{out}) coming out of the motor. The following equation shows the relationship: $\eta = \dfrac{P_{out}}{P_{in}}$.

 a) Compute the value of η, if P_{in} = 100,000 and P_{out} = 90,000.

 b) Compute the value of P_{in}, when P_{out} = 800 and η = 0.95.

 c) Calculate the value of P_{out}, for P_{in} = 16 and η = 65%

 d) Express the value of η as a percent (%) in part a) of this question.

99. In Electric Power and Machinery, the synchronous speed of a motor (η_s) is directly proportional to the frequency (f) and inversely proportional to the number of poles of the motor (p). This equation for this relationship is shown below.

$$\eta_s = \frac{120 \times f}{p}$$

a) Compute the value of η_s, when $f = 60$ and $p = 6$.

b) Compute the value of f, when $p = 4$ and $\eta_s = 1500$.

c) Compute the number of poles (p), when $f = 60$ and $\eta_s = 3600$.

100. In an induction motor, the slip (s) is defined as the percentage difference between synchronous speed (η_s) and the actual speed (n) that the motor is turning. The relationship of the variables is shown below.

$$s = \frac{\eta_s - n}{\eta_s}$$

a) Compute the value of the slip (s) when $\eta_s = 1800$ and n = 1760.

b) Express the value of s computed in part a) as a percent.

c) If the slip is given as 4% and η_s is 1500, compute the value of n.

d) If the slip is 0.0125 and n is 1185, what is the value of (η_s)?

101. In Electronics, the two possible states for a single diode is on and off. For multiple diodes in an electronic circuit, the equation is governed by $X = 2^n$. The variable n represents the number of diodes and X represents the total number of possible states.

a) What are the possible number of states when three diodes are present in the electronic circuit?

b) How many diodes are present in the circuit, if 16 total states are possible?

102. Solve for R_T in terms of R.

$$\frac{1}{R_T} = \frac{1}{3R} + \frac{1}{7R}$$

103. The equations below are used to calculate the temperatures in Celsius (°C) and Fahrenheit (°F). T_C represents the temperature in Celsius. T_F represents the temperature in Fahrenheit.

$$T_C = \frac{5}{9}(T_F - 32°)$$

$$T_F = \frac{9}{5}(T_C + 32°)$$

a) What is 75°F on the Celsius temperature scale?

b) What is 20°C on the Fahrenheit temperature scale?

104. The distance traveled by an object is directly proportional to both the rate and time associated with that object. The variable for the distance is d. The variable for the rate is v. The variable for time is t. Find the rate of a car that moved a distance of 385 miles in 7 hours using the equation below.

$$d = v \times t$$

105. Gasoline moves through a pipeline at 40 gal per minute. How many gallons per hour can move through the pipeline?

106. A toll station can accommodate on average 30 vehicles per minute. How many vehicles can be accommodated in an hour?

107. For the following matrix, find the cofactors of a_{21}, a_{33}, and a_{13}.

$$\begin{bmatrix} 4 & 1 & 2 \\ 3 & -1 & 2 \\ 6 & -1 & 0 \end{bmatrix}$$

108. Find the cofactors of a_{31}, a_{11}, and a_{23} of the matrix given in Problem 1.

109. Find the cofactors of a_{22}, a_{13}, and a_{21} of the matrix given in Problem 1.

110. Find the cofactors of a_{12}, a_{32}, and a_{33} of the matrix given in Problem 1.

111. Find all cofactors of the following matrix.

$$\begin{bmatrix} 1 & -1 \\ 3 & 2 \end{bmatrix}$$

112. Find the determinant of the matrix below.

$$A = \begin{bmatrix} 3 & 1 \\ 2 & -4 \end{bmatrix}$$

113. Find the determinant of the matrix below.

$$A = \begin{bmatrix} 4 & -6 \\ 1 & 1 \end{bmatrix}$$

114. Find the determinant of the matrix below.

$$A = \begin{bmatrix} 1 & 2 & 3 \\ 0 & 0 & -1 \\ 4 & -2 & 0 \end{bmatrix}$$

115. Find the determinant of the matrix below.

$$A = \begin{bmatrix} 2 & -1 & 3 \\ 0 & 1 & 2 \\ 3 & -2 & 1 \end{bmatrix}$$

116. Find the determinant of the matrix below.

$$A = \begin{bmatrix} s-2 & 4 & 3 \\ 1 & s+1 & -2 \\ 0 & 0 & s-4 \end{bmatrix}$$

117. Find the determinant of the matrix below.

$$A = \begin{bmatrix} 1 & 2 & 2 & 3 \\ 1 & 0 & -2 & 0 \\ 3 & -1 & 1 & -2 \\ 4 & -3 & 0 & 2 \end{bmatrix}$$

118. Perform the following expression.

$$\begin{bmatrix} 1 & 7 \\ 2 & 6 \end{bmatrix} + \begin{bmatrix} 3 & 5 \\ 1 & 1 \end{bmatrix}$$

119. Perform the following expression.

$$\begin{bmatrix} 7 & 6 & 6 \\ 5 & 4 & 1 \\ 9 & 8 & 2 \end{bmatrix} - \begin{bmatrix} 1 & 0 & 0 \\ 0 & 1 & 0 \\ 0 & 0 & 1 \end{bmatrix}$$

120. Perform the following expressions.

$$\begin{bmatrix} 2 & 1 \\ 0 & 0 \end{bmatrix} \times \begin{bmatrix} 3 & 2 \\ 1 & 1 \end{bmatrix}$$

121. Perform the following expression.

$$\begin{bmatrix} 1 & 9 \\ 7 & 2 \end{bmatrix} \times \begin{bmatrix} 2 & 1 & 3 \\ 4 & -1 & -7 \end{bmatrix}$$

122. Perform the following expression.

$$\begin{bmatrix} 1 & 2 & -3 & 4 \\ 0 & -5 & -1 & -2 \end{bmatrix} \times \begin{bmatrix} 2 & -5 \\ 3 & 0 \\ 6 & 1 \\ -2 & 3 \end{bmatrix}$$

123. Perform the following expression.

$$\begin{bmatrix} 2 & 3 \\ -5 & 0 \\ 1 & -4 \end{bmatrix} - \begin{bmatrix} 1 & 0 \\ -2 & -1 \\ -3 & 5 \end{bmatrix} + \begin{bmatrix} 0 & 1 \\ 1 & -1 \\ -2 & -1 \end{bmatrix}$$

124. Perform the following expression.

$$\begin{bmatrix} 1 & 6 \\ -3 & 4 \end{bmatrix} \times \begin{bmatrix} -1 & 0 \\ 3 & 2 \end{bmatrix}$$

125. Perform the following expression.

$$[2 \ -1] \times \begin{bmatrix} -4 \\ -5 \end{bmatrix}$$

126. Perform the following expression.

$$\begin{bmatrix} 3 \\ -1 \end{bmatrix} \times [2 \ 5]$$

QUESTIONS 127- 137 refer to the following matrices

$$A = \begin{bmatrix} 2 & 0 & 4 \\ 1 & 4 & -1 \\ 3 & 1 & 2 \end{bmatrix} \quad B = \begin{bmatrix} 3 & 5 & 2 \\ 0 & 8 & 4 \\ 1 & 0 & 9 \end{bmatrix}$$

$$C = \begin{bmatrix} 1 \\ 2 \\ 3 \end{bmatrix} \quad D = \begin{bmatrix} 1 & 4 \\ -2 & 3 \end{bmatrix}$$

127. What is the transpose of **A**?

128. Solve for the determinant of **A**.

129. Calculate the inverse of **D**.

130. What is the product of **A** × **C**?

131. What is the rank of **B**?

132. Compute the sum of **A** + **B**.

133. What is the product of **3** × **D**?

134. Calculate the product of **C** × **D**.

135. Write a set of equations that describe the matrix equation **A**×**X** = **C**.

136. Show that **A** + **B** = **B** + **A**.

137. Show that **A** × **B** ≠ **B** × **A**

138. What is the rank of the following matrix?

$$\begin{bmatrix} 2 & 1 & 1 \\ 1 & 1 & 1 \\ 3 & 2 & 1 \end{bmatrix}$$

139. Given the following matrix:

$$A = \begin{bmatrix} 1 & 2 & 0 \\ 3 & -1 & 1 \\ 0 & 2 & 0 \end{bmatrix}$$

a) compute the determinant.

b) find the rank.

140. Solve the simultaneous linear equations by using the following methods:

a) Substitution Method
b) Algebraic Elimination Method
c) Cramer's Rule Method

$$2x - 3y = 5$$
$$3x + 7y = -2$$

141. Solve the set of simultaneous linear equations by using the Cramer's Rule Method.

$$3z + 2y = x + 1$$
$$3y + 2x = 8 - 5z$$
$$3x - 1 = y - 2z$$

142. Given the following system of simultaneous equations:

$$4i_1 + 2i_2 = -2$$
$$5i_1 + 3i_2 = 2$$

a) Substitution Method
b) Algebraic Elimination Method
c) Cramer's Rule Method

143.   Given the following system of simultaneous equations:

$$2x + 3y = -5$$
$$\frac{1}{2}x + 2y = 3$$

a) Substitution Method
b) Algebraic Elimination Method
c) Cramer's Rule Method

144. Given the following system of simultaneous equations:

$$V_1 + \frac{1}{2}V_2 = -5$$

$$-\frac{1}{2}V_1 - 2V_2 = -15$$

a) Substitution Method
b) Algebraic Elimination Method
c) Cramer's Rule Method

145. Given the following system of simultaneous equations:

$$5R + 3V = 4$$
$$2R + 5V = \frac{1}{2}$$

a) Substitution Method
b) Algebraic Elimination Method
c) Cramer's Rule Method

146. Given the following system of simultaneous equations:

$$\frac{1}{2}a + 2b = 4$$
$$2a + \frac{1}{2}b = 5$$

a) Substitution Method

b) Algebraic Elimination Method
c) Cramer's Rule Method

147. Given the following system of simultaneous equations:

$$3a + b = 7$$
$$-\frac{1}{2}a - 2b = 9$$

    a) Substitution Method
    b) Algebraic Elimination Method
    c) Cramer's Rule Method

148. Given the following system of simultaneous equations:

$$-2R + 3V = -1$$

$$2R - 3V = -\frac{1}{2}$$

    a) Substitution Method
    b) Algebraic Elimination Method
    c) Cramer's Rule Method

149. Solve the set of linear algebraic equations by using the Gauss Jordan Elimination Method.

$$x - y = 1$$

$$x + y - 2z = -3$$

$$y + z = 5$$

150. Solve for the eigenvalues and eigenvectors of the matrix $\mathbf{A}$ without using MATLAB?

$$\mathbf{A} = \begin{bmatrix} 1 & 4 \\ 2 & 3 \end{bmatrix}$$

151. Solve for the eigenvalues and eigenvectors of the matrix $\mathbf{C}$ without using MATLAB?

$$C = \begin{bmatrix} 3 & 5 \\ 2 & 4 \end{bmatrix}$$

152. Use MATLAB to find the eigenvalues and eigenvectors of the matrix **A**?

$$A = \begin{bmatrix} 2 & 3 & 5 \\ 1 & 1 & 1 \\ 5 & 9 & 4 \end{bmatrix}$$

153. Use MATLAB to find the eigenvalues and eigenvectors of the matrix **A**?

$$A = \begin{bmatrix} 6 & 10 \\ 5 & 12 \end{bmatrix}$$

APPENDIX B

CONVERSION FACTORS

Time

1 day = 1.44×10^3 min = 8.64×10^4 s
1 year = 8.76×10^3 h = 5.26×10^5 min = 31.5×10^7 s
1 h = 60 min = 3600 s
1 min = 60 s

Displacement (Length)

1 meter (m) = 100 cm = 1000 mm = 39.4 in = 3.28 ft
1 centimeter (cm) = 10 millimeters (mm) = 0.394 in
1 kilometer (km) = 10^3 m = 0.621 mi = 3280.8 ft
1 foot (ft) = 12 in = 0.305 m = 30.5 cm
1 inch (in) = 0.0833 ft = 2.54 cm = 0.0254 m = 25.4 mm
1 mile (mi) = 5280 ft = 1.61 km = 1760 yd
1 yd = 3 ft = 36 in = 0.9144 m
1 revolution = 360° = 2π rad

Area

1 m^2 = 10^4 cm^2 = 1.55×10^3 in^2 = 10.76 ft^2
1 cm^2 = $10^{-4}m^2$ = 0.155 in^2 = 100 mm^2
1 ft^2 = 144 in^2 = $9.29 \times 10^{-2}m^2$ = 929 cm^2
1 yd^2 = 9 ft^2
1 ft^2 = 144 in^2

Volume

1 m^3 = 10^3 liters (L) = 10^6 cm^3 = 35.3 ft^3 = 6.10×10^4 in^3
1 ft^3 = 1728 in^3 = 2.83×10^{-2} m^3 = 28.3 L

Velocity (Speed)

1 m/s = 3.28 ft/s = 2.24 mi/h = 3.60 km/h
1 ft/s = 0.305 m/s = 0.682 mi/h = 1.10 km/h
60 mi/h = 88 ft/s
1 km/h = 0.278 m/s = 0.913 ft/s = 0.621 mi/h
1 mi/h = 1.47 ft/s = 0.447 m/s = 1.61 km/h
1 rpm = 0.10472 rad/s
60 rpm = 1 cps = 1 Hz

Mass

1 kilo-gram (kg) = 10^3 grams (g) = 0.0685 slug

1 kg = 2.2 pounds (lb) = 2.2046 lbm

1 slug = 14.6 kg

1 slug = 32.2 lb

1 g = 1000 mg

Force

1 newton (N) = 0.225 lb = 3.60 ounces (oz)

1 pound (lb) = 16 oz = 4.45 N

1 lb = 0.454 kg = 454 g

Pressure

1 pascal (pa) = 1 N/m^2 = 2.09×10^{-2} lb/ft^2 = 1.45×10^{-4} lb/in^2

1 lb/in^2 = 144 lb/ft^2 = 6.90×10^3 N/m^2

1 atmosphere (atm) = 1.013×10^5 N/m^2 = 14.7 lb/in^2

1 kPa = 20.89 lb/ft^2

Work (Energy, Torque)

1 joule (J) = 0.738 ft-lb = 2.39×10^{-4} kcal = 0.0009485 Btu = 6.24×10^{18} eV

1 foot-pound (ft-lb) = 1.36 J = 1.29×10^{-3} Btu = 3.25×10^{-4} kcal

1 kilocalorie (kcal) = 4185 J = 3.97 Btu = 3077 ft-lb

1 Btu = 0.252 kcal = 778 ft-lb = 1054.8 J

1 kilowatthour (kWh) = 3.6×10^6 J = 3.6 MJ = 2.655×10^6 ft-lb

Power

1 watt (W) = 1 J/s = $0.738 \dfrac{ft \text{-} lb}{s}$ = 0.001341 hp

1 kilowatt (kW) = 10^3 W = 1.34 hp

1 horsepower (hp) = $550 \dfrac{ft \text{-} lb}{s}$ = 745.7 W = $33,000 \dfrac{ft \text{-} lb}{min}$

Temperature

$$T_C = \frac{5}{9}\left(T_F - 32°\right)$$

$$T_F = \frac{9}{5}\left(T_C + 32°\right)$$

APPENDIX C

METRIC OR SI PRE-FIX CHART

Prefix	Symbol	Value
Tera-	T	10^{12}
Giga-	G	10^9
Mega-	M	10^6
Kilo-	k	10^3
Hecto-	h	10^2
Deka-	da	10^1
Base Unit	--------	$10^0 = 1$
Deci-	d	10^{-1}
Centi-	c	10^{-2}
Milli-	m	10^{-3}
Micro-	μ	10^{-6}
Nano-	n	10^{-9}
Pico-	p	10^{-12}

APPENDIX D

MATHEMATICAL REFERENCE TABLES
ENGLISH-METRIC EQUIVALENTS

LENGTH MEASURE

1 inch (in) = 25.4 millimeters (mm)
1 inch (in) = 2.54 centimeters (cm)
1 foot (ft) = 0.3048 meter (m)
1 foot (ft) = 12 inches (in)
1 yard (yd) = 3 feet (ft)
1 yard (yd) = 36 inches (in)
1 yard (yd) = 0.9144 meter (m)
1 mile (mi) = 1.609 kilometers (km)
1 millimeter (mm) = 0.03937 inch (in)
1 centimeters (cm) = 0.39370 inch (in)
1 meter (m) = 3.28084 feet (ft)
1 meter (m) = 1.093 61 yards (yd)
1 kilometer (km) = 0.62137 mile (mi)

1 rod = $16\frac{1}{2}$ feet (ft)

1 rod = $5\frac{1}{2}$ yards (yd)

1 statute mile = 5,280 yards (yd)

AREA MEASURE

1 square inch (in^2) = 645.16 square millimeters (mm^2)
1 square inch (in^2) = 6.4516 square centimeters (cm^2)
1 square foot (ft^2) = 0.092903 square meters (m^2)
1 square foot (ft^2) = 144 square inches (in^2)
1 square yard (yd^2) = 0.836127 square meters (m^2)
1 square yard (yd^2) = 9 square feet (ft^2)
1 square millimeter (mm^2) = 0.001550 square inches (in^2)
1 square millimeter (mm^2) = 0.000001 square meter (m^2)
1 square centimeter (cm^2) = 0.15500 square inches (in^2)
1 square centimeter (cm2) = 0.0001 square meters (m^2)
1 square decimeter (dm^2) = 0.01 square meter (m^2)
1 square dekameter (dam^2) = 100 square meters (m^2)
1 square hectometer (hm^2) = 10,000 square meters (m^2)
1 square meter (m^2) = 10.763910 square feet (ft^2)

1 square meter (m^2) = 1.19599 square yards (yd^2)
1 square kilometer (km^2) = 1,000,000 square meters (m^2)
1 square rod = 30.25 square feet (ft^2)
1 acre = 160 square rods
1 acre = 4,840 square yards (yd^2)
1 acre = 43,560 square feet (ft^2)
1 square mile = 640 acres

VOLUME MEASURE FOR SOLIDS

1 cubic inch (in^3) = 16.387064 (cm^3)
1 cubic foot (ft^3) = 0.028317 (m^3)
1 cubic foot (ft^3) = 1,728 cubic inches (in^3)
1 cubic yard (yd^3) = 0.764555 (m^3)
1 cubic yard (yd^3) = 27 cubic feet (ft^3)
1 cubic centimeter (cm^3) = 0.061024 cubic inches (in^3)
1 cubic centimeter (cm^3) = 0.000001 cubic meters (m^3)
1 cubic millimeter (mm^3) = 0.000000001 cubic meters (m^3)
1 cubic meter (m^3) = 35.314667 cubic feet (ft^3)
1 cubic meter (m^3) = 1.307951 cubic yards (yd^3)
1 cubic decimeter (dm^3) = 0.001 cubic meter (m^3)

VOLUME MEASURE FOR FLUIDS

1 gallon (gal) = 3,785.411 cubic centimeters (cm^3)
1 gallon (gal) = 3.785411 liters (L)
1 quart (qt) = 0.946353 liters (L)
1 ounce (oz) = 29.573530 cubic centimeters (cm^3)
1 cubic centimeter (cm^3) = 0.000264 gallon (gal)
1 liter (L) = 0.264172 gallon (gal)
1 liter (L) = 1.056688 quarts (qt)
1 cubic centimeter (cm^3) = 0.033814 ounces (oz)

MASS MEASURE

1 pound (lb) = 0.453592 kilogram (kg)
1 pound (lb) = 453.592 grams (g)
1 ounce (oz) = 28.349523 grams (g)
1 ounce (oz) = 0.028350 kilogram (kg)
1 kilogram (kg) = 2.204623 pounds (lb)
1 gram (g) = 0.002205 pound (lb)
1 kilogram (kg) = 35.273962 ounces (oz)
1 gram (g) = 0.035274 ounces (oz)

APPENDIX E

MEASUREMENTS

LENGTH

1 foot (ft) = 12 inches (in) = 0.3048 (m)
1 yard (yd) = 3 feet
1 yard = 36 inches = 0.9144 (m)
1 mile (mi) = 5280 feet (ft)
1 mile = 1760 yards (yd)
1 millimeter (mm) = 0.001 meter (m)
1 centimeter (cm) = 10 millimeters (mm)
1 centimeter (cm) = 0.01 meter (m)
1 decimeter (dm) = 0.1 meter (m)
1 decimeter (dm) = 10 centimeters (cm)
1 meter (m) = 100 centimeters (cm)
1 dekameter (dam) = 10 meters (m)
1 hectometer (hm) = 100 meters (m)
1 kilometer (km) = 1,000 meters (m)

LIQUID

1 cup (c) = 8 fluid ounces (oz)
1 pint (pt) = 2 cups
1 pint = 16 ounces (oz)
1 pint = 4 gills
1 quart (qt) = 2 pints
1 gallon (gal) = 4 quarts (qt)
1 imperial gallon = 1.2 US gallons (gal)
1 liter (L) = 1000 meters (m)
1 liter (L) = 1 cubic decimeter (dm^3)
1 milliliter (mL) = 0.001 liter (L)

WEIGHT

1 pound = 16 ounces (oz)
1 pound = 0.4536 kilogram (kg)
1 short ton = 2,000 pounds (lb)
1 long ton = 2,240 pounds (lb)
1 long ton = 1,016 kilograms (kg)
1 milligram (mg) = 0.001 gram (g)
1 centigram (cg) = 0.01 gram (g)
1 decigram (dg) = 0.1 gram (g)

1 gram (g) = 0.0352 ounce (oz)
1 kilogram (kg) = 1,000 grams (g)
1 kilogram = 2.2046 pounds (lb)
1 metric ton = 2,204.6 pounds (lb)
1 metric ton = 1,000 kilograms (kg)